The Death of Science

Science

The Retreat from Reason in the Post-Modern World

The Death of Science

The Death of Science

The Retreat from Reason in the Post-Modern World

Edited by

Paul R Goddard
and
Angus G Dalgleish

With major contributions
from
Dr Nabil Jarad
Prof. Chandra Wickramasinghe
Prof. David Nutt
Jeremy Goddard
Mark Goddard
Dr. Rosamond Jones
Dr. Clare Craig
Foreword: Professor Karol Sikora.
Finale: Sir Richard Dearlove

Clinical Press Ltd

The Death of Science

Clinical Press Ltd Publishers, Bristol, United Kingdom

© *Paul R Goddard, Angus G Dalgleish,* Chandra Wickramasinghe, Sir Richard Dearlove *and Clinical Press Ltd.* **2023**
First published in the UK 2023

A catalogue record for this book is available from the British Library
ISBN: **978-1-85457-113-7** *The Death of Science*
Published by:
Clinical Press Ltd. Redland Green Farm, Redland, Bristol, BS6 7HF

© Cover by Mark T Goddard

Contents

Quotes

"If liberty means anything at all, it means the right to tell people what they do not want to hear."
The unpublished introduction to Animal Farm (1945) George Orwell

1. Everyone has the right to freedom of expression. This right shall include freedom to hold opinions and to receive and impart information and ideas without interference by public authority and regardless of frontiers.
From Article 10 of the European Convention on Human Rights

"…we have forgotten how to analyse risk. If you don't accept that you will die some day, that you can never be safe, then you are a sitting duck for authoritarian policies which purport to be for your safety."
From *A State of Fear* by Laura Dodsworth

"…a new Dark Age made more sinister by the lights of perverted science."
Winston Churchill

"The duty of a university is to teach wisdom, not a trade; character, not technicalities. We want a lot of engineers in the modern world, but we do not want a world of engineers. We want some scientists, but we must keep them in their proper place."
Winston Churchill

"This reluctance to consider a new idea in the face of strong evidence is one reason why I think people should worry about science."
Roger Penrose (2022)

Acknowledgements

Many thanks to all the friends who have contributed to this book by discussion and argument. In particular we acknowledge the role of Lois Tutton and Stephen Goddard in the inception of this work, Dr Birger Sørensen of Norway for much of the science with regard to Covid-19, and Pete Bishop for help with the sub-editing.

Foreword

Science, throughout history, has been the bedrock of human progress and understanding. It has enabled us to comprehend the world around us, unravel the mysteries of the universe, and develop groundbreaking technologies that have transformed our lives. However, in recent times, there has been a growing concern about the waning influence and significance of science in society. This book explores in detail the notion of the "death of science" and the detrimental consequences that arise from its decline.

Throughout the ages there have been three powerful drivers to the pursuit of science – religion, politics and money. Beliefs from primitive sun worshipers to the powerful dominance of the Roman Catholic church, with its complex rules, have moulded the questions that science has been permitted to ask and more importantly those that it is not. The dissection room in Padua is a great example where the early anatomists, thwarted by religious doctrine, lowered the bodies into the canal below when the Vatican agents arrived.

'What is truth?' Pontius Pilate famously asked. Sometimes religions across the world simply suppressed it for their own ends.

Politics is a murky business even in democracies and here too we see undue influence over scientific endeavour. Just look at the Covid years fully discussed in this book. *We are following the science* was the strap line that led in the UK to a national catastrophe from which we are still recovering.

Research is expensive so money talks in choosing projects. Just look at the billions poured into drug development by big pharma. Huge salaries, bonuses and corporate jets dwarf even the well-funded cancer charity executives round the world and sway the choice of topics investigated.

The main contributing factor to the death of science is probably the diminishing appreciation for scientific inquiry in public discourse. In an age of misinformation and pseudo-science, scepticism and mistrust have eroded the credibility of scientific research. As a result, scientific findings are often met with incredulity and disregarded, or dismissed entirely. This disregard for empirical evidence hinders the progress of scientific inquiry and leaves society vulnerable to the consequences of ignorance. There is an increasing tendency to form a conclusion first and then collect the evidence to achieve that outcome. We have seen such approaches during the recent pandemic.

Another crucial aspect of the death of science lies in the dwindling financial support for scientific research. As governments and institutions face budget constraints, funding for scientific endeavours often takes a backseat. This reduction in financial support stifles innovation, inhibits the development of groundbreaking technologies, and limits our ability to tackle pressing global challenges such as climate change, public health crises, and resource scarcity. It also changes the balance of power to those institutions with massive financial capacity such as the pharmaceutical industry. By paying huge sums personally to advisors as 'key opinion leaders' it can control the decision making of future progress in high places. This leads to ideological stagnation. The rise of anti-intellectualism and populist movements further exacerbates the decline of science. In some instances, scientific expertise is viewed as elitist or disconnected from the concerns of ordinary people. This sentiment is fuelled by a rejection of evidence-based reasoning and a preference for emotional appeals and personal beliefs. When public opinion and policy decisions are driven by emotions rather than facts, the death of science becomes an imminent threat to societal progress.

The death of science is also reflected in the disregard for scientific consensus. When overwhelming scientific evidence is rejected or undermined, policymaking becomes susceptible to biases and vested interests. Issues such as climate change, vaccination, and genetically modified organisms (GMOs) have become battlegrounds for ideological debates rather than reasoned discussions based on scientific consensus. This erosion of trust in scientific consensus hampers our ability to make informed decisions and address critical challenges effectively.

The decline of science is perpetuated by the neglect of science education at various levels. Inadequate funding, outdated curricula, and a lack of emphasis on scientific literacy contribute to a society that lacks the necessary knowledge and critical thinking skills to engage with scientific advancements. The death of science, therefore, begins with the failure to cultivate a scientifically literate body capable of discerning reliable information from misinformation. It poses a dire threat to human progress and the well-being of society. It hampers our ability to understand and address complex challenges, perpetuates ignorance, and undermines evidence-based decision-making.

The following chapters examine the forthcoming crisis in topics such as Covid, recreational drug policy, medical education, climate change and several others. To avert this crisis, society must prioritise and rekindle a passion for scientific inquiry, foster scientific literacy, invest in research and development, and ensure that policymaking is informed by scientific consensus. Only by recognising the value of science and its profound impact on our lives can we prevent its demise and secure a brighter future for humanity. This book is a wake-up call to all of us.

Karol Sikora, Oncologist
June 2023

Preface

Science is moribund, lying on its death bed. Technology is developing fast, not least in the area of artificial intelligence, but not even the developers know how it works. Unbridled technology is dangerous and does not inform. It is not science. We have seen this in the development of weapons of war and the creation of new viruses.

Lies, specious argument and fraud abound in a variety of scientific endeavours including the treatment and vaccines for Covid-19. Managers and politicians have taken over where previously the scientists were in charge. They have been able to utilise the bizarre language and contradictory processes of political correctness, making themselves into the high priests of a new religion, one which spawns more politically correct managers and despises experts.

Decisions are taken in the name of science but with no grounding in logic except, perhaps, a perverse desire to undermine the professionals or on solely financial grounds. Medical scientists in particular find that they make advances, proven by trials, only for the commercial interest to evaporate even though the benefit has been proven.

It is not doubt or scepticism that is the problem but misplaced certainty. If the scientists or their masters are totally certain about something it is highly likely that the scientific principles are not being followed.

This book is a frightening but informed look at the parlous state of science from some honest and outspoken critics working within the scientific world. They have written the book not to criticise but as a warning. This has shown bravery as it is always difficult to go against the flow, buck the official line and the prevailing fashion. The recently unearthed secretive UK Government department known as the Counter Disinformation Unit has done their best (worst?) to discredit the authors but the authors have prevailed. There is always hope and possible answers are proposed. If we can understand where the problems lie we can give the kiss of life to science and resuscitate the dream.

Paul R Goddard and Angus G Dalgleish (Co-Editors)

Chapter 1

Introduction and Overview

Why have we chosen to create a book on The Death of Science when we "all know that science is still highly active". After all science has created the modern world in which we live so how can it have died?

Perhaps the phrase "we all know" sums up the problem. Many people now believe that we live in a post-modern world in which each and every person has a right to their own truth and there is no objective reality. Thus, in that scenario, we do not know that science is highly active and do not believe that it has created the modern world....or, if we wish to, we might believe exactly that. Such is the world of the post-modern person. They are convinced that they can believe just exactly whatever they like and, in their belief system, nobody has the right to disabuse them of their notions.

That's one side of the problem. The other is that, whilst most scientists are honest, hardworking and motivated for the good of all, some of the very scientists who should have been supporting the scientific process and scientific philosophy have recently done exactly the opposite.

This very small but influential minority have resorted to bullying, specious argument and outright dishonesty to get their individual agendas accepted as the legitimate scientific mantra as if that was not by its very nature the opposite to the way in which science should advance. Worst of all have been the so-called scientists who have set themselves up as The Science Which All Should Follow. Politicians have latched onto this with *We Are Following The Science*. This has been particularly obvious with regard to the Covid-19 pandemic and examples from the management of the pandemic will be used throughout the book. Which brings us to the politicisation of science. Once politics gets its grubby hands on scientists their science suffers.

So this book sets out to give a brief overview of the philosophy of science and then to give examples where postmodernism is damaging science, where scientists have cheated and lied and where politics has ruined science. Much of the book will be dedicated to the terrible outcomes when scientific principles are not adhered to and where politics and fashionable causes abuse science for their own aims. The final chapters will ask what can be done to save science and its mission to discover scientific truths about our world and the cosmos.

Science has not yet died but many of the problems mentioned above could be the death of science if they are not recognised for what they are. Be warned!

The History of Science

The word Science is derived from the Latin word *scientia*, which means knowledge. Science is usually considered to have started with the Greek philosophers but this is a particularly Eurocentric view. The pursuit of knowledge did not start with the Greeks and, curiosity being a human characteristic, it must have been a preoccupation of human beings for the past million years or so since they started knapping stones to make tools. Agriculture permitted some people to concentrate on more than just keeping alive and the development of writing allowed the culture to be passed on to future generations.

The Egyptians, the Indus Valley civilisation and the Mayans were all renowned for their medical skills and for astronomy. The Greeks codified philosophy and advanced rational thinking rather than superstition. Medicine in particular was moving away from reliance on magic and belief in gods but the Justinian plague (541-549 AD) showed up the weaknesses in medical knowledge and turned people back to religion and superstition. Whilst the Justinian Plague moved people towards superstition the Black Death (1350) did the opposite and labour was at a premium. With the movement of people from Byzantium science in Europe was rekindled in the Renaissance.

In 1794 the French Revolution allowed medical science in particular to flourish, The same year *The Age of Reason; Being an Investigation of True and Fabulous Theology* was published by English and American political activist Thomas Paine.We were now in the early Modern Period when logical thinking was the pre-eminent mode in philosophy and scientists were known as Natural Philosophers.

Postmodernism appears to have partly emerged from mid 20th century literary criticism rejecting the stability of meaning but was spurred on by the uncertainty rooted in some interpretations of Quantum Mechanics and the relativity of Einstein. This uncertainty has now engulfed all areas of education and hence re-entered the realm of science, the endeavour to seek out knowledge. But discarding certainty and stability has come with its own major drawbacks and in this book we point out that, taken to its extreme, postmodernism negates science leaving us with unbridled technology, misdirection and superstition.

Glastonbury High Street:
Sons of Asgard, Witchcraft Emporium and Magical Apothecary

Many of the examples in this book are from health care and medical science and are all the more serious because they can affect our lives directly. No less serious in the long run are failures in psychology, physics, cosmology etcetera and they are also discussed in the text.

What could be behind the death of science?

There are myriads of causes for the retreat from reason and apparent demise of scientific thinking. Many of these will be discussed in this book and some have already been mentioned. Here is a list of a few more possible causes with a comment or two:

General reasons for the demise of scientific thinking

Complacency. Perhaps there has been little reason for most people to be involved with science. There has been a massive increase in individual wealth but scientists are not usually in the top 1% unless they have developed an app that encourages online gambling or are working in the arms business. People are generally more comfortable than they were fifty years ago. Necessity is the mother of invention and if there is no necessity people will not be pushing innovation and science.

The Internet and Social media. Fake News and propaganda spread rapidly around the world via social media. Many people get all their news from social media. There has been a decline in the circulation of newspapers and a concomitant reduction in the number of journalists and a paucity of editors. The traditional media had many problems but generally had to keep to certain (rather ill-defined) standards.

Computers, Artificial Intelligence and Algorithms: The social media are partially controlled by poorly understood computer programs. The algorithms behind the programs tend to push reports and advertisements that coincide with the users previous likes and dislikes. Thus nonsense can be reinforced.

Media control and control of the media: A small cadre of rich people now control the traditional media. Governments also have considerable input.

Hubris (overweening pride): Scientists, like everybody else, can suffer with hubris. If they have written a book on a subject they are unlikely to want somebody to come along and show that it is all wrong. Children are now being taught that their ideas are of equal validity to everybody else's notions. This promotes hubris and downgrades the importance of expert opinion.

Change in funding and obsession with profit. The universities are now expected to be self-financing, the health services do not encourage research and commercial businesses have always needed to make a profit.

Education. Schools have often laboured under the mistaken belief that science is a lower form of thinking compared with the arts and literature. Now they are also a hotbed of political correctness (PC). The importance of good education has often been ignored by politicians.

Politics and PC. When the politicians get their hands on science it suffers. Political Correctness (PC) stifles debate.

Bureaucratic control. Working people are controlled by managers who know little or nothing about the subject matter and follow "managerial principles".

The wrong sort of scientist. There are, for example, too few scientists in medicine and too many in the arms industry.

Overpopulation. The increase in population has occurred due to advances in medicine and public health measures. These advances were not coupled with a decrease in fertility. The population demand attention to agriculture and industry for production of food and goods. They do not demand attention to science.

Reasons at the Individual level

Pursuit of pleasure. Pursuing a career in science of any sort takes hard work and application. It is easier and maybe more fun to be into gambling, drug taking, alcohol and tobacco.

Ambition. Some scientists deceive in order to further their individual ambition or simply to make a profit.

Fear (of war, disease, famine, loss of job or status). Many people are afraid of science and try to ignore it. People who are educated and could correct poor science may not do so if they are afraid of their managers or if their ideas could invite scorn and punishment. Fear of losing a job can also affect journalists and politicians who might otherwise have been in a position to influence science.

Error and Accident. It is certain that all human beings make mistakes and accidents can happen to anyone. Learning from mistakes is an important part of life but some people do not wish to learn or are afraid to admit they are wrong. *"The threat of malpractice suits, burdens related to electronic health records, intrusion by insurers, and other reasons plague all physicians today."* This tweet from Dana Corriel, MD, quoted in Medscape sums up how many doctors feel these days.[1]

Incompetence. The concept put forward by Laurence J. Peter explains this well: *"In a hierarchy every employee tends to rise to his level of incompetence... [I]n time every post tends to be occupied by an employee who is incompetent to carry out its duties... Work is accomplished by those employees who have not yet reached their level of incompetence."*

Malice and spite. Some people are consumed by malice and spite and this affects scientists, managers and politicians as much, if not more than most people. *"Cutting your nose off to spite your face"* comes to mind when thinking about some recent government advisers…

Lack of belief in traditional 'benign' religion and the rise of superstition and fundamental religion. Superstition is the antithesis of science. It has to be remembered that even Christianity just a short time ago burnt heretics at the stake.

Post Rationalism as a cause of the demise of scientific thinking

"I have a right to my opinion and my opinion is right…." Anonymous.

"…there's just as much truth in what I remember and how I remember it as there is in so-called objective facts." Prince Harry

A good friend recently told me about a conversation he had with his brother. My friend, in England, was talking over the telephone to his sibling in Australia. The guy in Australia stated that he believed in the Earth being flat.

'Then how did you get to Australia?' asked my friend.

'We flew round the rim,' the brother replied.

'So why are the planets and the moon round?'

'They're flat discs,' answered the brother.

'How do you explain the curving of the horizon and how do you explain gravity?'

'Now you are bamboozling me with science,' answered the brother. *'You know you're cleverer than me but I still believe that Earth is a flat disc so don't try to dissuade me.'*

In the book we will concentrate on the dearth of scientific thinking leading to the death of science. But is it possible that this is merely a side effect of a much bigger phenomenon? Perhaps we are witnessing and participating in the disintegration of rationalism- a key feature of the Enlightenment which has dominated Western thought since the late 18ᵀᴴ century. And maybe science is but one casualty.

Rationalism is a view that the world is logical. In the UK rationalism, empiricism, reason and enlightenment went hand-in-hand with a watered down version of Christianity. Even the affirmed atheists had usually been brought up in an Anglican or Catholic tradition. Rationalism gathered momentum during the Age of Reason in the seventeenth century followed by the Age of Enlightenment in the 18th century.

Rationalists believed that reality has a logical or rational structure that can be described and explained through logic and mathematics without the need for sensory experience.[2] For some rationalists, such as Descartes, a devout Christian, religion fitted firmly into their philosophy. In contrast the British Empiricists were of the view that we acquire ideas through experience of the world and that a broad and liberal toleration of religious and non-religious beliefs might lead to a better understanding of the truth.

The scientific method of investigation dates back millennia but a pivotal figure was Francis Bacon (1561 – 1626) who *"proposed a great reformation of all process of knowledge for the advancement of learning divine and human".*[3]

Empiricism was not really at such odds with Rationalism. The Empiricists still believed that a rational or logical meaning lay behind reality but that we developed the knowledge from *"evidence derived from observation tested hypotheses which in turn are re-tested when subsequent evidence becomes available"*…. another way of describing the scientific method.

Perhaps one of the nails in the coffin of rationalism was the development of Quantum mechanics and its many problems, including *"spooky action at a distance"* and indeterminacy, the inability to determine all the properties of matter simultaneously. Lord Kelvin had stated that *'there is no science without measurement.'* But indeterminacy puts a limit on the ability to measure things at the smallest, or quantum level and adds a sprinkling of randomness such that particles may be where you most expect them to be or, perhaps, on the other side of the universe.

The concepts of Newtonian physics were easy, or at least possible, for the educated public to understand. The principles of Quantum theory are difficult for even the most skilled scientist to explain and few who

The Death of Science

have not studied physics can get any grasp of the concepts.

Whilst Christianity was a supposedly logical belief system based on the idea of creation and redemption many new religions have sprung up and old, half-forgotten creeds resurrected.

The old Anglican version of religion did not impinge too directly on most people in the UK…they went to church for weddings, christenings and funerals. In 1900 church membership in the UK was about 25% but it has since dropped to 10%.

So where are we now? Some people nowadays have the attitude that all opinions, all 'stories' are equally valid and that firmly held views, however illogical or ill-informed, deserve to be respected. Politicians such as Michael Gove have espoused that *"The people of this country have had enough of experts.."* [4]

So is it now OK to believe in fairies, magic wands, witches and wizards? Some follow the mumblings of new-age Druids or flat Earth proponents. In this environment it is difficult to get people to accept scientific concepts. If you are happy to believe in fairies why would you believe in science? You can justify this by calling your irrational belief system as "my truth." The assumption is that other people are not allowed to question your own personal truth.

Most people do believe in science but, perhaps very reasonably, do not think that they are being told the truth in the press or even in the science journals. The media require sensationalism to sell their wares and this mitigates against the plain facts. Moreover the press do not have the time or expertise to explain difficult scientific concepts and therefore have to simplify in order that their readership can follow the story.

Of course this is compounded by the fact that science is seen as a fixed entity rather than a process aimed at developing a growing understanding of the world. Phrases such as 'we follow THE science' are nonsense and represent a cynical and ill-informed political hand washing much beloved of our leaders during the pandemic and championed by pharmaceutical companies etcetera. [5,6,7,8,9]

There is no *one* science and pundits who claim that they are the only fount of scientific truth are deceived, deluded or dishonest. As we shall see in the next chapter science proceeds like a many-headed hydra with the potential that any head may be removed when shown to be false.

The Death of Science

One important way in which human beings understand the world is by storytelling. We strive to understand reality by making up stories and passing them on to other people. We divide our stories into fiction and non-fiction but there is a crossover between the genres. It is often surprising when scientists tell us that nobody predicted a problem that has arisen because of science..... perhaps they had not bothered to read the many dystopian science fiction stories warning us about over population, reliance on machinery, killer robots taking over the world and our own creations coming back to bite us!

So within fiction there is truth and within non-fiction there are lies. Problems arise when individuals who love stories pass on fictions as if they are facts -sometimes in mischief or as a confirmation of prejudice. When a chance speculative posting of an unlikely idea goes viral then we have a problem.

This is compounded by a kind of perverse rationality where an idea, no matter how implausible is taken on and on to its fantastical conclusion. We have to remember that sometimes coincidences do happen!

Education

Maybe students should be equipped to be sufficiently skilled and confident to meet the unexpected and to view the world with a robust scepticism rather than regurgitating the name of a fictional character in an ancient poem.

In the 1960s there was some dismay that girls were not performing as well as boys when it came to examinations. Admirably there was a concerted effort to change this and one measure was to take into account course work. Recently the examinations were scrapped completely due to lockdowns and the GCSEs and A-levels were assessed by the class teachers. As will be mentioned later in the book nowadays more girls in the UK have sufficiently good enough grades to get into university than boys, a trend in many developed countries.

10

Analysis

A-level data shows record grades and biggest gender gap in a decade

Pamela Duncan, Ashley Kirk, Cath Levett and Niamh McIntyre

Number of students reaching A or A* doubles in 12 subjects since 2019 and girls beat boys in top maths grades

10 Aug 2021

Unfortunately the business of using marks assessed by the teachers has a built-in bias as shown by researchers at the University of Trento in Italy who looked at 40,000 test results. When marked anonymously boys did better than girls but when teachers marked their own class the girls came out top. [110]

Higher education was expanded under Blair and Brown, supposedly in order to ensure that Britain remained economically competitive. We needed more graduates. Unfortunately this apparently enlightened democratisation resulted in the monetisation of the university sector and coincided with the introduction of student loans to replace grants coupled with tuition fees.

Policy makers failed to articulate why young people should be educated in a university apart from saying they'll get a better job, be better paid and that this justifies the expense to the student and his parents. Hierarchies of subjects and disciplines are starting to be mouthed by politicians. Science, Technology, Engineering and Mathematics (STEM subjects) are to be considered more valuable than the arts or social sciences because of the better paid careers that follow. This, of course, misses what used to be the major point of a university education, namely to assist the recipient in knowing how to think in a broad way. In fact those actually involved in science and technology are increasingly looking to the arts for innovative insights. The arts and music make up an important percentage of the UK's GDP.

"The British record industry earned £519.7m overseas last year, the highest figure on record. Export revenues for music in 2020 grew by 6% compared to 2019, aided by the "explosive growth of music streaming", said record label association the BPI. One in 10 tracks streamed globally hail from the UK, with 300 British artists receiving 100 million streams or more. According to the BPI, the UK is still the largest exporter of music in the world, after the USA - but its share of the global market has dropped from 17% in 2015 to 10% last year. [12]

"In 2019 arts and culture contributed £10.47 billion to the UK economy. This corresponds to **0.5%** *of total UK economic output. There were an estimated 226,000 jobs in the arts and culture sector in 2019, 40% of these were based in London"*[13]

Why does everyone need to go to university at eighteen? Why is there not a greater focus on non-university further education, such as the training of plumbers, builders, electricians, care assistants, nursery nurses and such? All training for future jobs should be deemed as meritorious. Why are essential workers so frequently badly paid? University courses are being altered to suit the preconceptions and foibles of the students.

Lecturers forced to 'dumb down' for fear of being cancelled

By Louisa Clarence-Smith
EDUCATION EDITOR

UNIVERSITY professors are "dumbing down" their courses because they are concerned about being cancelled by intolerant students, according to an academic who feared for his life after he was falsely accused of Islamophobia.

Prof Steven Greer, a former human rights lecturer at the University of Bristol, has raised the alarm about freedom

a five-month investigation, the university exonerated him of all allegations.

An independent QC appointed during the inquiry also concluded that Prof Greer had not been guilty of harassment under the Equality Act 2010.

Prof Greer said universities were not doing enough to protect staff from "intolerant students" who could place academics at risk of reputational and physical attack "based on nothing but lies and distortion".

Daily Telegraph 13/2/2023

Lastly, one of the most frequently articulated ambitions for the school sector is to 'narrow the gap' between the levels of attainment of children coming from disadvantaged backgrounds and those from better off backgrounds. When children get to school at five they are already massively behind their better off classmates. When they get to secondary school it's probably too late to make a difference. We should invest heavily in pre-school education. In his great wisdom Michael Gove abolished Sure Start. A catastrophe.

Religion

When religion determines scientific ideas it is clear that the outcome is likely to be a compromise. It is hard to keep completely contrary ideas in one's mind so it is likely that the proposed theories to be tested by the scientific process will be biased.

Thus it is no surprise that the idea of a Big Bang comes from the scientists educated in the Christian tradition. They state that the universe appeared 13.8 billion years ago as a dimensionless point and then expanded into the massive space we now observe. This is akin to the Biblical creation story. Scientists from a Buddhist background may believe that the universe has always existed, perhaps expanding and contracting endlessly. Neither view is actually testable at present so the

Big Bang and the continuous universe theories are presently metaphysics rather than science. The new telescopes and further research may change this situation.

Historical Revisionism

Symptomatic of the post-rational mindset is the mad rush to re-write history, painting all the achievements of the western democracies as evil and ignoring the ongoing wickednesses in the developing world.

Thus Britain's role in the slave trade has full focus but its endeavour to prohibit slavery, throughout its empire and the rest of the world, is ignored. The greater the "white man" hero the more, in the modern idiom, he has to fall.

Winston Churchill is one example. The man was no saint but as a national leader in the time of crisis he was unparalleled. His role in defeating Hitler and his gang of racist criminals must never be diminished or forgotten. The revisionists, however, are having a particularly nasty try. This has led to a mob spray painting graffiti on his statue in London adding the words *"was a racist"* under his name. Reporting this the BBC ran the headline *"27 police officers injured during largely peaceful anti-racism protests."* [14] The BBC seems completely unaware of the irony in their reporting.

Now the former colonies, such a Barbados, are asking for reparations for slavery. Are they asking them from their cousins in Africa who actually sold them into slavery and benefitted from the trade? Of course not….they want the reparations from the country that actually called a halt to the slave trade and had to pay many millions of pounds to the slave owners in order to do so without a civil war. But who paid those millions of pounds? They came from the UK government from taxation of the masses via income tax and excise duty. The British people bore the burden and they would have to do so again if even more reparations are expected in addition to enormous foreign aid and the willing relinquishment of foreign countries to the people in those colonies.

Were the people in Britain living in unadulterated luxury when slavery was abolished in the British Empire? Far from it… during the industrial revolution the life expectancy of a Londoner reached a low of 35 years, children under ten were being forced up chimneys and into mills to work in appalling conditions.

What about slavery in Africa and the former Ottoman empire? There are still residues of slavery in these places and when the forced labour of political prisoners in China is taken into account there are probably numerically more slaves right now than there were in the 18th and 19th centuries.[14]

Going along with this revisionist approach to Western culture are the lead journal of medicine, *The Lancet,* and that of science in general, *Nature*.[14,15] In *The Lancet* an article was published entitled *"Racism is the Public Health Crisis"*. *Nature* stated *"Tackling systemic racism requires the system of science to change."*[13,15] Given this belief that science as we know it is inherently wrong it is no surprise that the editors of *The Lancet* and *Nature* managed to prevent any criticism of the Chinese laboratory and their role in making the Covid-19 pandemic. They did this by refusing to publish any rebuttal or reply to the opinion pieces that denied the involvement of the Wuhan Institute of Virology and that claimed, without any evidence, that the virus was natural and zoonotic. This will be discussed fully in this book. What other forms of censorship are they enacting preventing valid scientific discourse? We just don't know.

Medical Sciences

At the start of the Covid-19 pandemic in the UK it was clear that more people from the minority ethnic groups were dying than from the white population. Of the first ten doctors to die, many of whom had been called back in from retirement, nine were from ethnic minorities and only one was a white man. The pundits claimed, without any evidence, that it was due to racial prejudice. Unfortunately this was a very dangerous concept as it really implied that, in the short term, nothing could be done about it. A few "maverick" doctors were brave enough to point out that the deceased doctors were well respected consultants and something physiological had to be the cause. Possibilities included co-morbidities such as sickle cell trait and vitamin D deficiency. Tackling the former with pulse oximeters and oxygen via continuous positive airway pressure (CPAP), and the latter with D3 supplements brought down the mortality rate.

The suppression of repurposed drugs will also be discussed as will nuanced arguments about the efficacy of vaccines, a subject that few doctors are prepared to question.

Medicine is a scientific subject but, due to the unique nature of each individual, medicine also has to be an art and a learning process. We will argue in the book that a scientific approach to medicine is needed and that this is best fostered by encouraging medical doctors to concentrate on writing medical research papers as well as training in their specialties.

Physical Sciences

The physical sciences have a tendency to become hidebound in their theories just as much as any other subject. For years their has been a desire to justify results that do not comply with predictions and claim, quite erroneously, that they do. Frequently the originator of new ideas are derided as cranks and mavericks but when their suggestions turn out to be correct the new proponents of the ideas try to ignore the forerunners or alternatively claim that they knew the findings all along.

The layout of this book

In this book we first examine what science is by discussing the philosophy behind it. We then look at the ways in which people control science deceiving us by the use of clever but fallacious argument.

The third chapter examines political lying and the rise of political correctness (PC) and examines the rise of the managerial system which we argue has stymied scientific thinking. This is followed by a chapter on censorship, another obvious way of controlling scientists and science. The failure of the Peer Review system is tackled, particularly but not exclusively with regard to the Covid-19 pandemic. In later chapters we shall show that poor science led the catastrophic response to the Covid-19 pandemic, having started it in the first place! We also detail the outcomes of a lack of good science in health care, the loss of research acumen in medical training, poor science in climatology, cosmology and a myriad of other areas.

NB. The editors do not necessarily agree with every word written by the contributors but value their right to present their scientific hypotheses.

Paul R Goddard and Angus G Dalgleish (Co-Editors) Spring 2023

References: At the end of the book

Chapter 2

Philosophy of Science

The Editors with Jeremy Goddard & Mark Goddard

Lord Kelvin, the famous Victorian physicist, stated categorically that there was no science without measurement. The prevailing wisdom held that physics was complete and there was no need for further theories or discovery. This restricted view held by many scientists was challenged by Roentgen's serendipitous discovery of x-rays in 1895. Lord Kelvin arrogantly dismissed this as a hoax on the grounds that if they existed he would have discovered them himself!

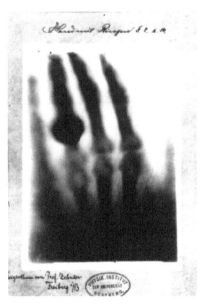

Anna Bertha Ludwig's hand 1895
The first medical X-ray by Wilhelm Röntgen.,
Public domain, via Wikimedia Commons

Lord Kelvin was wrong as the X-ray pictured above proves. Serendipity had allowed Roentgen to make a major scientific discovery.

So if it is true that science is not simply measurement what is it?

Science is the pursuit of knowledge by use of the scientific method but there is some debate as to what comprises the scientific method.

Karl Popper (1902 – 1994), the Austrian-British philosopher, suggested that any idea put forward as science should be open to tests that might falsify it. If there are no tests for an idea then it should not be considered as science. [1]

It is important to point out here that Popper was not decrying other forms of knowledge and expression such as art or music…simply that a theory should not be considered as science if there is no way of testing it. Whilst some people might like to think that science will eventually encompass everything and all knowledge there are aspects of human endeavour, and thus human knowledge, that do not lend themselves to this form of scientific testing and later in the book we will argue that science will always be incomplete.

So Popper believed that the main thrust of science is to try to disprove a theory as it may basically be impossible to prove it right. If the tests show the theory to be wrong this should be embraced and the theory altered or discarded for a new theory, which in turn should be tested.

In this book the Karl Popper approach is considered as the mainstream version of the philosophy of science. If a theory cannot be tested in any way it might be in the realm of art, metaphysics or religion, but generally is unlikely to be accepted as science.

Inductive reasoning is often cited as the method of science, inferring the validity of a general statement from a number of specific instances. This, although often used, is actually an illogical method and it is likely that most scientists use inference to the best explanation [1] which is often considered to be the simplest one. This is the essence of the Occam's razor … with competing theories the simplest one should be considered as the best unless or until a test falsifies it. The simplest theories are often more easily tested than complex ones because they rely on fewer assumptions.[2]

The human mind tries to create order from the events that affect it in order to better predict the future. We will never understand everything because we are within the system and ultimately cannot be objective. The scientific method is the nearest we can come to a method of finding a model of reality that is closest to the truth. If, of course, truth actually exists.

Medical Ethics and Bioethics

There are several codes of conduct. The Hippocratic Oath was written in Ionic Greek between the fifth and third centuries BC. The main principle stemming from the oath is *primum non nocere*, translated as 'first do no harm'. This is a principle that many non-medical scientists should also be advised to follow.

In Britain the Hippocratic Oath has been superseded by the General Medical Council's document *Good Medical Practice* which provides an overview of medical ethics.

The difference between Technology and Science

Technology and science are often confused. Technology, the practical application of science, relies on the knowledge created by scientists. However it does not necessarily aim to create new knowledge and a faith in technology *per se* can be a very dangerous and mistaken thing. The ongoing problems with so-called "Smart Motorways" are a good example. The UK government has been forced to halt alteration of more motorways to all-lane running due to the dangers correctly perceived by the public when the hard shoulders have been removed. But Westminster still puts faith in the technology saying *"Every new all-lane running motorway will open with technology in place to spot stopped or broken-down vehicles quickly."* [3,4] The fact is that building additional lanes would have been difficult and expensive and technology offered a quick fix which has turned out to be lethal.

Daily Mail
https://www.dailymail.co.uk › news › article-11945661

No more 'deadly' smart motorways to be built in Britain

Daily Mail 6.4.2023

Smart M-ways show Tories' child-like faith in technology

Daily Telegraph 24/4/2023

Sophistry and Specious Argument

It is important to understand how people can use argument to deceive in order that the deception can be detected. Sophistry is the use of clever but purposely misleading argument. Specious argument is superficially plausible, but actually wrong. So who uses such arguments?

The simple answer is that we all do. It is known as lying and, surprisingly enough, successful lying is a higher mental function. It is easier to tell the truth than it is to lie….to lie successfully requires imagination and a good memory.

If we all lie why does it particularly harm science? Because the whole object of science should be to seek out better and better models of reality. Put simply science is only worthwhile if it is trying to find out the truth and is worthless when people deliberately lie about it. (Except in very special circumstances which we shall discuss later).

So what type of specious arguments are there and how do we spot them?

Klemm in *Psychology Today* [5] made these bullet points:

- *Specious reasoning sounds good, but it is deceptively flawed.*
- *Specious reasoning is everywhere, and usually used to advance agendas.*
- *In a post-modern world in which everyone is allowed to have their own truth objective thinking is hard to find*

Disdain for Evidence

People who have no interest in evidence hold opinions without facts. Their logic may be sound but it is not based on any evidence, just opinion. It is hard to argue with such people unless you have a body of information to refute the groundless opinions.

Previous to the the Covid-19 pandemic many people had no knowledge of plagues or particular interest in medicine. Suddenly they have firmly held views on the science and are happy to disagree vehemently with other people. Their disagreements seem to be along political divides. Society has become more fragmented with firmly entrenched views towards the left and right wing of politics and this has spilled over into views on science. The nuanced argument and debate is being lost with politics leading views even among scientists themselves.

Changing the subject:
The straw man argument set up as a red herring.

One way of conducting an argument is to purposely misrepresent the views of the other side and then argue against the misleading ideas. The more reprehensible you can make the false position the easier will be your task. The opponents then have the difficult job of persuading the onlookers that the heinous views do not represent their position.

For example: *Debater A, argues logically that positive discrimination for one group results in negative discrimination for another.*

Opposing debater B then states that A is saying discrimination against minorities should continue. B then expresses strongly that such a view is immoral and that you are therefore not just wrong but also a despicable person. The debater B, gaining support from the audience, continues to argue against a view that A never professed in the first place!

In an appendix to this chapter at the end of the book the letter written by Peter Daszak (and pals) published in *The Lancet* in February 2020 will be discussed. It is a good example of a straw man argument.

Ignoring unfavourable evidence

The argument may appear sound but is based on evidence that only points in one direction. The perpetrator purposely selects evidence that supports their cause whilst ignoring evidence that they know is to the contrary. Such arguments use selective evidence. Drug companies are often guilty of this type of sophistry. Trials that are successful are always published but negative results are usually buried, never to see the light of day. Consider this when later reading about the actions of Pfizer.

Flawed premise

Syllogistic argument is a form of logic much used by Socrates. The correct form of syllogism works this way:

If all A are B
And this is A
Then A must be B

Many syllogistic arguments are based on one or more flawed premise. So here is a famous syllogistic argument supposedly put by Socrates:

All men are mortal
I am a man
Therefore I am mortal

Are the two premises necessarily correct? Do we know that all men are mortal? Despite the apparent fact that people have died in the past we cannot say with certainty that all the people alive now are going to die. Whilst it seems highly likely it is not a certainty. And what is mortality and immortality? This may seem to be a daft question but there are already cell lines from human beings that have outlived their original host and appear to have achieved immortality. And what if the person speaking the lines is not a man?

Thus even the simplest of logical arguments can be at fault.

Inverted Syllogism

The illogical inverted syllogism:

> *If all A are B*
> *And this is B*
> *Then B must be A*

If presented very quickly this type of specious argument may be accepted.

Here is an example:

People with pulmonary tuberculosis show cavitating lesions and lymph nodes on computed tomography of the chest.

This person has cavitating lesions and lymph nodes on computed tomography of the chest.

Therefore they must have pulmonary tuberculosis.

Knowledge of the correct form of a syllogism immediately indicates that something is wrong here. The answer is that the person *may* have pulmonary tuberculosis but there are many other causes of the same appearance, cancer (or other malignancy) being one of them.

Do people actually argue this way in medicine? Unfortunately they do so repeatedly.

Another particularly pertinent example goes like this.

SARS 1 came to human beings from bats via an intermediate animal

MERS came to human beings from bats via an intermediate animal

Therefore SARS 2 came to human beings from bats via an intermediate animal

This seems logical and certainly was worth pursuing as a theory. However the logic is not impeccable … two instances do not show that all unusual coronaviruses have arisen that way. Moreover the circumstances were different…within a short space of time the researchers were able to discover the interim animals with SARS1 and MERS but have not done so for SARS2…. Apart from a humanised mouse from the laboratory.

(Note: The poor pangolin and the raccoon dog have been exonerated).

Circular logic

This is argument that appears to be supported by self referral.

"Survival of the fittest" is a slogan deeply embedded in Darwinian and neo-Darwinian evolutionary theory. It is put forward as the driving force for natural selection and hence evolution itself. But is this really true? When discussing this with biologists and discussing any particular species you may receive the reply that they must be the fittest if they are the species that survived because survival itself proves they are the fittest. The biologists seem unaware that this is circular logic. Sometimes the species may be the fittest but at other times it might be sheer chance that one species survived and another demised. The circular argument does not advance the case though it appears to do so.

Take an example: There are two species of mammals on two separate land masses, A and B, surrounded by the sea. Maybe the species on island A is better fitted for survival than that on land mass B or perhaps the opposite way round. The sea level rises and because A is lower than B the entire landmass is inundated and the species on island A is wiped out…..not because A is less fit to survive but due to bad luck.

Survival of the fittest only works when two species are directly in competition with each other and even then chance must play a large part.

Taking the moral high ground: virtue signalling

Symbolic statements and gestures that convey virtue are frequently used to impart authoritativeness. Who can argue against virtue? Klemm .[5]

Argue that you are providing benefit to all and the poorest must come first and you instantly acquire an air of saintliness. The facts must not stand in the way of righteousness and politicians often use such arguments. *(See the example below)*

| *From The NHS Constitution* | **6. The NHS is committed to providing best value for taxpayers' money** |

Religion constantly employs such tactics. Mother Teresa is an example. Made a saint in 2016 many are still critical of her and her virtue signalling:*"The New York Times reviewed the British documentary Hell's Angel, a film that highlighted some of Mother Teresa's flaws, the paper concluded that she was "less interested in helping the poor than in using them as an indefatigable source of wretchedness on which to fuel the expansion of her fundamentalist Roman Catholic beliefs."* [7]
Virtue signalling has become rife in the younger generation who, keeping to the tenets of political correctness, glory in being *"Woke"*.

Misuse of Statistics

Looking at the headline reproduced above you might be forgiven for believing that the Belfast doctor always misdiagnosed nearly half of his cases. The statistics are not exactly a lie: they are simply misleading. Of the deaths of patients in his care nearly one half were misdiagnosed, an appalling statistic but not nearly as bad as if he misdiagnosed half of all his patients. Clearly misdiagnosis may have contributed to the deaths thus raising the percentage of wrong diagnoses in the group of fatalities. A survey of 2,500 patients showed a misdiagnosis rate of about 20%, still bad but under half the rate of the headline.

So are statistics often misrepresented in this way? The answer is, of course, yes they are!

One of the best books on this subject was written by Darrell Huff and entitled *How to Lie with Statistics*. [8] The book was written in 1954 and reprinted in 1973 and 1991. Secondhand copies are readily available on the internet. We would thoroughly advise buying one.

Here are the three first chapter headings :

1. *The sample with the built-in bias*
2. *The well-chosen average*
3. *The little figures that are not there*

We will give a couple of examples from our own experience.

Some years ago there was much debate about cyclists wearing helmets. Should it be made mandatory in order to avoid head injuries? A neurosurgeon weighed into the debate. He looked round his ward and through his records and said that there were equal numbers of cyclists with head injuries who had worn helmets as those who had not and therefore decided that wearing a helmet made no difference. In fact his intervention was unscientific and the statistics meaningless because of the built-in bias, and the little figures that are not there. In particular the neurosurgeon had no details about the populations the samples came from(see the appendix to this chapter for more information.)

Recently we have been regaled with huge numbers of statistics with regard to Covid-19. Deaths within 28 days of testing positive for Covid-19 were used whether or not the person had actually died from the disease. A relative caught the Covid in January 2021 and phoned up a month later. He wittily remarked that at least he could now be run over in the street and killed without being a Covid statistic!

Part of the graph is missing? Here is an example from NASA. Note that 0 to 3 are missing making it look as if nearly all the sea ice has gone. The loss has plateaued out but NASA suggest that the trend continues.

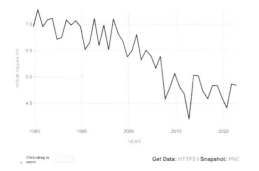

Key Takeaway:

Summer Arctic sea ice extent is shrinking by 12.6% per decade as a result of global warming.

Parametric statistics versus non-parametric statistics

Many forms of statistics used in medicine rely on the figures measured being part of a normal distribution. This is known as the bell curve because of the bell like shape. Whilst height, weight and IQ do tend to comply with such a curve most measurements in sick people do not. Thus it might be possible to use parametric stats for height, weight and IQ but using them for medical conditions brings in a lot of unwarranted assumptions. Why should diseases conform to such strict distribution?

In fact they don't and assumptions based on the idea that they do conform to the normal distribution curve are gravely misleading.

Graphs of normal distribution curves (from Wikipedia)

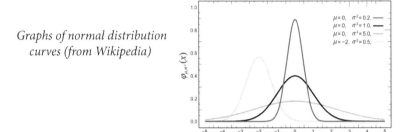

Non-parametric statistics can, for example, use the ranking of the results rather than using the actual measurements. For example one could ask judges to give beauty contestants a score of 1 to 10. Say there were 10 contestants and 4 judges. Three of the judges may have considered the contestants were all very similar and gave them all scores between 4 and 6. The fourth judge decided one of the contestants, person A, was exquisite (or perhaps A had bribed the judge) and the judge gave A a score of 10 and the other 9 just a score of 1 each. Parametric statistics would use the actual figures and A would win whether or not he/she was placed highly by the other three judges. Non-parametric stats may give a completely different result as it is the ranking that is totalled and averaged, not the score. If the other three judges put A on a lowish score (4 or 5) then A would get a low ranking in their results and, despite the high ranking by the 4th judge, A would lose (see also the Appendix at the end of this book).

How to lie well !

There are many other ways of presenting misleading argument. A knowledge of psychology can help if you wish to lie successfully. The police and cross-examining barristers use a trick to spot whether or not people are lying ….. simply keep asking the same question! Maybe, if they are clever, the questioners will alter the form of the question although it is really asking the same thing. In essence, however, what they are trying to do is test the person's memory and ability to confabulate.

A lie is something made up, it is fiction. It is therefore harder to remember than the truth which is why, if you want your lie to be successful, it should be as near to the truth as possible without actually deviating from the fiction you wish to impart. Perhaps also you should keep the answer a little vague so that you can incorporate later interpolations.

Rhyming and Alliteration

If you wish to convince a large number of people then a rhyming slogan helps. Psychologists have discovered that rhyming slogans, aphorisms etcetera are believed more often than simple prose. For example *"What sobriety conceals, alcohol reveals"* was judged more accurate on average than: *"What sobriety conceals, alcohol unmasks."* [9] This is known as the rhyme-as-reason effect, or Eaton-Rosen phenomenon or even the Keats' Heuristic[10-15]. So beware of slogans and particularly beware of conclusions that rhyme…. we have a built-in tendency to believe rhymes. Can you remember the following?

- *A Mars a day helps you work rest and play.*
- *Bounty, the quicker, picker upper*
- *A million housewives every day, pick up a tin of beans and say "Beanz meanz Heinz"*
- *No battery is stronger longer*
- *Once you pop, you can't stop*
- *You Only Get an 'OO' With Typhoo.*

They may all be basically untrue but they rhyme, are easy to remember and *seem* true. Of course a million housewives don't say *"Beanz meanz Heinz"*. For a start it is bad English so very, very few people would ever say it even if the sentiment was true but we forgive the advertiser because it is amusing and it rhymes.

A Mars bar a day is probably not really good for you but we still remember the slogan. But what about old homespun wisdom?

'An apple a day keeps the doctor away' seems more convincing and easier to recall than *'If you eat an apple a day you will not get sick.'* (Throwing the apple at the doctor would certainly keep her away but that is probably not what is meant.) Try changing the following so they do not rhyme and then see if they are as convincing:

- *"Red sky at night, shepherd's delight. Red sky in morning, shepherd's warning."*

- *"A friend in need is a friend indeed."*
- *St. Swithun's day, if thou dost rain, For forty days it will remain;*
  St. Swithun's day, if thou be fair, For forty days 'twill rain no more

Alliteration works in a similar way. Do you recall *Guinness is good for you?* We really wish it was! *Safe and effective* (the NHS vaccine motto) is an alliterative form of rhyme so immediately suspect (see chapter 12).

Lying by joking

Saying a lie as a joke is a way of getting the idea into somebody's mind whilst having the excuse that you were only trying to be humorous:
'Many a true word is spoken in jest'

Lying in a foreign language

Usually for English speakers the other languages that would be best for convincing people are Greek, Latin or French. The foreign quote gives an unwarranted air of superior knowledge.

For example at the end of your discourse you could say *"quod erat demonstrandum, Q.E.D."*. This means 'what was to be demonstrated' and implies that you have logically proven your point, and you have hammered this home by speaking in Latin.

We all know of politicians who do this to show how clever they are!

Nondisclosure

Scientists have a duty to disclose whether or not they have a conflict of interests. Even if someone is trying to be impartial when conducting research they may be subconsciously biased.

A person working for a tobacco company would, for example, not be the best person to trust with regard to the harmful effects of cigarette smoking, a person working for a brewery might be biased in favour of alcohol, a virologist might be biased in favour of virology experiments and a surgeon biased in favour of surgery.

If the person's employment relies on a particular mode of action they might well find excuses to support their activity. Even worse they may purposely mislead by stating they have no conflicts of interest whilst presenting misleading information.

Peter Daszak (mentioned earlier) did not disclose in his published *Lancet* letter that he had been working on coronavirus research with the very laboratory in Wuhan that he stated could not possibly have been the source of the novel coronavirus that caused the present pandemic. All the evidence pointed towards that source yet he failed to disclose his clear conflict of interest! (see the appendix to this chapter).

Nondisclosure is a form of lying…*we have left undone those things that we ought to have done and there is no truth in us* (Book of Common Prayer). Put simply, it is fraud.

Lying by necessity

Are we arguing that lying is always wrong and, as in the Vera Lynn song, *It's a Sin to Tell a Lie*?

No! That is not what we are saying. Lying functions as a necessary part of human existence permitting people to socialise and work together in a complex society. Where would fiction, art and religion be without some lies? How could marriages be sustained without the occasional white lie?

But science is supposed to be unlike other aspects of human endeavour. It is the search for truth and knowledge, whether or not that truth exists. Lies should not generally be employed in science unless they serve a higher purpose.

Having stated that it is clear that there will be occasions when scientists are morally bound to lie. We have to be grateful that German physicists convinced the Nazi high command that creating an atomic bomb was impossible.

So where does lying, a higher mental function, fit in with science, the pursuit of knowledge?

The lying or fiction is the imaginative part at the beginning of scientific research….make something up then try to test it. Imaginative people are good at this but it goes wrong when they try to hold onto their ideas when they are proven to be manifestly wrong. Or, even worse, purposely lie to hide their failures.

Comment

So there we have it. Lying is a common behaviour but does not fit well with science. Belief in peculiar ideas is also common, spurred on by people who may know full well that the things they are saying are not true. In a recent lecture about the Covid-19 pandemic we were reminded of the many strange ideas people had about the cause of the disease.

The lecturer lumped together the beliefs he called pseudo-scientific lies or "scientism." These included the idea that the symptoms were due to the 5G masts, that there is no virus and that it is a bioweapon. Also he mentioned the "microchips in the vaccine" theory.

Are these science or pseudoscience? Can they be tested and potentially falsified?

Firstly the 5G masts. In some of the places that they pulled down masts there was no 5G technology so any cases could not have been caused by 5G. In the UK Huawei were installing some of the masts. Did Chinese installers inadvertently spread the Covid virus? This could have supported the 5G myth but the disease was not caused by 5G as there is no correlation with the places that 5G is up and working.

Viruses are very small infective agents that pass through a filter. It is true that their distinction from bacteria is not as clearcut as people may have thought. Some bacteria, such as Tuberculosis, can have a stage in which the organism has no cell wall, much like a virus. Moreover many of the bits of so-called junk DNA in the human genome do code for virus fragments……quite why this is the case nobody really knows, though there are many theories. People who do not believe in viruses at all are similar to flat-earthers. They have a fixed opinion and no facts.

There are no microchips in the vaccine. Microscopy proves this, so the theory is shown to be false.

Suggestions that the Covid -19 virus is a bioweapon are much harder to disprove. In later chapters we shall attempt to convince you that the virus was made in a laboratory in Wuhan. It was almost certainly released accidentally but since the laboratory in Wuhan was under the control of the military and the virus and vaccine were tested on political prisoners it almost does fit the description of a bioweapon and certainly was unethical and criminally negligent. So that is not pseudoscience and it is not a conspiracy theory.

We shall see in subsequent chapters that many scientists do lie, to the huge detriment of the subject. Moreover there are lies and half-truths from the people with influence in science, be it the government, royal colleges and societies, governing bodies or simply the media. At other times they are simply mistaken but prefer not to admit their mistakes.

References: At the end of the book

Chapter 3

Politics and Science

Part 1
Political Lying, Political Correctness and the Managerial Process
The Editors

The Problem With Liberal Democracies

The rise of science has been inextricably linked with the development of the modern world and modern government.

We live in a "liberal" representative democracy. It is unlikely that science would have developed the way that it has if such governments had not come into existence. In a liberal democracy such as the one we live in, the United Kingdom, the tacit agreement has always been that the business of government is left to the politicians who we elect periodically. In return they leave us, the populace, alone to get on with whatever we like as long as it is within the law. There is some overseeing of the politicians by the partially elected, partially inherited House of Lords and the entirely hereditary royalty (for 70 years QEII, now Charles III) and the politicians' job is to keep the peace and prosperity in the country.

There is no standing army in the UK and the policing of the UK is generally light, relying on the population agreeing to be policed. But this policing has broken down with precious few of the "classical" crimes, such as burglary or theft, being solved or even investigated and peculiar new crimes being punished severely.

In recent years big changes have occurred to our country's governance.

Firstly we joined Europe (1973) and then, with Brexit, we left (31.1.2020). But many of the laws passed by the EU have been absorbed into British law without being overseen by our system and most of them remain. Back in 2008 PRG wrote about this pointing out that the laws absorbed into our system from the EU were well over one hundred thousand by 2003. [1]. They may well be past 200,000 by now but we will probably never know as the politicians told us there were too many even to list! Added to this is the slavish adherence by British courts to a peculiar version of Human Rights. Too often the Human Rights of the criminal, often a terrorist who the Government wishes to deport, trump the views of the UK Government. Thus a criminal, who has preached hate and convinced people to bomb innocent citizens, can claim that being deported back to his country of origin would interfere with their right to a family life. So when did one hate-filled person's human rights to a family life become so important that they are more important than an elected government that represents the people? Why are one person's human rights more important than another and when does a criminal act eventually become so heinous that the person forfeits basic human rights?

Secondly we have, by stealth, been taken over by "political correctness" (PC). This apparently means *"the avoidance of forms of expression or action that are perceived to exclude, marginalise, or insult groups of people who are socially disadvantaged or discriminated against".* [2] In practice the one group who are usually perceived as not being socially disadvantaged or discriminated against are white men. All other groups are tacitly considered as possible targets for un-PC activity even if they are in a majority.

The country is now divided into those people who consider themselves to be "Woke" and therefore believe that they fully understand how people should behave (mostly young and left-wing leaning in political terms) and those (mostly older white males) whose behaviour is considered to be offensive even if no offence is intended.

In the past it was possible to understand most laws with just a little bit of study. Now older people are bewildered by the complexity and the large number of laws. How can you have a law whereby the person "offended" is the one who judges whether or not the person they accuse of offence was offending them even when such offence was entirely non-intentional? Intent was always part of law but has now been removed as an important distinction. This has reached such a parlous state that a person can judge that they have been offended by someone using the wrong pronoun when addressing them….. a woman can decide to "change gender" with no obvious change in appearance and then decide they are offended because someone thinks they are female…and, of course, vice versa. Bristol University has even suggested that people can self-gender as a cat if they wish to do so. [3]

It is commonplace for university students to "deplatform" speakers if they, the students, do not agree with the speaker. But what does "to deplatform" mean? Google states *"To prevent (a person holding views regarded as unacceptable or offensive) from contributing to a forum or debate."* Is it still a debate if people with opposing views are prevented from taking part? Are young people unable to consider ideas and opinions that differ from their own and thence becoming unfit for the workplace as recently suggested by the Channel 4 chief?[4]

Thirdly …there has been an enormous change in the disparity between the rich and the poor. In the past the top boss of a firm might expect to earn twenty times as much as his average employee. Now many of the chief executives earn thousands of times the average wage. Moreover their loyalty to their staff is very questionable. Fire and rehire (at a lower rate of pay) has almost become a normal practice. There are now some individuals that are so rich that they have more money at their disposal than governments. Arguably these unelected oligarchs are now more powerful than the elected governments.

Thus we have nations which seem at times on the brink of major civil unrest. For example, one day there may be a huge protest about excessive use of oil which the protesters believe is fuelling climate change. The next day there is an equally noisy and abusive protest about the high cost of fuel.

In these circumstances how can the normal role and practice of science continue? Put simply: it can't.

In the past academics were allowed to beaver away at some obscure area in science with no expectation that their pure research would pay for itself. Now governments want "value for money" from universities and the universities in turn are constantly looking at ways of making money, attracting fee-paying students, making profitable discoveries that can be patented or copyrighted and getting huge grants from corporations or individuals.

Meanwhile the NHS, where many medical researchers flourished in the past, has gradually starved the frontline of cash whilst feeding the managers with higher and higher salaries. Individuals are no longer encouraged to do research and doctors are now appointed as consultants without having published a single paper. This will be discussed later in the chapter written by Dr Jarad.

Moreover in medicine the pharmaceutical model of research now rules the roost and is called *"evidence based medicine"* as if none of the previous research and development, experience and knowledge constitutes evidence at all. Double-blind, randomised cross-over techniques are the mantra ....something we have known about since studying for degrees. We are, however, fully aware that much of medical practice cannot fit into such research and does not need to. So this is the background to the writing of this book.

The Rise of Political Lying

Lying has always been part of politics but the way in which it has become almost universal has only been apparent in the past twenty-five years or so. [5]

Winston Churchill was famous for his use of rhetoric. His excellence at writing and delivering speeches enabled him to persuade people to follow his line of argument even when it was not completely factual. In times of crisis, such as the two world wars, political leaders have been economical with the truth for the sake of national security.

Latterly the situations have not deserved such behaviour but political expediency has. In other words the politicians have lied in order to further their own goals.

At one time, if a politician was found to be lying, he or she would be expected to resign. Latterly that has rarely been the case until the falsehoods have become so egregious that the politician's own party turn against them, as has happened to Boris Johnson recently.

Take the example of the Labour manifesto of 1995/6. This promised that the Labour Party, if they won the election and formed the government of the UK, would not bring in private finance initiatives (PFIs) to finance the NHS. As soon as they were in power in 1997 that is exactly what they did with no resignations and no apologies. Now we are reaping the harvest from those bad decisions and paying vast amounts for a health service that is barely functioning.

In 2002 the Department of Health was busy publishing star ratings for hospitals. In the spin that they put out they told everybody that they had collected data on all aspects of the performance of hospitals: the clinical results, the management, the complaints and the budgetary achievements. The hospital that editor PRG was working at, University of Bristol Hospital Trust (UBHT), was given zero stars which hardly seemed fair as they were doing some very good clinical work. So he looked at the published figures collected by the Department of Health inspectors and noticed some amazing anomalies. The hospital had apparently performed the best in England on clinical scores but had overspent. Another large teaching hospital on the other side of the country had achieved only half the UBHT score on the clinical results but had stayed within budget. They had been awarded three stars whilst UBHT had been given zero. Other hospitals followed the same trend. If they had overspent they received a very low rating and if they were within budget they were awarded three stars. Not surprisingly the trusts that had overspent had mostly performed very good clinical work and staying within budget was a sure-fire way of achieving poor clinical results. So the star rating system was not, as put out to the public, a judgement on which was the best hospital from a patient's perspective. In fact the three star hospitals were the worst ones for a patient.[6]

Around that time it became apparent that the political class had a new word for lying. They called it spin and the unelected assistants, or special advisers, who concocted the lies were called spin doctors. By 2013 the average pay of a special adviser was standing at £73,470 per annum (about three times the starting salary of a real medical doctor.) There is a special section in this book on the UK government's reaction to the Covid-19 pandemic but it is important here to point out that there has been a considerable degree of spin and some downright lying. In addition behavioural scientists were employed to "nudge" people to obey the UK Government's policies. They did this by creating a climate of fear, always exaggerating the risks.[7]

It is our contention that the biggest sin conducted by the NHS, with special powers granted by the government, was seeding the nursing homes with untested people discharged from hospital thus spreading Covid-19 right through the care homes and killing thousands of the most vulnerable. Remember… that was at a time that they were spinning the line that the lockdowns and hardship were necessary to protect the NHS *and* save the vulnerable. Perhaps the lockdowns did protect the management of the NHS but in no way were they protecting the vulnerable and we contend that the actions were entirely incompetent and we are now living with the consequences.

Recently civil servants in the UK have become politicised and many pursue a "woke" agenda, even to the point of accusing ministers of bullying because they "stare at them too hard."

Wokeness and Political Correctness

Some of the most well-meaning people have been co-opted into pushing an agenda that is categorically opposed to scientific thinking. There is no doubt that many of the views regarding gender, race, disability and age that were prevalent up until the end of the Twentieth Century were cruel and wrong. However the ideas brought in by political correctness (PC) have often done little to improve the situation and have frequently inflamed disagreements.

How can PC be defined? In its simplest form it is the avoidance of statements or views that exclude, marginalise or insult a minority group. On the surface this would appear to be a very laudable aspiration. It is, however, a one-sided approach. It is better to treat everybody equally rather than to constantly side with one group, be they in the majority or minority. Thus political correctness has become very unbalanced.

In practice there is one group of persons who are considered fair game: white, heterosexual "Anglo-Saxon" males. This is considered to be fair as according to PC they, apparently, are the ones who have been oppressing everybody else. The exponents of Woke are very proud of their views and try hard to let people know how Woke they are. *(See Chapter 2 "Virtue Signalling).*

Hence quotas are set up in which a much higher percentage of women, ethnic minorities and minority sexual preference is represented than the average in the main population. In fact we have been in the situation where we have been told that to suggest that "the best person should get the job" is a bigoted, racist and sexist statement. No, the best person cannot be allowed to get the job any longer …. it has to be the person who best fits the PC agenda not the job specification.

This is very discouraging for all parties. The people who get the jobs may think that it is simply because they are meeting diversity requirements and feel diminished because of that. The people who do not get appointed despair that the appointments committee have been biased. Organisations are thus being encouraged to be unfair.

Recently one of the editors of this book was invited by the University College Alumni to a meeting entitled *Emerging women's leadership course.* Naturally, being a man, he had not really been invited as it was only for women or people who identify as women. Imagine the outcry if this had been a course for men, *The Emerging Men's leadership course.* The sexist nature of such a course would have created a furore. The recipient replied to the actual University College Alumni invitation *"Why are sexist courses such as this occurring? Can you not see that this is divisive?"* and invited reply *"I would be interested to hear your views on this."* No reply was forthcoming. In universities it is OK to have racist or sexist courses as long as they point in one direction….against white men.

In the UK there is an active organisation entitled *Women in Medicine.* No such organisation exists for men despite the fact that it is the male of the species who are in a serious minority in healthcare.

In the music industry there are awards for Music of Black Origin. Where are the awards specifically for music of white origin? It is our belief that all music is a fusion of ideas from multiple cultures so we would not want to see the latter award but why just pick out the Black origin? And why do people try to suggest that white people playing blues, jazz, soul or hip-hop are appropriating black culture? Can they not understand that there have always been people of many backgrounds playing the music unless an extremely remote tribe is involved? Even a little study reveals the fact that the Blues, for example, are the result of European and African music combining, that there were many people of different races combining to create jazz and as one of the originators of soul music, the genius Ray Charles declared when criticised for playing Country Western standards, *"If it's good music, it's good music."*

How has this become possible and why have we allowed it to pervade society and, in particular, academia to the extent that it has?

Some would argue that we are completely wrong and the facts are the opposite. The prevalent PC view is that women and minority ethnic groups are being discriminated against in all areas of UK society.

But let us consider university places:

Female/Male as University Undergraduate Students

In the UK every year since 2010, females have been in the majority of undergraduate students. [8]

2019-2020
56.6% female, 44.1% male
Compare this with the general population UK
50.59 % female, 49.41% male

The Death of Science

White/Ethnic: as University Undergraduate Students

Starting undergraduate study in the 2019 to 2020 academic year:
72.6% White, 12.2% Asian, 8.7% Black, 4.5% Mixed ethnicity 2.0% other. [9]
Compare this with the general population
White 87.2%, Black/African/Caribbean/black British 3%, Asian/Asian British: Indian 2.3%, Asian/Asian British: Pakistani 1.9%, mixed 2%, other 3.7% (2011 est.) [10]

These simple figures show that white students are not getting the percentage of places in university that they should do commensurate with their proportion in the population and in particular white males are very under-represented. But the constant outcry is that the "minorities" are under-represented in higher education.

We are not arguing that the students have been chosen incorrectly. We have no idea about that. All we can tell from the figures is that the PC outcry about "minorities" in this particular case is now completely untrue. They are not under-represented on a simple percentage basis.

Deprivation and family income

It is wrong to assume that families identifying as "white" have the highest income. In fact the Indian, Chinese and Arab households have higher income on average than white households and Black, Bangladeshi and Pakistani have lower income. [11] Moreover going to an expensive school does not mean the families are wealthy…they may have used up all their spare cash to send the child to the school!

Living in an expensive area also does not mean a family is wealthy…in fact it often means the opposite as a poor family in an expensive area is often very badly off. It is better to be poor in a poor and cheap area than in a wealthy and expensive area. It is, of course, better still to be wealthy!

There has been a recent push to take more university entrants from people in poorer areas. This has been achieved by taking fewer from wealthier areas without knowing whether those excluded *were* actually wealthy.

Universities stifling free speech?

As mentioned earlier the PC lobby has many laudable aims, trying to prevent offence to minorities being one of them.

But what if the views of a minority are simply wrong, demonstrably wrong and even harmful? Surely in such a situation offence has to be accepted since without it mitigation of a harmful situation cannot occur.

Undergraduates are now significantly less supportive of free expression than they were six years ago [12]. 61% of one thousand students surveyed now believe that their own university *"should ensure all students are protected from discrimination rather than allow unlimited free speech."*

A cynical view of this might be that the majority of the students surveyed have benefitted from the politically correct attack on white males and owe their places to the PC lobby, thus they will support their twisted view of the world in which the word discrimination can be applied to anything that upsets their supposed minority.

In fact the Woke mode of thinking has mostly emanated from a strong left wing bias in British and American government financed schools. It is now *de rigour* for teachers to attend management courses where they are told how they should think on these issues. If they move out of line they are likely to be reprimanded and even dismissed from their posts. Similar brainwashing is occurring to doctors, nurses and other professionals in the UK's National Health Service.

Freedom of speech in universities is under attack. A record number of speakers and events at English universities and colleges were cancelled in 2021 according to the Office for Students. OfS is an executive non-departmental public body, sponsored by the Department for Education. They are worried that lawful debate is being stifled and it really does look as if they have cause to be concerned.

Let us look at some real life examples of the way that the censorship of thought and deed due to political correctness can potentially harm people and patient care suffers:

Political Correctness and health problems

Obesity

Short Case Report
A man in his late fifties had his weight and height measured. The general practitioner, an honest cove, told him that on the Body Mass Index (BMI) he was not just overweight but bordering on obese. Shocked, the man

decided to lose weight and did so successfully losing twenty-two kilograms in a couple of years. As a result the pains in his knees and hips considerably reduced and his overall health improved.

This happened a decade ago but many GPs are now afraid to tell patients that they are obese as it is considered "too offensive" and, because the doctor is being too obscure, they are not shocked into losing weight. Some pressure groups are telling the public that "fat-shaming" is "inappropriate behaviour" and that fat people should accept their body shape.

The charity Obesity UK, have recently tried to create guidelines so that doctors avoid using terms that upset patients. The charity also says clinicians should avoid using "threatening" phrases such as telling patients: "If you don't lose weight you will end up with your leg chopped off, or just plain dead." [13]

However, if the doctors use 'unthreatening' words it is likely that the seriously overweight will not listen to the advice.

According to Roger Collier[14] obesity is a clinical term, applicable to a person whose body mass index (BMI) is 30 kg/m2 or higher. In most Western nations, about 20% of people fall into this category. Obesity even has a code in the International Statistical Classification of Diseases.

The health risks from morbid obesity (above 40 kg/m2) include: [15]

- Type 2 Diabetes
- High Blood Pressure
- Heart Disease
- Stroke
- Sleep Apnoea
- Metabolic Syndrome
- Osteoarthritis
- Gall Bladder disease
- Some cancers
- Kidney Disease
- Problems in pregnancy
- Emotional and social problems
- Mental illness including clinical depression and anxiety
- Low quality of life, body pains, difficulty with physical functioning

The number of people with obesity is truly alarming. At the World Health Assembly in May 2022 the World Obesity Federation predicted that one billion people globally (1 in 5 women and 1 in 7 men) will be living with obesity by 2030. [16] In the UK the cost to the NHS of obesity is truly appalling.

Self-Gendering

Sex is not as binary as most people think however there is obvious science behind the view that most people can be viewed as either male or female. It is the Y chromosome that determines the sex. The standard Female genetics reside in the XX chromosomes whilst the Male chromosomes are XY. The most common divergence from this simple state of affairs is XXY occurring in about 1 in 500 to 1 in 1000 males. This is known as Klinefelter's syndrome and their phenotypes (body parts etc.) are always male. They do not usually know that they have the syndrome until they are tested due to fertility problems.

There are also genotypes XXX (1 in 1000 females) and XO (1 in 2500 live female births) and other much rarer variations.

Recently the terms gender and sex have diverged in their meaning. Nowadays many people consider that gender is socially derived whilst sex is genetically determined. In this view it is possible to decide that a person can change their gender. Some people believe that it is possible to go further than this and change sex. This is purely a belief and, as yet, the science does not agree with this since the chromosomes in every cell in the body cannot be altered.

There has been a growing trend to let children choose their gender. In the UK this has been encouraged in the school setting and often the news of a gender change has been kept from the parents of the child in direct contravention of the law. Many children have been pushed towards having gender changing drugs and surgery without sufficient counselling.

Legislation has been pushed through allowing gender changed individuals to alter their documentation. Even the health record will no longer include the information that the person has changed gender.

Short Case Report 1

A person assigned the male gender at birth, who now self-identified as a woman, suffered from prostate cancer. This was not picked up at an early stage because she now insisted that her gender was female, that all her medical notes should register her as female. Thus no screening occurred and the cancer was only picked up at a late stage when treatment options were limited.

Short Case Report 2

Dr Stefan McAndrew was not permitted to donate blood because he would not confirm that he was not pregnant. He is obviously male and had indicated that on the form.

Reported in numerous newspapers

Daily Mail
https://www.dailymail.co.uk › news › article-11968813

Male GP turned away by Scottish NHS

The vast majority of people's gender determined at birth is in accordance with their genetic sex. Despite considerable surgery it is unusual for transgender women to have undergone prostatectomy during the period of male to female gender transitioning. Thus the risk of developing prostate cancer persists although it may be lowered due to orchidectomy and oestrogen therapy.[17]

In recent years Germaine Greer and JK Rowling have been attacked on social media and deplatformed because of their views on what the definition of a woman should be. In addition Keir Starmer, leader of the Labour Party and leaders of the Church of England have refused to define the term "woman".

It is reasonable to consider that people who wish to self-gender as something other than their biological sex are deluded. Nowadays they may be protected in their delusions rather than risk offending them. It is a different matter if chromosomal abnormalities have been discovered but it is highly likely that this is not the case with most individuals wishing to change their gender.

Delusions are often a sign of mental illness and if the delusion is adhered to and the patient's obsession treated without proper attention to the mental disorder there are major risks, such as suicide, when the patient discovers that the surgery or drugs have not cured their problem.

The law courts in the United Kingdom have prosecuted persons presenting themselves as male when they know that they are biologically female. It is considered to be fraud.

However you may also risk prosecution for offending trans-males and trans-females by using the wrong pronouns…..so you cannot win either way! Even trying to write in scientific terms about the subject is difficult and carries the risk of the writer being labelled transphobic.

Fear of Crime Gender Paradox

Recently there have been some shameful attacks on women in public spaces. One of these, the murder of thirty-three year old Sarah Everard in South London, was perpetrated by a policeman. This was particularly terrible as the man was exactly the sort of person who should have protected Everard. This has led to an outcry about violence against women and led many people to believe that most random attacks in the street occur against women. But is this the case? The answer is quite the opposite. Quoting from SBS News [18] *"The most recent statistics from the Australian Institute of Criminology indicate that men are 11.5 times more likely than women to be killed by a stranger. Women are, however, at much higher risk than men of random sexual harassment and sexual assault in public."*

The overall homicide rate in the UK in the year ending March 2021 was 9.9 per million population, with the rate for males (14 per million population) more than twice that for females (6 per million population) [19] Women were more likely to know their murderer but much less likely to be attacked randomly. Women are more frightened of street crime but men are at much higher risk – criminologist Dr Michelle Noon states that this is known as the 'fear of crime gender paradox' [20] Because of this paradox it is difficult to have a sensible conversation with people about street crime. The prevailing opinion will be that it is women who are in the greatest danger and therefore the ones who must be protected when in fact the men are the ones whose risk is a magnitude greater.

Where the women are right is that men are usually the violent offenders....it is a fact that women are rarely attacked by people they do not know.

Prediction of Crime

Another problem occurs when the police try to predict who will perpetrate the crimes and the places where crimes are likely to occur. A modern liberal democracy is a strange thing. In some ways it is a mechanism by which the majority of people can divorce themselves from the work of running the country. It has been said that the modern state is a successful, legitimate controller of violence.

Certainly the police are the enforcing arm of the government and policing in a modern democratic state is only possible if the public are prepared to be policed. The number of police in the UK is really very low and they could not possibly force the entire public to obey them by coercion. Trying to predict where crime will occur and who will be the criminals does seem like a good idea but it also risks reinforcing stereotypes. Computer models, algorithms, that predict who and where crimes will occur have been widely condemned because they appear to be biased and that bias in particular affects black people and black communities. Political correctness will thus not permit such systems to be widely used. However, the algorithms are usually based on neural nets, taught about the crimes and criminals by learning from examples. If more crimes are committed by the black people they will automatically be targeted by the algorithms, if more are done by white people they will be the ones targeted.

There have been many outcries about stop and search because black people are more frequently stopped. This must be a very humiliating and upsetting experience for the people searched but if they are the ones who most commonly carry illegal weapons and drugs it is understandable that the police target them. It is a denial of the science of criminology to refuse to address a problem because it offends people. Perhaps the answer is to improve the living conditions, income and education of the people likely to offend. However this cannot be done if the science is denied…you have to know who the likely offenders are going to be including such factors as gender, race, age, religion, parentage (married, divorced, single etc.), family income, schooling, living accommodation and location. It is no good shirking away from these factors if you want to do something about them. A major driver of the death of science in any subject is deciding in advance what the acceptable answer is and refusing to look at the facts.

Short Case History

Recently in Rotherham the police refused to help young white girls who were beaten, tortured and raped by a gang of paedophilic Muslims. The police did not want to upset race relations. One victim, talking about her abusers, states "Like terrorists, they firmly believe that the crimes they carry out are justified by their religious beliefs." Political correctness has for years prevented the girls from getting justice.[21]

White girls are not the only victims of this situation. Young Muslim girls have been subject to "honour killings" and their murderers have not been apprehended and once again it has been due to the reluctance on the part of the police to upset race relations.

It is significant that the Swedish government has stated *"Sexual violence is being used as a tactic of terrorism"*. All religions have been used at some time or other to justify sexual violence and torture…. it is, however, simply the case that it has no place in a modern society.

Recruitment into the Armed Forces

Recently the criteria for joining the US armed forces have been changed in order to fit in with political correctness. Clearly women would not be able to pass the tests of physical fitness, strength and endurance that men can so the army tried to create a gender and age-neutral test. That did not make much sense since a young man might pass such a test easily but not really be fit…and that is exactly what happened. Half the female recruits failed the test whilst the men passed easily.[22] So, after years of trying the gender neutral route, they will allow women and older recruits to pass at a reduced standard.[23]

Similar problems have beset the British Army in their push towards politically correct testing.

The Rise of Managerial Dictatorship

The Managerial Structure and Process

Over the last fifty years or so the position of the manager in liberal democracies has become significantly more entrenched. Now it is usual for everybody who is employed by a company to have a line manager above them and so on (ad infinitum) up to the chief executive level. They, in turn, answer to the board of directors.

Managers were an emerging class in the Industrial Revolution, being employed mainly in the manufacturing industry. In the mid to late Twentieth Century managerial processes started to be employed in human activities that had previously not traditionally utilised formal management. Previously professions such as medicine, law and education managed themselves….they did not employ professional managers. Charities rarely had professional managers until the 21st century.

The NHS started employing managers in the early 1970s and this trend was accelerated by Thatcher's administration in the 1980s.

Professional management was also introduced into other areas where they had not previously been employed. These included law, education, religion and charities.

According to Google *"managerial processes are organisational routines that underpin the dynamic capabilities of an organisation by controlling and reconfiguring the organisation's resource base, thus impacting on the organisation's ability to attain, sustain or enhance performance in the long-term*

At the most fundamental level, management is a discipline that consists of a set of five general functions: planning, organising, staffing, leading and controlling. These five functions are part of a body of practices and theories on how to be a successful manager."

Having been on management courses and read management books we are aware of the belief amongst the doyens of the management process that management is the same whatever the endeavour. The mantra they believe is that you do not need to understand the lower level of work to manage a firm. The management process will sort it out.

Thus a top manager of a biscuit manufacturing company could usefully be brought in to develop management in the health service or a planner could manage a firm of architects. Conceivably a Wellington boot factory manager could manage the Church of England.

We believe that this is arrant nonsense but many holders of the great MBA believe it to be true.

Management in the NHS

The UK's National Health Service, the NHS, was, genuinely, at one time, the envy of the world. Despite claims by politicians that this is still the case it has become clear in the past three decades that the NHS is no longer fit for purpose. Even before the Covid-19 pandemic it was obvious that waiting lists were far too long and that many services were outrageously poorly run.

This, in part, is due to the culture of management and the management process and failure of the NHS as a system to learn from its failings.

Take the example of the *Bristol Cardiac Scandal*.[24] When Thatcher decided that an internal market was needed to sharpen up the NHS hospitals she created the Trust system, which later became Foundation Hospitals. Each Trust would compete for work and was obliged to stay within its budget.

In Bristol the children with congenital heart disease had traditionally been sent away to national centres of excellence. The management of the United Bristol Healthcare Trust decided that in the future this would cost too much so the work would have to be done in Bristol. There already was a highly successful adult cardiac surgery unit so they were asked to take on the children's cardiac service. The surgeons and their team stated that they needed a dedicated operating theatre, that the assessment, surgery and follow up needed to all be on one site and, crucially, new surgeons would have to join the team as the adult surgeons were not trained for the work on children.

The finance director decreed that none of these conditions could be met but that, for the sake of saving the expense, the work still needed to be done in Bristol or it would not be done at all.

The chief executive of the Trust asked the surgeons to come up with solutions, and, browbeaten by the finance chief, they agreed to try to undertake the work.

Several years later one of the anaesthetists realised that there was quite a high mortality rate in the paediatric cardiac cases and this led to the Bristol Cardiac Scandal. The surgeons were defamed by irate parents who claimed that the surgeons were arrogant murderers. The Ian Kennedy enquiry decided in advance that the fault lay in the way that doctors had clinical freedom and that this needed to be curtailed.

The professor of paediatric pathology demonstrated the pathology of the hearts to the Ian Kennedy enquiry.... despite cries to the opposite it turned out that after operating on hundreds of cases there were only twenty cases that might have been saved and of these only four were due to poor surgery. Overall the results were little different from other centres. In the end the Ian Kennedy report advised that a dedicated operating theatre was needed, all the work should be on one site and, crucially, new surgeons would have to join the team. Exactly what had been asked for in the first place! Curtailing of clinical freedom was highlighted as essential.

The paediatric professor agreed with the surgeons that they had been prepared to operate on cases that the other centres had turned down. This was in order to give the poor children a chance, *not* because the

Bristol surgeons were arrogant. Other surgeons did not want to spoil their statistics by taking on nearly hopeless cases. Jumping on the bandwagon the GMC suspended one surgeon, struck another off and struck off the chief executive, who happened to be a doctor. The finance officer emerged unscathed and later became the acting chief executive!

The Ian Kennedy team also castigated the professor of paediatric pathology for keeping the "hearts of babies" claiming that it was an evil thing to have done. He pointed out that they were all coroner's cases and he had no choice…. by law he had to keep the specimens. When this cut no ice with the lay members of the Kennedy committee the pathologist resigned on the spot. The way he put it was: *'I realised that the lunatics had taken control of the asylum.'*

This example is from the 1980s and 1990s but is symptomatic of what has happened to the NHS. Moreover finance officers in the NHS are busily cooking the books to keep within targets.

Private Eye 20.4.2023

NHS SCANDALS

Hole truth

FINANCIAL misreporting became "the norm" at the University Hospitals of Leicester NHS Trust, with staff fearing for their jobs if they blew the whistle on serial irregularities in the accounts, according to a damning 2021 auditors' report.

Waiting Lists

Not surprisingly no form of medical science can work if the patient has to wait too long for an appointment.

Some twenty years ago editor PRG was appalled to find that patients were not having timely appointments for radiology because the manager was gerrymandering the waiting list. When the requests came in the clerks were being told to hold them back in a pile if the waiting list was at its official limit whether the request was urgent or routine. The patient was not put on the waiting list until the form had been ratified by a consultant. PRG remonstrated about this much to the annoyance of the manager.

Today we can read about a similar ruse occurring on the e-referral system. Between January and June this year, "appointment slot issues" affected an average of almost 400,000 referrals each month and if a patient does not receive an appointment due to such issues and they have waited 180 days they are automatically removed from the system! Nearly 10 million patients are now waiting for some kind of patient care and many may be taken off the waiting lists automatically having never been seen.[25]

Dentistry has frequently been the Cinderella specialty in medicine. It appears that twenty percent of people in the UK are now turning to DIY dental care, either using temporary dressings, taking antibiotics or pulling their own teeth out! The science of dentistry has no hope in the NHS. [26]

In the case of Covid-19 elderly patients were sent out to nursing homes without testing and without adequate personal protective equipment. Patients or relatives who complained were ignored, mistakes were not investigated and people were lied to. Staff were afraid to speak out because of bullying by management. Indeed some medical staff were even struck off by the GMC if they disagreed with the policies being enacted by the NHS.

The recent case of the murderous nurse Lucy Letby has highlighted the fact that the NHS management cannot be trusted. As Allison Pearson put it…. *'the unforgivable complacency of those self-soothing, feeble-minded, cowardly, risible, overpaid, under-qualified…Stalinist apparatchiks…and their only guiding principle; cover thine own sorry backside.'* [26] As usual the whistleblowers were the ones who were made to apologise and threatened with the GMC.

When will the managers, NHS or whatever, be properly qualified and accredited such that *they* can be struck off if they offend? Such a move has been suggested before and is heavily overdue.

Equal Opportunities Managers

Despite the huge waiting lists and general lack of cash for frontline services the NHS management are still advertising for managers and senior managers to work on diversity, involvement, equality, inclusion and human rights. When PRG discussed this with a person in a local government managerial position she could see no wrong in such recruitment. *'They're definitely needed. For example, how else would they know that people of a particular ethnic group have worse obstetric outcomes?'* she asked , oblivious to the fact that the persons who should have been able to tell her this are the obstetricians themselves if they were doing their job properly!

Moreover the NHS already has the most diverse staff in any UK business ….

Involvement and Equality
Manager

Moorfields Eye Hospital NHS Foundation Trust 3.8 ★
Equality, Diversity & Inclusion Manager
London, England
✓ Employer Est.: £56K - £62K ⓘ

Diversity and Inclusion Manager

NHS Blood and Transplant (NHSBT)
Bristol

Director of Equality, Diversity and Inclusion

Nottingham University Hospitals NHS Trust
Nottingham

The Telegraph

NHS hires diversity managers on £77,000 a year despite 'war on wokery'

A government review had suggested the roles should be cut back

By **Lizzie Roberts**, HEALTH CORRESPONDENT
27 August 2022 · 7:00pm

It does appear that the priorities of the NHS have been lost. The diversity managers earn two to three times the starting salary of a junior doctor and more than the highest paid and most senior "junior" doctor. Equality of opportunity for health care is no longer a priority and the focus is on equal results.

Unfortunately as more rigid control is enacted the worse is the outcome. There can never be equality of result since each person is unique.

The NHS is given as an example but similar dictatorial behaviour is seen from managers in education, law and, of course, the civil service. They all use the same tactics: accuse the whistleblower of bullying and ignore the problems.

Comment on Management and Political Control

It is easy to understand this development in dictatorships but how has management been able to take such control in so many industries and endeavours in the democratic countries? They have been able to utilise the bizarre language and contradictory processes of political correctness, making themselves into the high priests of a new religion, one which spawns more politically correct managers.

Moreover right now governments all over the world are planning to introduce their own programmable Central Bank Digital Currencies (CBDCs). The politicians and their managers will have Orwellian control over every transaction and determine exactly how you can spend your money or even if you are allowed to keep it![27] Once they have that power they will undoubtedly use it.

References: At the end of the book

Chapter 4

Politics and Science

Part 2: Censorship
The Editors

Censorship has, for many people in the Western democracies, been a taboo subject. We kid ourselves that there is no censorship and that we live in a free society with one of the major tenets being freedom of speech. That much vaunted freedom of speech has come under attack from many quarters, not least of which is the pressure from the politically correct lobby as discussed in the last chapter. But in addition to the censorship by the PC brigade there is a developing lobby to control that which is written in scientific journals and the forces behind this developed into a perfect storm during the lockdowns of Covid-19. In this chapter we will explore these forces which are pushing for conformity of thought as well as conformity of output.

The Liberal Nation State and Censorship

The examples of censorship discussed previously in this book have their origin in political correctness and occur at the individual level. But does censorship occur at the government level in a modern liberal democracy?
Of course it does!
In 1975 PRG was involved in the Junior Hospital Doctors' Dispute between the doctors and the Labour government of the UK. The Department of Health and Social Security (DHSS), led by Barbara Castle, tried to impose a contract that would have meant detriment to most of the hardest working junior doctors. In order to prevent the doctors knowing exactly how much money they had earned in the previous year the government put a D notice on doctors' pay. This was an official request that newspapers or other publications should withhold information for reasons of state security. The administrators would also refuse to give the information to the doctors' representatives. The government had decided that the public and the doctors should not know exactly how much they had been paid. [1]

The press were not particularly sympathetic to the doctors but the public were and, when an audit of doctors' pay was eventually forced on the government and the predicted underpayment demonstrated, it was Barbara Castle who paid the price of the DHSS's duplicity. Eventually, the Labour government were forced out of office. In 1979 Thatcher won a convincing majority for the Conservative party. The censorship had not protected the government from humiliation but they had definitely instigated it.

Yes, censorship is part of everyday life in liberal democracies. The government try to convince the public that it is all voluntary. D notices are now called the DMSA notice system and they state *"Standing notices: The DSMA-Notice System is a means of providing advice and guidance to the media about defence and security information, the publication of which would be damaging to national security. The system is voluntary, it has no legal authority and the final responsibility for deciding whether or not to publish rests solely with the editor or publisher concerned".* [2]

It is clear that doctors' pay should not have been subject to a D notice as it could not be considered as a threat to national security. Governments may, however, consider a threat to their continuing role as a threat to security when most of the public actually believe it is only a threat to the political party in power, a subtle but important difference.

A quick glance at the DMSA notices posted on the DMSA website shows that they all now relate to military information. So has censorship at the national level now stopped in the UK apart from subjects of obvious military significance? Unfortunately this is not the case.

The national news media, led in a substantial way by the BBC, seriously self-censor themselves. *The Oldie*, an online and print journal, provides many examples in an article entitled *"Why does the BBC censor the news?'* written by Michael Cole.[3] Self-Censorship frequently means that important information is missed out in a story….perhaps that the attacker in a case of assault was a particular ethnic group or that the person attacked was known to be homosexual. When this happens it might protect the minority group but misinforms the public.

The BBC leads this self-censorship and they will bend to pressure put on them by government because their income is derived from a form of very special taxation known as the licence fee and it is the government who decide whether or not this special arrangement continues! Thus the government can co-ordinate censorship of the media without resorting to the DMSA-notice system.

Recently censorship has been very effective in preventing the public from hearing about the origin of the Covid-19 virus, about the effectiveness of repurposed drugs and the harmful effects of Covid vaccinations and boosters.

At present there is a war between Russia and Ukraine. Russia has undoubtedly been the aggressor and has perpetrated war crimes. Russia has taken a strip of land in the east of Ukraine and is trying to consolidate its hold on Crimea, which it invaded in 2014. But how many people are aware of the fact that Russia only gave Crimea to Ukraine in 1953, that it is a very important strategic military base for Russia and that the present conflict was partially sparked off by Ukraine damming a Soviet-built canal that provides 99% of Crimea's fresh water? *Algeciras* was the only news channel that reported this in any detail. BBC World news and Sky news gave no hint of these problems,

Dictatorships and Censorship

If the liberal democracies use censorship, and clearly they do, then what about the dictatorships? They only survive because they use censorship, propaganda, coercion and terror to a very huge extent. We will group the communist regimes (China, North Korea) with the right wing and religious dictatorships (such as Erdogan in Turkey, Khamanei in Iran) as they use the same tactics.

In 2020 to 2022 there was considerable reporting on the Chinese success in controlling Covid-19 and very little on the Chinese role in creating the problem in the first place. But the big question is why did we listen to the Chinese and why did we believe their medical science when we know that they censor everything that comes out of China? And why was the WHO so blinded by Chinese propaganda? We do know that the Chinese government try various tactics to extend their censorship and intimidation overseas.

Guardian 16.10.2019   The Guardian https://www.theguardian.com › world › oct › think-of...   'Think of your family': China threatens European citizens

The Daily Telegraph 17.4 23   China accused of targeting Tories' families

Exceedingly Rich Individuals, Corporations and Social Media

The digital revolution has led to the development of many exceedingly rich corporations (such as Apple, Microsoft etc.) and a number of ineffably rich individuals. Many of them have considerable control over the information disseminated by the traditional media and even more control over the social media (YouTube, Facebook, Twitter etc.). The original idea was that the internet would be a free for all with no censorship but this is no longer the case. Now algorithms are used to decide on which posts are acceptable and which are not. To what extent these algorithms are led by corporate or individual decisions is not generally known. The media bosses can now decide what is permitted and what is not permitted on their platforms and these decisions are undoubtedly skewing the output.

It is possible that the action of censoring people on social media may be illegal. Right now three famous doctors are suing Twitter for suspending their accounts. The three are internist/immunologist Robert Malone, MD, who is licensed to practice in Maryland, Brian Tyson, MD, of El Centro, California, and Peter McCullough, MD, MPH, a clinical cardiologist in practice at Dallas-based HeartPlace, which offers cardiovascular and related services. [4] It will be very interesting to see the outcome of the court case.

As stated in Chapter 1 a particular problem with the new social media is that the users may not get to see a range of opinions. The search engines automatically tend to find results that the user wants to see thus reinforcing opinions, right or wrong, and missing out on the serendipity that reading a newspaper or a magazine automatically created. Whilst writing this chapter we have received an email stating that the Daily Sceptic, an independent news source, critical of much of the media orthodoxy, has had all its Paypal accounts closed.

The Daily Sceptic states: "*There are five issues in particular where it's completely verboten to express sceptical views and if you do you can expect to be cancelled, not just by PayPal but by YouTube, Facebook, Twitter, Instagram, etc.: the wisdom of the lockdown policy and associated Covid restrictions, the efficacy and safety of the mRNA vaccines, Net Zero and the 'climate emergency', the need to teach five year-olds that sex is a social construct and the war in Ukraine. Dissent from the prevailing orthodoxy in any of those areas is no longer permitted.*"
.......They clearly will not like this book!

Extreme Religion and other fanatics

Not surprisingly there is censorship due to fear of reprisals from fanatics. It is well known that any mention of the Islamic name for God can invoke violent response from a very small minority of Islamists who wish to demonstrate the peaceful and loving nature of their religion by bombing, stabbing or stoning people to death. The fearless press does not wish to be targeted in this way (who would?) so they try to avoid commenting. It is also considered great blasphemy to create an image of their prophet or even for school teachers to discuss the problem of such images existing. Religious debate in schools and universities is being stifled by fear of the response. The educational authorities and police will often immediately side with the fanatics, suspend the teachers and accuse them of "hate crimes".

Salmon Rushdie is a high profile victim of such intolerance and violence.

In a similar way the followers of "woke" customs, the high priests of political correctness, take it upon themselves to ruin the careers of lecturers who disagree with their extreme PC views. The attitudes of the "woke" brigade have much akin with the Puritans of yesteryear. They seem to be followers of a new non-theistic religion. Intolerance of alternative views whilst professing great personal virtue is a hallmark of their faith. Erich Fromm, the humanistic philosopher stated *"There is perhaps no phenomenon which contains so much destructive feelings as "moral indignation," which permits envy or hate to be acted out under the guise of virtue.*

Conclusion

Censorship has become more of a problem in the last few years because of the rising power of the media moguls and the malign influence of totalitarian states. However it is clear that government inspired censorship and political correctness is rife in democracies and freedom of the press is certainly not guaranteed.

Stop Press: *Reports are surfacing that a secretive UK Government unit called the Counter-Disinformation Unit (CDU) broke rules and targeted, as "domestic threats," people who disagreed with Covid policies,[5,6] including the editors, and Ros Jones and Clare Craig, authors of Chapters 12 and 13 in this book, who were quite rightly questioning the roll-out of Covid-19 vaccines to children.[7]*

References: At the end of the book

Chapter 5

Malpractice in Scientific Research?

Peer Review
Including the Origin of the Covid-19 Pandemic
The Editors

Peer review has always had its dark side. The idea, laudably, is that scientists send in their work for potential publication. The editor of the receiving science journal sends the paper out to referees who are experts in the same field. They referee the work and determine whether or not it should be published. They are supposed to do this based on its scientific value. If, for example, the work appears to be sound but the paper is badly written they may suggest that it is publishable if the writing is improved and ask for it to be resubmitted. On other occasions they may consider the work is correct but not publishable in that particular journal due to a lack of originality or that it is too long, too boring or whatever.

Did Darwin steal Wallace's idea?

The dark side is obvious. If the work is truly original the referees undertaking the peer-review may not understand it or may be enlightened by it. That does not mean that they will necessarily want it to be published. What if they consider themselves to be the foremost experts in the field? They might turn down or delay the publication of the article, repeat the work themselves and then submit their version to the journal in question or to another journal.

That is exactly what happened to Alfred Russel Wallace. In 1858 he sent Charles Darwin a paper that he had written explaining that evolution of species occurred because the fittest survived…it was a form of natural selection. Darwin had been working on the theory of evolution for twenty years, gathering information and honing his examples and ideas. He had not, however, managed to find an explanation that superseded Lamarck's idea that traits developed by an animal in its lifetime could be passed on to the next generation. In Lamarckian evolution if a giraffe stretched its neck to reach leaves on a higher branch, the offspring would then inherit a longer neck. Darwin was not happy with that explanation but he had not found a better answer despite having a huge body of facts at his disposal. Wallace had just provided the required theory. Darwin was in despair but his family and friends told him to write his own paper and that is exactly what he did. *"Two of Darwin's friends, the eminent geologist Charles Lyell, and Joseph Hooker, botanist, arranged a joint presentation of the ideas of Darwin, which they knew about but hadn't been published, and the paper that had just come in from Wallace. A joint presentation at a meeting of the Linnean Society, July 1st, 1858, in London".* [1]. Darwin then followed this up with a hastily written précis of the book on evolution that he had been working on for years and included Wallace's idea of survival of the fittest. He entitled it *"On the Origin of Species"*.

Charles Darwin

'An 1871 caricature following publication of The Descent of Man was typical of many showing Darwin with an ape body, identifying him in popular culture as the leading author of evolutionary theory.'
Public domain, via Wikimedia Commons https://en.wikipedia.org/wiki/Charles_Darwin

Lamarck was a Frenchman and it is no surprise that the French consider Lamarck to be the father of the theory of evolution. Interestingly scientists have dismissed Lamarckian evolution as utterly wrong but recently there has been a focus on epigenetic inheritance. Stresses to parents can affect offspring and these changes can be passed on for several generations so Lamarck was not so wrong as people have thought. Survival of the fittest may be a very important factor in evolution but other factors, such as sheer chance, deterministic chaos and unusual stresses, can also have an effect.

But have the dark days of scientific plagiarism, misdirection and fraud completely disappeared? Please read on….

Plagiarism in The Lancet?

We will now give similar examples from our own experience over the past few decades showing how peer review has failed. In 1982 one of the editors of this book (PRG), with colleagues, submitted papers to the journals *Lancet*, *Clinical Radiology* and *Clinical Pathology.* They were based on his MD thesis describing the diagnosis of pulmonary emphysema using computed tomography correlated with respiratory physiology and pathology. The papers sent to Clinical Radiology[2] and Clinical Pathology[3] were accepted but *The Lancet*, the most prestigious of the three journals, turned the paper down. The referee was DC Flenley who then published a paper in *The Lancet* in 1984 entitled *"Diagnosis of Pulmonary Emphysema by Computerised Tomography."*[4] Flenley, having read the original paper, went away, repeated the work with the same result as the original research by Goddard et al. and (surprise, surprise !) his 'me too' paper was accepted.

Three similar cases are known to the editors.

Sometimes it is the editor who turns down a paper that the referees have accepted. And occasionally it is the publisher who steps in and forbids publication of a paper accepted by the peer review and by the editor.

Record number of papers requiring retractions?

Yoshitaka Fujii: Anaesthesiologist who trained in Japan and Canada. He became an expert in the control of post-operative nausea and vomiting using granisetron (a serotonin receptor antagonist). Although granisetron *can* be effective in control of post-operative nausea at least 219 scientific papers published by Fujii had to be withdrawn because the data on randomised crossover trials had been falsified.[5]

According to Wikipedia the previous record for necessary retractions was another anaesthesiologist, **Joachim Boldt** (German. born 29

September 1954). Boldt has been stripped of his professorship and is under criminal investigation for possible forgery of up to 90 research studies.[6] He had fabricated data and failed to obtain ethical approval for his research into the use of colloids for use in intravenous fluid management.

More Misdirection in *The Lancet* and even *Nature Medicine?*

The Origin of the Covid-19 Pandemic. Recently there has been a perfect storm with regard to publication of articles describing the origin of the Covid-19 virus and with regard to vaccines against that virus. This will be discussed below.

In 2020 opinion articles were published as fact in *Nature Medicine*[7] and *The Lancet*[8] purporting to show that the SARS-Cov-2 virus (Covid-19) could not have been made in the Wuhan Institute of Virology, near which it was first discovered. No articles have been published in those journals refuting the points even though many researchers have questioned the validity of the articles and the independence of the writers of the papers.

Two researchers stand out from the others in their valiant attempts to get their work on Covid-19 published.

Berger Sorensen from Norway, and the co-editor of this book Angus Dalgleish (St George's University of London) immediately realised that the Andersen paper in *Nature Medicine* was fatally flawed. They wrote a carefully reasoned and researched letter refuting the Andersen article and this was rejected by the editor of *Nature Medicine*, presumably on the grounds that it was not of sufficient public interest. Sorensen and Dalgleish tried to get the paper accepted in a wide number of journals only to find that the editors would not even countenance the idea of publishing it or that two referees in the peer review process would accept it but a third would totally damn the paper.*(See Appendix to Chapter 5 at the end of this book).*One of the journals managed to reject the paper within five hours indicating that they had not used peer review.

After receiving rebuffs from the medical scientific journals they finally altered the paper such that the central premise, that the virus was made in the Wuhan laboratory, was not the main focus and instead the paper concentrated on the method of making a suitable vaccine against Covid-19.

This paper predicted that creating vaccines against the spike proteins would lead to harm and it would be better to target nonhuman epitopes. It was published in QRB Discovery and has now been downloaded 260,000 times but mysteriously only cited 27 times! [9]

Recently, since the climate of opinion has shifted away from the toxic abuse promoted by Daszak and *The Lancet*, Sorensen and Dalgleish tried again to get the original paper published. Accepted by a journal's referees and editor the paper was refused publication by the publishers.

So why the reluctance to support the process of scientific thesis followed by antithesis? Surely the point of science is that important suggestions such as those put in *The Lancet* and *Nature Medicine* should be questioned and tested. Clearly this has not occurred and the Sorensen and Dalgleish paper has been censored. Who and what was behind this censorship? To answer this we have to look at the evidence and follow the money trail.

The following has been excerpted from Pandemic (2nd edition) by Paul R Goddard. [10]

"In 2014 the Wuhan-based virologist Shi Zhengli (known as the Bat Woman) and her team were offered large sums of money to perform Gain of Function (GoF) studies on the viruses. Making the viruses infective between humanised mice was the aim.

….Dr. Peter Daszak, President of EcoHealth Alliance, a US-based organisation that conducts research and outreach programs on global health, had been provided with some of the money by Dr Fauci, Director of the National Institute of Allergies and Infectious Diseases, part of the USA's NIH, because the research in the USA was stymied by a moratorium. Too many outbreaks of novel viruses had occurred from the US based virology laboratories so the Obama administration had called for a halt on the research in 2014. Over a million dollars had been given to EcoHealth Alliance by the US Agency for International Development (USAID) for a sub-agreement with the Wuhan Institute of Virology. Funding also came from the US Department of Defence.

It is clear that the US State Department officials did not realise the threat that China represented.

"China under Xi Jinping is a very different place compared with the liberalising leaders for the previous thirty years. Under Xi Jinping there have been far-ranging measures to enforce party discipline, crackdowns on dissent in Hong Kong, border skirmishes with India and major threats to the security of Taiwan.

Jinping is more like Mao Zedong than any leader since Mao died. In 2018 Jinping abolished the presidential term limits. Under his rule there has been a deterioration in human rights, increased censorship and mass surveillance.

"Xi Jinping assumed the office of president of China in 2013. In 2015 the Chinese military were looking at the possibility of weaponising a coronavirus. Subsequently they also had at least one laboratory in Wuhan experimenting with the viruses. A new building had been devised for virology research and the project was initially a joint venture between the Chinese and French. France provided the laboratory's design, biosafety training and most of its technology using European Union money. However, when the building was completed in 2017 the French, much to their annoyance, were chucked out and the Chinese military were moved in. The French politicians had backed the project but their security experts were against the endeavour and were proven right. They had been warning the USA about the potential security risks from 2015 onwards.

"Gain of Function (or Make Another Disease, MAD) studies were used to make the viruses infective between humanised mice on the assumption that if they could be so adapted it showed that they were potentially harmful to human beings. And the work was successful as reported by Daszak and Shi Zhengli in 2017 to 2019. In 2018, however, US officials who had visited the lab were told they would not be allowed to return and they therefore warned the US Government that there were major safety concerns.

"In September 2019 some virologists in Wuhan had a peculiar respiratory infection. By October it was a growing and alarming problem and in December Dr Ai Fen, director of the emergency department at Wuhan Central hospital, was reprimanded after alerting her superiors and colleagues of a Sars-like virus seen in patients.

"….China continued to tell the world that the virus could not be transmitted from person to person but eventually it was clear that it was easily transmitted that way, something that the Chinese had known from the start of the outbreak. China immediately stated that the virus had evolved naturally and that the intermediate host was the pangolin. In fact no pangolin has been shown to harbour the virus and the nail in the coffin of the natural evolution myth is the fact that bats cannot be infected with COVID-19…..

"It is also interesting to note that Shi Zhengli and her team had tried to make a vaccine to combat the coronaviruses and had searched for drugs against them. Daszak reported that these efforts were unsuccessful but by February 2020 the Chinese vaccines had already been patented and by midsummer of 2020 the Chinese were already immunising their airport staff. The Chinese vaccines are based on inactivated COVID-19…….

"By March 2020 Kristian Andersen published a paper in *Nature Medicine (as mentioned earlier)* stating, in a bewildering about turn, that it was highly unlikely that the COVID-19 virus had been made in a laboratory. He used as proof that his analysis showed that the virus was not perfectly adapted to infecting human beings which he believed it would be if it was made in a laboratory. The ability of the virus to infect all races and ages of people has proven that assertion to be completely incorrect."

It is our contention that the censorship by science journals resulted from pressure put on editors and publishers by the Chinese Communist Party (CCP), by the NIH (Fauci and Collins) and by Ecohealth Alliance (Daszak). Once the party line had been established by *The Lancet* and *Nature Medicine* all other journals were expected to follow suit.

Why did the Chinese have so much influence over the West's journals and academics? Because they fund them.

Why did Fauci have so much influence over virologists. Because he funds them.

Why did Daszak have so much power over many of the virologists who wrote the letter with him to *The Lancet*? Because Ecohealth Alliance employs them and he is the CEO!

The old adage 'follow the money' does seem to fit the bill.

Direct Censorship and Intimidation of Medical Doctors

One of the most unnerving and perfidious sequelae of the Covid-19 pandemic has been the intimidation of doctors by the medical authorities. The Chinese authorities arrested the doctors who spoke openly about the virus and some subsequently died in mysterious circumstances including the Chinese man who had patented the vaccines. But the direct censorship and intimidation has not been confined to China. In the USA and the UK the doctors were strictly told to avoid using pharmaceuticals that in normal circumstances they would have used for other viral pneumonias. The reason given was "lack of evidence". If they transgressed they risked censure. Some of the doctors worst affected were those who questioned the efficacy of the vaccines.

Russell Blaylock has written about this [11]

: *...the recent suspension by the medical board in Maine of Dr. Meryl Nass' medical license and the ordering of her to undergo a psychiatric evaluation for prescribing Ivermectin and sharing her expertise in this field.*

....Dr. Peter McCullough, one of the most cited experts in his field, who has successfully treated over 2000 COVID patients by using a protocol of early treatment (which the so-called experts completely ignored), has been the victim of a particularly vicious assault by those benefiting financially from the vaccines. He has published his results in peer reviewed journals, reporting an 80% reduction in hospitalizations and a 75% reduction in deaths by using early treatment.... Despite this, he is under an unrelenting series of attacks by the information controllers, none of which have treated a single patient

...Another unprecedented tactic is to remove dissenting doctors from their positions as journal editors, reviewers and retracting of their scientific papers from journals.

....A careful review indicates that in far too many instances the authors dared question accepted dogma by the controllers of scientific publications—especially concerning the safety, alternative treatments or efficacy of vaccines.

What is so worrying about this is the fact that the vaccines do now lack efficacy and can be dangerous. Here is an article that is worth reading with an open mind. *"Could Vaccines Make Omicron Infection Worse? Scientists Weigh in on Antibody Dependent Enhancement"* [12]

This lack of efficacy and hazard was, of course, predicted by Sorensen and Dalgleish.

Another example of egregious intimidation of medical staff is that of Dr. Sam White, a general practitioner. He, very reasonably, pointed out his concerns about the lack of informed consent, vaccine harm and alternative, safe treatment. The GMC suspended him and then told him not to comment on Covid and the government's response. The case was taken to appeal in the High Court and all restrictions on him were repealed by the judge on the grounds of freedom of speech. So at the moment at least one judge is batting on the side of justice but the GMC has a lot to answer for. [13,14] The BMA's Annual Representative Meeting has very recently passed a vote of no confidence in the GMC [15,16] Incidentally recent reports suggest that the mRNA vaccines contain DNA that makes cells permanently produce spike proteins! [15]

HIV Research

The discovery of AIDS and HIV

In the 1980s a new syndrome causing immune suppression was described and became known as Acquired Immune Deficiency Syndrome (AIDS). Researchers in France and the USA determined that this was caused by a retrovirus, later called Human Immunodeficiency Virus (HIV).

For many years the medical researchers involved refused to accept that a similar syndrome could be caused by any other virus. It is now clear that maybe as many as half of the sufferers of AIDS-like syndromes are affected by other viruses, including Human Herpes Virus (HHV)6 (a and b), and by HHV 8 which causes Kaposi's sarcoma (often considered as a hallmark of AIDS).

AIDS Vaccines

Dr Anthony Fauci managed to persuade the US government to put trillions of dollars into the development of AIDS vaccines. The vaccines developed in the USA were a total failure and there were appalling cover-ups of deaths and other harm caused by the vaccines.

Dr Fishbein

Dr. Jonathan Fishbein was overlooking ethical concerns in the NIH and drew attention to the cover-ups. He was unfairly dismissed but won a claim against the NIH.

He is quoted in in Robert F Kennedy's book[16] as follows *"Dealing with Tony Fauci is like dealing with organized crime,"* says Dr. Fishbein. *"He's like the godfather. He has connections everywhere. He's always got people that he's giving money to in powerful positions to make sure he gets his way—that he gets what he wants. These connections give him the ultimate power to fix everything, control every narrative, escape all consequence, and sweep all the dirt and all the bodies under the carpet and to terrorize and destroy anyone who crosses him."*

Dr Robert Redfield

The "mistakes" did not stop with Fauci. Let us consider Dr. Robert Redfield who was later Donald Trump's Centers for Disease Control (CDC) Director during the 2020 COVID pandemic. Few people realise that the military wanted to court martial him for fraudulent research on AIDS vaccines!

Similarities between the response to Covid-19 and to HIV

The Covid-19 pandemic has been handled extremely poorly in retrospect, although many of us lobbied hard through any available channels, including the Great Barrington Declaration. Governments universally went along with a narrative which has many similarities with the HIV epidemic of the early 1980s. Interestingly the same formula seems to have been used, and by the same head of the National Institute for Allergy and Infectious Disease (NIAID): Dr Anthony Fauci.

The HIV epidemic came along at a most convenient time for Dr Fauci who had taken over as the head of the NIAID at a time when its very existence had been questioned as allergies and infectious diseases had fallen into relative obscurity in a nation that had made controlling cancer as its number one medical goal. The National Cancer Institute (NCI) was given large resources to achieve this, and was the first to get involved with the AIDS outbreak as clinicians had noticed outbreaks and clustering's of a very rare cancer called Kaposi's Sarcoma as well as an increased incidence of Lymphomas in gay men.

Dr Gallo, an NCI scientist specialising in retroviruses and leukaemia had been the first in the USA to claim the isolation and characterisation of a new retrovirus now known as HIV which he announced at a special press hearing before the publication of 4 papers from his laboratory. It was noted that the virus was very similar to the one previously announced by Luc Montagnier and his team at the Pasteur Institute in France.

Azidothymidine (AZT)

Dr Sam Broder head of the NCI, used this virus to screen drugs that might have anti-viral activity including ones discarded previously in anti-cancer screens. One of these was AZT which was put into clinical trials. As HIV was clearly an infectious disease Dr Fauci claimed control for all HIV and AIDS research and took charge of the enormous budget that followed, much to the fury of the NCI team who. unlike the NIAID, had a strong track record of conducting clinical trials.

Following the NCI interest and studies on AZT , Burroughs Wellcome (BW) retrieved it having regarded it as too toxic even as a cancer agent, patented it and placed an enormous price on it at up to $10,000 dollars a year per patient. Fauci used this to drive his own HIV drug platform using BW and their huge army of Principal Investigators (PIs) with expertise in running the complex regulatory hurdles. BW PIs dominated the NIAID clinical trial system which included the selection or dismissal of drugs which could compete with AZT. Fauci was to use this model to populate approval committees in the Federal Drug Administration (FDA), CDC and other Institutes.

AZT was to prove very toxic and made designing trials to make it look safe and effective difficult, at the same time preventing trials for other less toxic drugs.

There was an enormous number of such drugs that Fauci would not recognise, even those which clearly treated opportunistic infections that were fatal such as pneumocystis pneumonia which responded well to Bactrim and Septrin. This is very reminiscent of the failure to recognise drugs which were clearly effective in early Covid-19 such as Vitamin D3, steroids and Hydroxychloroquine.

The resultant AZT trials were designed purely to get FDA recognition. The official trial of the BW sponsored AZT study, known by the first author as the Fischel study, was published in the New England Journal of Medicine (NEJM) and was immediately hailed as an elaborate fraud.

The study was criticised for its abbreviated duration, fatal methodological flaws, some clearly as a result of corruption and deliberate falsification. An investigative reporter John Lauritsen rapidly discovered that not a single table in the report made sense and that the authors were unable to explain them! He was to expose these findings in two reports, *Poison by prescription: the AZT story, and the AIDS war,* and *Propaganda, Profiteering and Genocide from the Medical Industrial complex.* Using Freedom of information documents, he showed that Fauci had aborted the studies at the halfway point, and that the claim that AZT prolonged lives was mainly due to the repeated blood transfusions they were given and widespread cheating on nearly every patient, with patients already on AZT recruited into the placebo arm!! The AZT toxicities were clearly hidden on the official case report forms.

Professor Dalgleish states: *'The first time I met Tony Fauci was at an AIDS meeting just after I had published our paper showing that CD4 was the major HIV receptor. He was very loud and super confident having just taken over as the director of the NIAID. I was unaware of the political fights between him and the NCI regarding control of the war on HIV/AIDS and the enormous budgets involved. I was however, impressed by his confidence in predicting a successful vaccine within months to 2 years, a prediction which has yet to be fulfilled nearly forty years later.*

I was to listen to many of his talks over the years and his fantastically original discoveries many of which I was to later discover were pre-confirmed by others!

Fauci predicted that Histone Deacetylase (HDAC) inhibitors would cure AIDS and put the majority of his AIDS budget that year into developing these drugs. I stood up at a meeting and said it would never work for some obvious and very simple reasons. He was furious with me and shouted me down.

The host of the meeting said he loved having me there as I was the only one willing to stand up to Fauci. I noted I was the only one there not dependent on his funding which in HIV research in the US was the only non-commercial source!'

It is worth noting that in the three years from taking over the AIDS programme Fauci could only claim credit for one drug which was found to be highly toxic and rapidly dropped. It was at this time Fauci was able to muzzle any critics and media which did not idolise his every word, even though his claims were outrageous and never justified, and start to control what was allowed and what Trump would call fake news. Once again, this trend was to continue with COVID vaccines. When questions about possible side effects were aired directly to him, by someone concerned, regarding a link between COVID vaccines and testicular swelling, his denial of cause and effect was gospel. Anyone questioning it on Twitter was immediately ejected, in spite of the lack of any evidence or investigation to refute the association. Fauci had heralded in the age of "the death of science" with his blatant lies and cover up of the failure of the AZT trial. He has certainly continued to hammer the nails into the coffin with gusto in his approach to Covid treatments and vaccines.

Once again, he was to suppress all useful drugs that doctors were clearly reporting benefits for in the clinic whilst promoting useless and toxic drugs. These drugs, such as Remdesivir, had strong patents and profit potential. One thing Fauci should have learnt from HIV vaccines is that all the vaccines he promoted with his big Pharma chums and Bill Gates, had failed to work over thirty-five plus years, in spite of promising an effective HIV vaccine within two years in 1984!!

Scientists such as co-editor of this book AGD, and Birger Sorensen from Norway successfully predicted that vaccines based on the HIV envelope (plan A) would fail and that a few core vital epitopes should be selected instead. One such vaccine based on this principle, Vacc-4x, has clearly shown efficacy even in chronically infected HIV people, and an improved mark 2 version is even better. It is worth noting that all applications for this plan B were turned down by the agencies within Fauci's control.

It is amazing that all attempts to make an effective Covid vaccine included the use of the whole spike (read HIV envelope) protein , even though Sorensen and Dalgleish had warned that it was 79% homologous to human epitopes and would induce a wide variety of side effects including clotting and neurological conditions.

The fact that the receptor binding region had been engineered and selected for strong ACE-2 receptor binding made cardiac and clotting issues even more guaranteed. Fauci was personally informed by Sorensen and Dalgleish of these findings and concerns but chose to ignore them.

HIV saved Fauci's career and taught him that epidemics/pandemics could give him, and his agency, enormous powers and funding.

Perhaps Voltaire would observe that if future epidemics were not to occur then they must be invented: "*If God does not exist, then man must invent him.*"

This was to prove to be Fauci's strategy for staying in post and building his career and power base.

Robert F. Kennedy in his excellent book on *"The Real Anthony Fauci"* distinctly sums up Anthony Fauci's strategy, which was so overblown in the COVID crisis[16] and was carried out by Fauci in the USA and Hancock in UK:

- Pump up pandemic fears to lay the groundwork for large budgets and greater powers.
- Incriminate any elusive pathogen
- Fan hysteria by exaggerating transmissibility
- Stoke waning fear levels with warnings of super mutants etc.
- Control how people live to save their lives
- Keep making confusing and conflicting announcements (public engagement)
- Push faulty tests such as polymerase chain reaction (PCR) to manipulate epidemiology
- Ignore or dismiss effective off the shelf remedies
- Direct all public monies to patented and profitable agents
- Partner with big Pharma and fast track approval
- Allow them to skip key testing metrics
- Curtail clinical trials to conceal side effects
- Sabotage the competition, especially cheap effective competitors.
- Prevent debate and censor dissenting voices in mainstream media, social media and scientific publications
- Promise salvation through vaccines

Effectively what Fauci states as "following science" actually equates to the killing and ultimate death of science.

Fraud in Sciences other than Medicine (nevertheless harming people)

Science has never been and never will be perfect. In addition to the people who simply get it wrong there are, as we have noted, some scientists who purposely create fraudulent research papers.

The Piltdown Man (1912) is perhaps the most famous fraud. The cranium of a human and the jaw of an ape were adapted to fit together and presented as if it was an ancient, early man. Fascinatingly this was exactly the wrong way round. It appears that in ancient man the jaw became more like that of a modern human being before the increase in size of the braincase! This fooled the anthropologists until the 1950s.

In 2006 the world of science was shaken by the news that the work of Dr. Hwang Woo Suk, a South Korean animal-cloning expert, was fraudulent. As well as unethically obtaining human ova he had not managed to produce the stem cells he claimed to have created by cloning. The work had been funded to the tune of $30 million. Hwang is still working in the field of animal cloning.[17]

Fauci, one of the 'scientists' who has overseen more harmful and misleading research than almost anyone in history, continued in post until December 2022 when he retired with full pension and innumerable honours. Contending with Fauci for such an ignoble title as worst scientific fraudster are the CEOs of the large car companies (especially but not only VW) who purposely cheated the scientific testing that was supposed to ensure that the cars would not produce toxic emissions.... And then went on to boast in a series of adverts that the cars were environmentally friendly, clean, efficient and had a high resale value! Now we have an excess of diesel vehicles clogging our towns and cities. The evil carbon smuts and nitrogen oxide waste from these fraudulently produced cars pollutes our atmosphere and will probably cause as many early deaths as that other great scientific polluter of our air, Thomas Midgley.

Wikipedia reminds us that Thomas Midgley (1889-1944), was an American scientist and inventor. His two most famous inventions are both now banned because they are globally dangerous for the environment: the use of lead in petrol (gasoline) and the use of chlorofluorocarbons (CFCs) in refrigerators. Midgley was accidentally killed by something he was inventing.[18,19]

More examples will be mentioned later in the book but a particularly egregious case is that of paraquat, the highly dangerous herbicide. The manufacturer Syngenta knew about paraquat's neurological risks as early as the 1960s but kept the information away from the regulators.[20,21] Paraquat is causally linked to Parkinson's disease.

References: At the end of the book

Chapter 6

Virology

Gain-of-function studies

First presented to the British Society for the History of Medicine Biennial Congress September 2021 by PG
The Editors

".... Pestilence may be spread far and wide, and met by preventive inoculation. A hideous kind of warfare may be waged by scientists commanding armies of innumerable microbes which will fight for and against us in the battlefield of our unhappy bodies."
(From Winston Churchill's *"Mankind is Confronted by One Supreme Task,"* 1937)

Two myths have hindered investigations into the origins of the SARS-CoV-2 virus: one, that viruses seldom escape from laboratories; and two, that most pandemics are zoonotic (caused by a natural spillover of a virus from animals to humans). Whether or not these myths are deliberate lies, tantamount to fraud, is up to the reader to decide.

Promoters of the first myth include the World Health Organisation (WHO). At a press conference in Wuhan, China, in February 2021, Peter Ben Embarek, the head of the WHO inspection team tasked with looking into the origins of the virus, said [1] it was *"extremely unlikely"* that it had leaked from a lab and as a result the lab escape hypothesis would no longer form part of the WHO's continuing investigations.

Dr Peter Daszak, president of the EcoHealth Alliance, has promoted both myths. As long ago as 2012, Dr Daszak co-authored a paper [2] in *The Lancet* claiming that *"Most pandemics—e.g. HIV/AIDS, severe acute respiratory syndrome, pandemic influenza—originate in animals"*. Since the start of the pandemic, he has claimed [3] that *"lab accidents are extremely rare"*, and that they *"have never led to large scale [disease] outbreaks"*. He also said that suggestions that SARS-CoV-2 might have come out of a lab are *"preposterous"*, *"baseless"*, *"crackpot"*, *"conspiracy theories"*, and *"pure baloney"*. He made all these damning statements aimed at other scientist who were pointing out that he and Shi Zhengli had published papers showing that they had made chimeric coronaviruses in the Wuhan Institute of Virology. Moreover these novel coronaviruses had spike proteins inserted in exactly the same place as the virus causing the Covid-19 pandemic [4].

In September 2020 Dr Anthony Fauci, director of the US National Institutes of Health's (NIH) National Institute of Allergy and Infectious Diseases (NIAID), and his co-author wrote in a paper about COVID's origins,[5] *"Infectious diseases prevalent in humans and animals are caused by pathogens that once emerged from other animal hosts."*

Fauci has tried to quash the notion that SARS-CoV-2 could have come from a lab. In May 2020 he said[6] that the virus *"could not have been artificially or deliberately manipulated"* and in October 2020 that year that the lab leak theory was *"molecularly impossible".*

But emails uncovered [7] by a Freedom of Information request in the US reveal a wide gap between what Fauci was being told by experts about the virus's origins and what he was saying publicly. In January 2020, a group of four virologists led by Kristian G. Andersen of the Scripps Research Institute told Fauci that they all "find the genome inconsistent with expectations from evolutionary theory" – in other words, it didn't come from nature and could have come from a lab.

Fauci hastily convened a teleconference with the virologists on 1 February 2020 [8]. As the New York Post reported,[7] *"Something remarkable happened at the conference, because within three days, Andersen was singing a different tune. In a Feb. 4, 2020, email, he derided ideas about a lab leak as 'crackpot theories' that 'relate to this virus being somehow engineered with intent and that is demonstrably not the case'."*

Andersen and his colleagues then published an article [9] on 17 March 2020 in the journal *Nature Medicine* that declared, *"Our analyses clearly show that SARS-CoV-2 is not a laboratory construct or a purposefully manipulated virus."* The article was highly influential persuading the mainstream press not to investigate lab leak theories.[7]

While the emails do not prove a conspiracy to mislead the public, they certainly make it more plausible. Just one day after the teleconference at which his experts explained why they thought the virus seemed manipulated, Francis Collins, then-director of the NIH, complained about the damage such an idea might cause[7].

"The voices of conspiracy will quickly dominate, doing great potential harm to science and international harmony," he wrote on 2 February 2020, according to the emails.

But there is another reason why Fauci and Collins might not want the lab leak idea to take hold. Dr Daszak's EcoHealth Alliance had channelled funding from the NIH's NIAID to the Wuhan Institute of Virology (WIV) in China, for gain-of-function (GoF) research on bat coronaviruses[10]. So money from organisations headed by Fauci, Collins, and Daszak funded research that could have led to the lab leak that some believe caused the pandemic.

While it should have been clear from the beginning that Drs Fauci and Daszak have strong vested interests in denying the lab leak theory, until recently their assertions were taken as objective fact by most science writers and media.

But a brief look at the history of lab leaks and the origins of pandemics confirms that their claims are highly misleading. Research shows that the escape of viruses from laboratories and supposedly contained experiments, such as vaccine research and programmes, is a common occurrence. In addition, many pandemics have arisen from lab escapes and almost all have not been directly zoonotic. Even when viruses do ultimately originate in animals and make the jump into humans, they mostly fester in a separated community of human beings for many years – centuries or millennia – before spreading during abnormal movements of people due to wars and famines.

What is GoF research?

In its broadest definition[11], Gain of Function research (GoF) provides a virus or other microbe with a new function, such as making it more virulent or transmissible, or widening its host range (the types of hosts that the organism can infect). Through GoF, researchers can create new diseases in the laboratory.

GoF can be achieved by any selection process that results in changes in the genes of the organism and as a result, its characteristics. One example of such a process is passing a virus through different animal cells, which can result in a loss of function (weakening it) or a gain of function (making it more able to replicate in a new host species). The researcher can then select the altered organism, depending on the purpose of the research.

In the last decade, GoF researchers have used genetic engineering to directly intervene in the genome of viruses to enhance a desired function.

But long before GoF studies involving deliberate genetic alteration, researchers had started to experiment with widening the host range of certain viruses, in order to develop vaccines. Often these experiments had unintended outcomes, including causing outbreaks of the disease being targeted.

Smallpox

An example is the development of the smallpox vaccine. Most of us are aware of how Edward Jenner in 1796 put cowpox to work in a new way, to infect humans. This led to the successful vaccination programme that eventually eliminated smallpox from the world.

But what many people do not know is that the experiments of 1796 were not his first attempts at using an animal pox in humans. His first subject was his baby son, who had been born in 1789. He inoculated the lad with swinepox and later tested the inoculation's effectiveness with smallpox. As Greer Williams[12] pointed out in the book Virus Hunters, *"The best we can say for this experiment is that it muddied the water... whether the experimental infections had anything to do with (the son's) mental retardation it is impossible to say."*

Vaccination does not give immunity from smallpox for life. Indeed, for such immunity, a booster is required every few years. The last person to die from smallpox was Janet Parker, a photographer who worked on the floor above a lab in Birmingham, UK, where research on the virus was being conducted. She had been vaccinated against smallpox in 1966 but contracted the disease in 1978 when the virus escaped from the lab by an unknown route. She died some days later (Table 1).

Introducing a virus or other microbe to a new host has historically been associated with problems. Before Jenner, inoculation with variola minor (smallpox from a sufferer with minor disease), had been used as a preventive measure in China as early as the tenth century.[13] Variolation, as it was termed, was introduced to the UK in 1717, but is reported to have killed 1 in 25. So Jenner's experiments have to be viewed in the light of the contemporary practice, which was killing 4% of those inoculated. What is more, as Greer Williams noted, variolation was an "excellent way of spreading the disease and starting new epidemics".[12]

Yellow fever

In 1900 the French had given up on building the Panama Canal due to yellow fever decimating the workers. Eventually the disease was conquered in the region by a mosquito eradication programme [14] based on the experiments of the US Army surgeon Major Walter Reed. This success was crucial to the completion of the project in 1914.

But what is often forgotten is that a series of doctors and laboratory workers died trying to combat yellow fever. In 1900 Dr Jesse W. Lazear was the first researcher to die from yellow fever after he apparently allowed[15] himself to be bitten by an infected mosquito as part of his experiments. Between 1927 and 1930, yellow fever caused thirty-two laboratory infections, killing five people.[16]

As the research into viruses continued, so did the infection rate amongst the researchers and the death toll of researchers and those inoculated against diseases rose. We do not doubt that the final outcome was to the good of mankind, but occasionally a "vaccine" would go spectacularly wrong.

Polio

In the 1930s, 40s and 50s the infection that seemed to most frighten Western society was poliomyelitis. Perhaps it was the fact that, unlike with most infectious diseases, cleanliness did not seem to be a protection and exercising could be positively harmful. In fact polio struck those who were healthy and wealthy and was worse if the person was fit and active. Much effort was put into finding a vaccine and among the first to succeed was Dr Jonas Salk. There had been abortive attempts in the 1930s but the 1935 vaccination programme had actually killed people.

Salk was a meticulous researcher and his technique was excellent. Unfortunately this was not the case with all of the laboratories that prepared the vaccine for public use. In particular, the Cutter Laboratories failed to kill the virus and poliomyelitis was spread by their version of the Salk vaccine, paralysing and killing the recipients. Eventually the proper controls permitted the successful rollout of the killed vaccine. It was later replaced by an attenuated polio virus vaccine, which has nearly eliminated polio from the world. It will not, however, succeed in completely eliminating the disease, as the attenuated virus can revert to a wild form. Thus the final push may require the use, once again, of the killed virus polio vaccine.

The infection of laboratory workers with the microbes they were working on was so common that steps were introduced in the 1940s to prevent escape of the organisms. According to Wikipedia,[17] the first prototype Class III (maximum containment) biosafety cabinet was fashioned in 1943 by Hubert Kaempf Jr., then a US Army soldier. The regulations were enhanced and the escape of dangerous organisms decreased, but has never disappeared. This is clearly demonstrated in Table 1, which lists some, but by no means all, of the known lab leaks since the 1960s

Escapes from bioweapons facilities.

Whilst all of the incidents in the table are of interest, some are more worrying than others.

Date	COUNTRY	Virus	Outcome
1966	Birmingham, England	Smallpox	72 cases, no deaths
1967	Germany and Serbia	Marburg Virus Disease	Simultaneous large outbreaks from laboratory work with Green Monkeys fatality rate about 50%
1971	Soviet Union (Aral Sea)	Weaponised Smallpox	Biowarfare field test 10 cases, 3 deaths
1973	London UK	Smallpox	4 cases, 2 deaths
1977	Edge of Russia and China	H1N1 Influenza	Put back together in a lab but escaped causing a pandemic, then returned in 2008/9 as Swine Flu
1978	Birmingham UK	Smallpox	The last person to die from smallpox, Janet Parker, worked on the level above a biosafety 4 lab. She had been vaccinated against smallpox in 1966 but contracted the disease and died
1979	Sverdlovsk, Soviet Union	Weaponised anthrax	Escape from Compound 19 a bioweapons facility, 100s infected, 60 dead
1995	Venezuela	Equine encephalitis	Major equine epizootic and epidemic
2003-2017	China	SARS 1	6 documented outbreaks from research labs, 4 of which were in China, plus Singapore and Taiwan. 13 infections, 1 death
2007	Pirbright, UK	Foot and Mouth disease	Epidemic in British Cattle.
2015	USA	Anthrax	US department of Defense accidentally shipped live anthrax to nine US States and to a US military base in South Korea

Table 1: Some serious leakage of viruses from laboratories (references 18-25)

In 1971 and 1979 there were outbreaks of smallpox and anthrax in the Soviet Union, caused by escapes of weaponised smallpox and weaponised anthrax from their own bioweapons facilities. In 1977 it is believed that a laboratory somewhere on the border of China and Russia put the H1N1 virus back together and it escaped and caused at least two pandemics. SARS1, which erupted first in 2003, later escaped from laboratories six times, four of which were in China, plus Singapore and Taiwan.

The more closely you look at the table, the more you wonder if there is any virus that has not at some time escaped from a laboratory. Laboratory workers have told us that it is common for technicians to become infected with the organisms they are working with and their usual response in the past has been to take multivitamins and hydroxychloroquine.

You also cannot help but wonder how people such as Daszak and Fauci have the gall to stand up in public and state that these things do not happen.

The recent history of gain-of-function studies

Since 2010, GoF studies have increasingly focused on finding out whether non-pathogenic strains of viruses could be made infective and harmful to human beings.[26] This was supposedly in order to know whether or not the microbe was likely to be hazardous to human beings and then, if it was, devise vaccines and drugs against it.

In our opinion, such work simply increases the sum total of different pathogens that can affect human beings. When medical doctors are made aware of this type of research, they are usually speechless at the stupidity that anybody would contemplate doing such work. We now call such studies *Make Another Disease* (MAD) research.

This type of MAD research dramatically increased in laboratories in the USA between 2012 and 2014. For example in the Netherlands the researchers gave an otherwise "harmless" avian influenza virus the ability to infect ferrets and thus very dangerous to human beings. [27] The resulting accidents in which small outbreaks of novel viral diseases occurred led to three hundred scientists writing to the Obama administration asking for GoF to be stopped. The US Government responded by calling for a moratorium on the research in 2014 because of the inherent dangers.

Immediately Dr Fauci and his committee started redefining the meaning of GoF studies. They now said *that the moratorium was only on those studies with the known "potential to enhance the pathogenicity or transmissibility of potential pandemic pathogens (PPPs)"*[28], ignoring the fact that enhancing the ability for any microbe to infect human beings carries a high risk of making it pathogenic.

In 2014 Dr Fauci, whose recorded belief was that the studies were worth the risk, gave money from the NIH to Dr Daszak, of Ecohealth Alliance, to continue GoF research on coronaviruses. This was carried out in the Wuhan Institute of Virology using genetically engineered humanised mice, culminating in reports in 2017 and 2018 that the researchers had successfully made harmless coronaviruses pathogenic to humans.[29]

In the autumn of 2019 the Covid-19 pandemic of SARS-2 started in Wuhan and, to date, over six million people in the world have died from the virus.

Are pandemics ever zoonotic?

In addition to stating erroneously that viruses only rarely escape from laboratories and/or that SARS-Cov-2 was unlikely to have done so, Drs Daszak and Fauci hold that most pandemics are zoonotic in origin. They say that pandemics start from a disease spreading from an animal but they do not state the time period involved. We would suggest that pandemics never occur from the *immediate* spread from an animal. In order for a pandemic to occur, a reservoir of the infection, adapted to human beings, must develop. This usually takes many years. Moreover the spread usually occurs due to the unnaturally large movement of people that occurs due to wars and famines.

We will give just a couple of well known examples.

When the Europeans invaded the Americas, 90% or more of the indigenous people of America died from the introduced diseases, which included measles, smallpox and mumps. In return, syphilis spread to Europe. Yes, the diseases had all arisen from animals initially, but the adaptation to make them pathogenic enough to cause a pandemic must have occurred over a period of the several thousand years during which the populations of Europe and America were separated.

AIDS was discovered in the early 1980s and it was soon clear that the Human Immunodeficiency Virus had arisen from the Simian Immunodeficiency Virus. However, studies have concluded that the first transmission of SIV to HIV in humans took place around 1920 in Kinshasa in the Belgian Congo[30] so that it had at least forty or fifty years of sporadic infection of human beings before it started to spread round the world as a pandemic and during that time there were many local wars in Africa and, of course, the 2nd World War.

In his book *PANDEMIC*, PRG documents the world's worst pandemics and concludes that it is only malaria that seems to be indifferent to wars, killing people whether or not there are hostilities. All other historical pandemics have at least some connection with war and occur when isolated groups with an endemic disease meet another group without the disease. Nowadays it is possible to follow this with antibody studies, the endemic group showing the antibodies of previous infection.

Conclusion

Thus historically we come to an impasse with SARS-CoV-2. This arose in a city many miles away from an animal population that might have harboured a similar virus, at a time when the supposed original host was dormant (late autumn), near a laboratory known to be working on the viruses. It then spread from person to person at an alarming rate and was seen to be totally adapted to human beings, to the extent that it was unable to even infect the bat it was supposed to have arisen from. PRG had studied the history of pandemics and lab leaks, imagine his surprise when authorities, not only in China but also in the USA and UK, stated categorically that the virus was obviously zoonotic and we were all conspiracy theorists if we proposed the opposite. We had to conclude that they were misguided or purposely lying.

Even *New Scientist*, a magazine that has not been exactly forthcoming in its criticism of unbridled science, in a recent review of *The Genetic Age* by Matthew Cobb states that Cobb identifies a streak of hubris running through the field of genetics. "*Many practitioners are too in love with clever technical solutions and can't resists implementing them without considering if the benefits are worth the risk.*" [31]

In particular Cobb identifies three areas of concern:
• Human germline editing
• Gene drive, a genetic chain reaction
• Gain of function studies.

It is now clear that the virologists have purposely misled the world by hiding their involvement in dangerous research and labelling critics as conspiracy theorists.

In case anybody thinks that this is all in the past and they no longer care where the virus originated we now (26/10/22) quote directly from the Mercola site [32]

STORY AT-A-GLANCE

Less than two months ago, scientists funded by the National Institutes of Health (NIH) and Dr. Anthony Fauci's National Institute of Allergy and Infectious Diseases (NIAID) announced they'd resurrected the Spanish flu virus through reverse genetics

Now, scientists at Boston University report they've engineered an Omicron strain of SARS-CoV-2 with an 80% lethality in mice. The new hybrid was created by extracting spike protein from the Omicron BA.1 variant of SARS-CoV-2 and attaching it to the original Wuhan Alpha strain

The research was funded by four grants from the NIH/NIAID, but because those funds were supposedly "earmarked" primarily for equipment, they did not clear the viral engineering portion of the experiment with the NIH. The NIH is reviewing the case to determine whether the University violated rules for enhanced potential pandemic pathogen (ePPP) research

Boston University denies the research qualifies as "gain of function" research as the Alpha strain's lethality was reduced from 100% to 80%. However, the Alpha strain did gain function, namely immune escape, which it didn't have before. The immune-evading properties came from the Omicron spike.

The likelihood of SARS-CoV-2 assembling itself into a Wuhan Alpha strain with Omicron spike protein "in the wild" is just about nil, as the Wuhan strain has mutated out of existence already. Were it not for these madmen, we would never have had to worry about this kind of recombination.

MP told to 'check his behaviour'

COMMONS Leader Penny Mordaunt has scolded independent MP Andrew Bridgen for sharing "conspiracy theories" in the House of Commons.

Daily Telegraph 30.3.2023

Unfortunately the clampdown on so-called conspiracy theories continues in the UK. Commons Leader Penny Mordaunt has scolded and warned MP Andrew Bridgen for sharing conspiracy theories in the House of Commons. Bridgen gave a very good talk about Covid-19 and the danger of the vaccines only to be cautioned by Mordaunt for promoting the theory that Anthony Fauci offshored the operation of making Covid to Wuhan.[33] Effectively that is exactly what Fauci did and all the parties involved should be prosecuted.

Meanwhile the vaccine companies are still busy making new viruses[34] (see below) and Chinese virologists working in Canada have been expelled because they apparently stole viruses from the Winnipeg Biosafety level 4 laboratory![35] **The rogue virologists must be stopped!**

Pfizer admits 'engineering' Covid mutants in lab studies to ensure its antiviral drug works on new variants — but pharma giant insists tests were not 'gain of function' and did not pose risk to public

 [34]

References: At the end of the book

The Response to the Covid-19 Pandemic:

Repurposed drugs: *The Editors*

We have seen earlier that the Chinese and American researchers who had been working on coronaviruses were trying to cover up their ill-gotten knowledge. Thus the origin of the virus was obscured. But what about the response to the virus by the authorities…was the response optimal or another example of poor science?

There were several responses that the UK government could have made to the Covid-19 pandemic. The guidelines on repurposed drugs appeared to have been produced by people in the thrall of "Big Pharma". The social interventions were partly in response to inaccurate predictions made by Neil Ferguson of Imperial College, London, and partly based on inaccurate information from China.

Perhaps unsurprisingly the response was guided by managers rather than by practising doctors. Even when doctors were involved they were people in management positions rather than the chest physicians who knew how to treat viral pneumonias and their sequelae.

Predictably the nations most in thrall to management and to "Big Pharma" fared very badly. Not only did they have the worst death toll but the actions showed how fragile are our liberties and how thin is the veneer of civilisation.

"Guidelines" on the use of drugs for Covid-19

In March 2020 many doctors in the UK and USA were in despair. The Covid-19 pandemic was now well underway and people were dying. Mysteriously the Chief Medical Officers of both UK and the USA had told doctors not to use drugs that they would normally have used in a patient with viral pneumonia. This, apparently, was because there was no scientific evidence that such treatment was effective, and the high priests of evidence-based medicine decreed that the treatments should not be used until full double-blind randomised cross-over trials had been conducted.

Put simply the authorities refused to let doctors use repurposed drugs even when they knew that the drugs had a high safety record and had been used for decades when treating viral pneumonia.

Covid-19 although a new virus was not a completely unknown entity. In broad terms it is a respiratory infection that leads to pneumonia and organ failure, something that can happen with many respiratory infections including influenza, Legionnaire's disease, pneumococcal infection and even measles . More specifically it is very similar to SARS (Severe acute respiratory syndrome) and MERS (Middle East Respiratory Syndrome).

With the knowledge of similarly presenting infections it was reasonable to assume that prophylaxis against such infections and treatment of the common sequelae of the infections may have mitigated against the worst effects of Covid-19. In the event many of the possible procedures, techniques and medicines were not initially used in the UK because of the instructions from the Chief Medical Officer and the Secretary of State for Health and Social Care effectively banning their use. Similar behaviour in the USA prevented simple treatments from being administered.

We contend that such drugs should have been permitted and would have saved lives. A full investigation into the advice given to the CMO and Secretary of State and the instructions given out by them is undoubtedly necessary. Moreover scientific discussions about the use of repurposed drugs and the clinical freedom of medicine are necessary, not in order to attribute blame but to prevent such occurrences in the future.

In a rapid response letter to the BMJ in April 2020,[1] Goddard, Jarad and Dalgleish supported the trials but pleaded for clinicians to be allowed to use their discretion in patients not entered on trials

We saw no conflict between enrolling patients in clinical trials and trying off-label HCQ, AZM, anti-viral drugs or anti-inflammatory agents in Covid-19 patients who were not being entered on the trials. We also advocated the use of Vitamin D3, social distancing including masks and breathing exercises (Facebook, Youtube, PANDEMIC 1ᵈ edition).

In the event high dose corticosteroids were not used in Covid-19 in the UK and USA until a report from the University of Oxford 16 June 2020 stated: *"Dexamethasone reduces death in hospitalised patients with severe respiratory complications of Covid-19"*.[2]

Hydrocortisone is also effective in reducing mortality rate as shown by a meta-analysis study by WHO rapid evidence appraisal (REACT)[3.]

But a textbook from 1972 stated that at the stage of peripheral circulatory failure due to viral pneumonia high doses of corticosteroids may be of some value [4] and Professor Landrey (lead of the RECOVERY trial) stated recently *"Had we been prescribing this drug from February 2020 we would have saved 4000 lives"*. [2] Previous experience with viral pneumonias showed that corticosteroids could be very effective. Banning the use of corticosteroids and killing four thousand people in the UK alone was probably criminally negligent. As usual no discussion was permitted and the belief that the pharmaceutical firms and large trials are always necessary to create the "one and only science" was wrong. Experience is useful in all sciences. Other drugs that have proven to be useful with very little risk if prescribed and administered correctly include non-steroidal anti-inflammatory drugs (particularly Aspirin, as a gargle when starting the infection), anti-histamines, Vitamin D3 [5] and anticoagulants.

Ivermectin and Hydroxychloroquine (HCQ), demonised by management, have been shown to be extremely useful in many studies but effectively banned in the USA and UK. The trials of Hydroxychloroquine (HCQ) were conducted using a massive dose that was known to be toxic.

The curtailment of the clinical freedom of medical personnel started in the UK with the Ian Kennedy Report. It has now reached a parlous state where the ability of the clinician to act in the best interests of the patient is severely limited.

The pessimism propagated about treatment of Covid-19 was understandable but misguided. Repurposed drugs including oxygen, anti-virals, corticosteroids, and other anti-inflammatory agents, and anti-coagulants have a major role in treatment of the infection and the inflammatory response. Vitamin D3 is useful in prevention of severe Covid-19 infection and has been shown to shorten in-patient stay.

The Death of Science

Antivirals developed for treatment of Covid-19

Here is a quote from an article by Dr Mercola [6]

So far, all of the drugs developed against COVID-19 have been disastrous in one way or another. Remdesivir, for example, which to this day is the primary COVID drug approved for use in U.S. hospitals, routinely causes severe organ damage and, often, death. Another notable one is Paxlovid, which was granted emergency use authorization to treat mild to moderate COVID-19 in December 2021. While not showing signs of being deadly like remdesivir, Paxlovid has become so widely associated with rebound infection that the U.S. Centers for Disease Control and Prevention has even issued a warning about it. According to the CDC's health advisory: "Recent case reports document that some patients with normal immune response who have completed a 5-day course of Paxlovid for laboratory-confirmed infection and have recovered can experience recurrent illness 2 to 8 days later, including patients who have been vaccinated and/or boosted."

Could we have done better?

Of course we could have done better! If management had not been so firmly in control of medicine in the USA and UK the repurposed drugs may well have brought the pandemic under control at an early stage saving many thousands, perhaps millions, of lives. But management was listening to the big players in this game. We quote again from Robert F Kennedy's book, *The Real Anthony Fauci* [7]

"In 2020, workers lost $3.7 trillion while billionaires gained $3.9 trillion…..

"The biggest winners were the robber barons—the very companies that were cheerleading Dr. Fauci's lockdown and censoring his critics: Big Technology, Big Data, Big Telecom, Big Finance, Big Media behemoths (Michael Bloomberg, Rupert Murdoch, Viacom, and Disney), and Silicon Valley Internet titans like Jeff Bezos, Bill Gates, Mark Zuckerberg, Eric Schmidt, Sergey Brin, Larry Page, Larry Ellison, and Jack Dorsey." and *"If the COVID-19 pandemic has revealed anything, it is that public health officials have based their many calamitous directives for managing COVID-19 on vacillating and science- free beliefs….."*

It is hard to imagine how the official response to Covid-19 could have been worse with regard to the potentially useful repurposed drugs. We shall, however, in further chapters show how badly informed all the other measures have been and how they worsened the situation.

References: At the end of the book

93

Chapter 8

Social Interventions

Part1: Background, Inception, Definitions and Effectiveness : *The Editors*

The social interventions brought in throughout most of the world in 2020 were the biggest curtailment of freedom in peacetime known to living people. Dictatorial control over people's lives was enacted, surprising many in power with the way in which people accepted the arbitrary rulings.

In this chapter we will examine what the interventions were, whether they were based on science, whether they were lawful and whether or not they were effective. We shall also look at the harm they did and balance it against any possible good.

Liberty is a difficult concept and difficult to maintain. Once freedom and rights are taken away it is often very hard to regain them.

The background to social intervention

Lockdown was the response to an unknown virus which appeared in Wuhan in China at the end of 2019. It was originally applied to the city of Wuhan and adopted by nearly all other countries where the infection spread and took hold.

The world officially first became aware of a novel coronavirus in December 2019 with reports that it was killing people in Wuhan. Even though the World Health Organisation (WHO) were involved, we were assured that it was a local problem, associated with a live meat market in Wuhan, and that the transmission was from bats to humans. In short there was no concern about it spreading from human to human and hence no fear that it would spread further.

We now know that this was a cover up and that had the WHO not withheld the obvious fact that it was spreading from human to human the virus may never have travelled outside China. It is now obvious to all that the failure to control this virus and instigate appropriate measures has led to the deaths of more than six and a half million people world-wide and brought the world's economy to its knees.

This is even more surprising when such a pandemic had been feared for many years. The last big pandemic that killed millions was, in what is a sadly relevant irony, caused by a virus that originated in China but became known as Spanish flu. It was bought to Europe at the end of the first world war by Chinese workers who were brought in to help clear up the battlefields of the war. It was remarkably infectious and lethal causing an estimated 50-100million deaths, far more than had died fighting the war, and about 10% of those infected. This was much higher than the subsequent flu pandemics of the fifties (Asian flu with less than 1% deaths), the Hong Kong flu of the sixties, (again with less than 1% mortality) and the more recent Mexican Swine flu in 2009/2010, with an even lower mortality.

We have had previous alarm bells over coronavirus infections (which are normally associated with no more than the common cold) when a virus from the Yunnan province in China spread from bats to humans and caused the severe acute respiratory syndrome (SARS), the virus was termed SARS-Cov-1. It occurred in 2003/4 and infected 8000 people and killed about 10% of those infected. Fortunately, it was contained and burnt out before vaccines and treatments could be developed. Another coronavirus was identified with an outbreak in Saudi Arabia in 2012 which was known as the Middle East respiratory syndrome (MERS). This virus was associated with a high mortality rate of 35% and once again rapidly attenuated and burned out.

The current pandemic is known as COVID-19 and the causative virus is known as SARS-Cov-2, implying similarity to the causative agent of SARS.

The condition of COVID-19 was first brought to the world's attention in December 2019 by Dr Li Wenliang (an ophthalmologist) who warned his colleagues via an on-line chat room that a mysterious virus was killing people in Wuhan and that it was very infectious and deadly and similar to SARS. What happened next was to stimulate the subject of this book. Despite being scientifically correct and acting in a responsible and public-spirited manner he was summoned by the Chinese police and other authorities to be reprimanded and forced to sign a statement that his early pronouncements were not true. He was declared dead supposedly from the very disease that he was warning everybody about just a few weeks previously.

The Chinese authorities with the connivance of the WHO assured the world that the disease was completely under control. Had this lie, which was only one part of a clear cover up, not occurred it is possible that the virus could have been contained and not spread to Europe or to the rest of the world.

An investigation in 2016 examined how prepared the UK was for a pandemic, which would likely emanate from China. We now know that Sally Davis, who was chief medical officer for the UK, had responded that systems were in place with the WHO which would make such an event an extreme impossibility!

The response to this initial infection clearly defined the worldwide outcome. It is obvious that the staff in the Wuhan hospitals were extremely concerned and that like Dr Li Wenliang they were told to keep quiet. This virus had infected hundreds of patients as far back as November 2019 but the possibility that it was caused by human to human infection was ignored or purposely played down. This was still the official line in late January when the first description of the virus was sent to Nature by an expert on bat viruses, Dr Shi Zheng-Li, who worked at the now world famous Wuhan Institute of Virology (WIV). The official Chinese origin theory was that it had spread from bats to an intermediate animal such as a pangolin and infected the meat market in Wuhan. The meat market was closed and thoroughly sterilised obliterating the possibility of testing such a theory. In a very short time other virologists had submitted papers in agreement that this was a natural virus.

However, *"the elephant in the room"* was deliberately ignored. The WIV was the world's specialist laboratory on bat viruses and hundreds of samples had been brought from caves over a thousand miles away for investigation. The laboratory was well known for Gain of Function (GoF) experiments where viruses are genetically altered so that different functions such as receptor binding and infectivity can be explored. The laboratory had published in top virology journals stating that they had engineered coronaviruses in order to enhance their infectivity to human cells.

This may make some sense of the NIH directive which was sent out to scientists a few months later to explain why SARS-Cov-2 is so perfectly adapted to infect human cells.

It is necessary to recollect that the Americans had inspected the WIV site in 2018, which was meant to be the only level 4 biosafety laboratory in China. The inspectors concluded the facilities and standard operating procedures (SOPs) were entirely unsuited for successful containment in a level 4 safety laboratory. Nothing is completely secure even when operated at the highest levels, as in the escape of smallpox from the freezers in Birmingham and the animal disease, foot and mouth, from Pirbright in Surrey, as noted in Chapter 6. It has subsequently been brought to light that laboratory staff in Wuhan had become infected with the Covid-19 virus as far back as September 2019 and that the WIV went mysteriously silent for a few weeks in October. Infections in humans outside the laboratory were clearly occurring in early November.

Wuhan was put into lockdown in December and interregional travel within China halted. However, the international airports remained open as did the train line that ran between the WIV and the international airport of Wuhan.

If the "lockdown" had been conducted as the WHO should have insisted then the virus would not have escaped to Europe and the world-wide pandemic not occurred. China could have been quarantined and millions of lives would have been spared.

However, the point of this chapter is to explore how effective or not, lockdown has been in containing this virus in the United Kingdom.

Lockdown of the whole population might possibly have made sense when dealing with an infectious disease that kills 10 percent or more of people infected such as the Spanish flu and SARS-1. However, as the pandemic progressed it became clear that COVID-19 kills less than 1-2% of infected people and that this is not a random event occurring in all ages of the population. Indeed, the majority of people who die from COVID-19 are elderly with an average age of death in the UK of 82, not much different from the average age of death from other conditions. Moreover, the majority have other underlying conditions such as diabetes and heart disease. Very few people under 65 have died from COVID-19 who did not have any other serious medical condition or co-morbidity.

It is against this background that we will later examine the benefits and negatives of imposing lockdown in its different degrees, on different populations and the UK in particular.

Inception of Lockdown

As discussed in Chapter 2 a major principle in the bioethics of medical practice and research is *primum non nocere*, translated as 'first do no harm'. An intervention is unethical if its harms outweigh its benefits. When, belatedly, they realised that the virus was a serious threat to life the UK government initially asked people to limit contact with other people then brought in lockdown measures by law. They also persuaded people that they needed to **protect the NHS and protect the vulnerable.**

UK Government

CORONAVIRUS
**STAY AT HOME
PROTECT THE NHS
SAVE LIVES**

In order that people obeyed the instructions experts in behavioural science were consulted and a climate of fear was ramped up. People were made extremely frightened of the virus, afraid of meeting each other, forbidden from usual social interaction and told that they might be passing on the virus unawares. Everybody was a potential enemy.[1] Unfortunately the measures taken lessened the "burden" on the NHS at a time when the duty of the NHS was to protect the populous, rather than the other way round. When did it become our duty to protect the NHS? Surely the burden they referred to is the actual job of the NHS, an organisation that takes an increasing proportion of the tax money paid by the citizens of the UK and nearly has a monopoly on the provision of healthcare in the UK?

Moreover the most vulnerable people turned out to be those over seventy years of age…..and any old people in hospital were turfed out into the care homes using hastily passed acts of parliament to ensure the care homes could not refuse their admission. The discharged patients had not been tested or protected and immediately spread the disease to the other vulnerable people in the homes.

In late 2020 vaccines were already being tested in Europe, South America, South Africa and in India. In 2021 they were rolled out in the UK. They had two immediate effects. To start with the vaccinated people avoided hospital admission and it appeared that they did not spread the virus. Then the variants started appearing (mostly from the UK or Europe, South America, South Africa and in India) and the whole picture changed: the vaccinated were spreading the disease more than the unvaccinated! [2,3]

Definitions of the Social Interventions

When the Covid-19 pandemic was confirmed as a major problem many of the governments introduced lockdowns, following the Chinese government's example as discussed in the last chapter. But what exactly is the meaning of the terms used ? We shall demonstrate that Sweden, whose government did not impose lockdown, fared better than many European countries that imposed strict restrictions. Here we wish to take time out from the flow of the book to clarify what was meant by the imposed loss of freedom, then show what ill-effects occurred and ask whether the way the UK's government has behaved was justified or whether it was illegal and harmful.

What is Lockdown?

What coronavirus lockdowns have meant around the world
Emma Graham-Harrison

The Guardian
18 March 2020

Effects of lockdown could be causing more deaths than Covid: Fears rise

Mail Online
19 Aug 2022

Lockdown feared to be killing more than Covid

Daily Telegraph
19 August 2022

A large number of new words have been brought into common parlance with the advent of the Covid-19 pandemic. First and foremost of these is Lockdown, the title of this section, but often confused with this are Quarantine, Self-Isolation, Social Distancing and Curfew. All these topics are inter-related but have distinctly different meanings and it is important to start by defining them.

How people used the new terms

A friend told us that her mother was vulnerable so she had been in *self-isolation*, a man on the allotments confided in me that the *curfew on pubs* was spoiling his life. Another person argued that shutting down businesses due to *quarantine* was an unwarranted breach of human rights. Were they right? Were they using the terms correctly or are they all interchangeable as those examples seem to indicate?

Lockdown: Few people liked the lockdowns but many grudgingly accepted it as necessary. But was it?

Lockdown is a North American term describing a situation in which the authorities impose a restriction on people entering, leaving or moving around in a building or area because of danger[4] . It has typically been used in the past to describe the confining of prisoners to their cells in order to regain control during a prison riot. [5] It is now being used to describe a period of time during which freedom of movement, commerce and general activity is curtailed by government diktat in order to protect the public or an institution from the effects of a disease. The probability is that the majority of the population affected from a lockdown for disease control are not actually suffering from the disease and, indeed, the lockdown may be enacted to prevent them from coming in contact with people who do carry the contagion.

Some activities are continued, such as shopping for food and essential items, exercising and walking the dog. Lockdown as described will never completely prevent social interaction as essential workers have to continue their activities and the public are obliged to meet them when shopping etcetera.

Quarantine: The word quarantine is a much older term than lockdown. It first appeared in the English language in 1663 during a period when the Bubonic Plague was rife. [6,7] The word is derived from quarantena, meaning "forty days", which was used in the Venetian language in the 14th and 15th centuries. [8]

People known to be an infection risk, either because they had a disease, had been in contact with a disease or had recently arrived from a place where the disease was prevalent, would be quarantined by being placed in isolation for a pre-determined period until no longer deemed to be a danger to others. This term was originally used solely for human beings but has been expanded to include animals, plants and objects. The time period of quarantine is determined by the nature of the contagious disease.

This may appear conceptually similar to lockdown but on examination it is actually the opposite. In lockdown the whole population of an area, such as a country or state, has their activity reduced but not completely stopped. In quarantine just those who are a risk to the population are constrained and prevented from leaving the place of confinement. The activity of those who *are a contagion risk to* the population is completely curtailed for a short determined period in quarantine compared with the activity of those who *are at risk from* a contagion being partially reduced for an often indeterminate period in lockdown.

Self-Isolation: Self-isolation is when a person does not leave their home because they have or may have a disease. Recently it has been used to describe people staying at home due to Covid-19 [9]. It could be considered as a semi-voluntary, self-imposed form of quarantine at home rather than in a detention centre or specified location.

Social Distancing: Social distancing, also called 'physical distancing' means keeping a safe distance between yourself and other people and taking specific steps to reduce social interaction with people in order to reduce transmission of disease. [10]

The NHS advice on social distancing was as follows [11]:

1. Try to stay at least 2 metres (3 steps) away from anyone you do not live with (or anyone not in your support bubble)
2. Wash your hands with soap and water often – do this for at least 20 seconds
3. Use hand sanitiser gel if soap and water are not available
4. Wash your hands as soon as you get home
5. Cover your mouth and nose with a tissue or your sleeve (not your hands) when you cough or sneeze
6. Put used tissues in the bin immediately and wash your hands afterwards
7. Let fresh air into your home by opening windows, doors and air vents as much as possible.

Shielding: People who are particularly vulnerable to infection are advised to "Shield". This is basically extended self-isolation with extra caution thrown in for good measure. The NHS advice [12] suggested that to reduce your risk from coronavirus, you may want to:

- Do your shopping online
- Ask family or friends to collect shopping for you
- Avoid busy times if you go shopping.
- You can also get help with food and medicine deliveries from an NHS volunteer.

Goddard in PANDEMIC [7] stated that the basic concepts for shielding and social distancing can be summed up as Time, Distance, Barriers and Cleanliness:

- Time: spend as little time as possible with other people
- Distance: keep your distance from other people
- Barriers: keep a barrier (eg mask, visor, window, screen) between yourself and others
- Cleanliness: frequently wash your hands and face with soap and water.

Curfew: A curfew is a regulation that people must remain indoors between specified times. This is usually at night and has been used to control dissent and activities deemed to be antisocial. With epidemics the purpose is to stop events that might lead to super-spreading , such as large parties, raves and concerts. The rest of the time the populace can go about their usual business.

Test and Trace: Tests for the severe acute respiratory syndrome coronavirus 2 (SARS-Cov-2) are carried out using several techniques. Tracing involves contacting individuals who have tested positive using telephone, email or texting or visiting them in person then determining who they have been in contact with and testing the contacts. Good test and trace would seem to be imperative if a pandemic is to be brought under control.

Apparently Test and Trace Consultants have been paid £1000 per day. Baroness Harding was put in charge of the UK Covid test and trace team and over £37 billion has been spent on it. That is equivalent to three-quarters of the annual salary bill for the entire NHS yet the results have been dire.

There were already, before Covid-19, people who were experts in test and trace. Medically the respiratory teams test for tuberculosis and trace contacts. The sexually transmitted disease clinics do the same for STDs. The police try hard to trace criminals and have large computer systems to assist them in the task.

So why was Baroness Harding, a novice in this field, entrusted with the task and why was it left up to commercial concerns?

As a BMJ blog points out the story could have been completely different. Volunteers would have been willing to run such a system, vast expense could have been avoided and the results much better. Here is their story : *"A small group of retired public health and primary care staff formed Sheffield Community Contact Tracers (SCCT) a year ago. We linked with a local community volunteer hub and the local Primary Care Network. We demonstrated in a small study that volunteers could be quickly and safely trained to undertake contact tracing of covid-19 cases identified by local GPs. We ensured that cases and quarantined contacts were supported throughout their isolation."*

There is no convincing evidence that the enormous expense has done anything to halt the pandemic. If it had been successful we would not be onto the fourth wave (plus!).

However useless the test and trace has been in its attempt to halt the pandemic it is absolutely clear that it has ruined livelihoods, education and leisure of numerous people. Whole schools were shut down by one positive case and the NHS app has even traced people who live in the next door house but have not left their home!

The examples: So in the examples at the beginning of the chapter the friend who told us that her mother was vulnerable so she had been in self-isolation should have stated that she was shielding and the man on the allotments probably meant the effect of lockdown on pubs was spoiling his life, although when the premises are told to close at a set time, such as 10.00 pm that is indeed a curfew. When the person argued that shutting down businesses due to quarantine was an unwarranted breach of human rights she probably meant lockdown and not quarantine though quarantine can also impinge on human rights as the effect on the person who is being quarantined is tantamount to being imprisoned.

It can be argued that human rights are not possible without responsibilities and somebody taking a position of power and enforcing the rights. However, any intervention must be weighed against the possible adverse outcome from that intervention. All the harmful effects of the socially isolating interventions were predictable before even the first "lockdown."

The Mistakes

Following the Science?

In the recent (and presently still ongoing) Covid-19 crisis governments all over the world brought in "lockdowns" to slow the spread of the disease. They did this announcing that they were "following the science". Was it a mistake to do this and what does the phrase mean?

In the UK the science that was supposedly followed was that put out by the SAGE committee. This is an unelected group of people who are supposed to represent the science community in the UK. But do they actually do anything of the sort? And when was there only one science to follow?

Lockdowns had never previously been used with the present meaning. As discussed earlier in this chapter *Lockdown* is a term from the USA where prison communities rioting were literally locked in and thus locked down. In that sense it is not a healthcare intervention. Clearly the term "lockdown" in the UK does not mean literally locking people in buildings since there were no places to imprison so many people. Moreover it seems that the people who were most inclined to disingenuously break such lockdown laws were the Government and the Government officials. Since they did not keep to the strict laws and directives that they tried to make us keep to, it is clear that they did not really accept the so-called science they were being told by the SAGE committee.

There was no science to follow so the officials were right to be sceptical but wrong to be so hypocritical.

Why was there no science? Because the one country that professed to have controlled the Covid-19 pandemic by lockdown was China itself, a country ruled by a government utterly different from our own Western democracies.

The Chinese government lied about the origin of the virus, which research has shown was undoubtedly made in the Wuhan laboratory. They lied about the way in which they locked down…it was done much more viciously than they led the world to believe. And they lied about the number of people who had died.

But Western governments swallowed their lies and continue to do so. As a result many countries passed very stringent laws to control the movement of their citizens and then, by a climate of fear, forced the populace to obey such laws.

One country that did not do that was Sweden. They advised people to stay at home but did not bring in stringent laws and huge fines. The latest figures show that their rate of Covid-19 infections and deaths were no worse than countries that did stringent lockdowns. When you look at excess deaths of all causes you find that the Swedes did better than most European nations.

It was noticed by the press a year ago that there are 1000 excess deaths per week that are not due to Covid.[13] These are still being blamed on Lockdowns. The other possibility, vaccine problems, are not being suggested, probably for political reasons. They will certainly be discussed later in the book.

Non-Covid excess deaths averaging 1,000 a week

The Daily Telegraph 19/8/22
Also reported in The Week,
Independent, and the Daily Mail

What is the SAGE Committee?

A discussion about the science of the UK's response to Covid-19 cannot be complete without a discussion of the Sage committee.

SAGE stands for "Scientific Advisory Group for Emergencies". Clearly the acronym has been chosen since it implies wisdom, something that has sadly been very much missing from the committees deliberations. Freedman[14] argues that the committee's decisions were flawed *"...a system geared to consensus, even in contentious areas, may mean that what comes through reflects the loudest or most senior voices, with dissenters marginalised and dismissed as mavericks."*

There was no true consensus about response to Covid-19. On the one hand the SAGE committee advised severe lockdowns and on the other equally eminent scientists, as reflected in the Great Barrington Declaration[15], suggested the opposite. An independent SAGE committee thought that the lockdowns were not severe enough![16] Frequently the SAGE output was based on predictions by Neil Ferguson of Imperial College that were disproved even at the time of dissemination to the government and shown to be manifestly wrong when seen by the greater public. Sitting on the Independent SAGE group was Professor Susan Michie FAcSS FMedSci, of University College, London. Her advice all along was for further restriction of movement and limitation of people's freedom, advice in keeping with her hardline communist views that greater government control is always necessary.

Lockdown was imposed in Wuhan to stop the spread of the unknown virus from person to person, which is quite ironic given that the Chinese authorities denied that this was possible for many, many weeks, when this was clearly the case. Lockdown was to contain the infection and the instance of disease leading to overload of the hospital and death. Meanwhile, even as this lockdown was imposed and flights and internal travel banned in China, thousands of Chinese students, business people and students from mainland China and Hong Kong continued to arrive in the UK The Foreign Office advised British citizens not to visit China. What China and the WHO should have done is prevent everybody from leaving China and spreading the disease outside. It is clear that what should have occurred was a complete prevention of dissemination of disease outside China, as they clearly were trying to do within China. WHO should have insisted that everybody who left China to go to another country should be quarantined on arrival to make sure they were not infected and would not introduce the infection into another country. Bizarrely, there were still thousands of people arriving from China and Hong Kong,, particularly into the UK and other parts of Europe, even though the populations were being severely locked down. When the absurdity of this was pointed out the CMO, Professor Whitty, said there was no point as the virus was already here.

This highlights a major issue and that is the difference between lockdown and quarantine. Whereas quarantine is useful and effective, lockdown at best merely delays the inevitable.

Because lockdown was apparently imposed quickly and effectively in Wuhan, it was adopted very quickly in Italy when the epidemic quickly got out of control there. It had been suggested that lockdowns were easy to impose in totalitarian regimens but would be very difficult in the liberal western democracies. However, the scale of the infection and rapid spread and the overwhelming pressure on hospitals and intensive care made the authorities believe they had little option and other countries, including the UK, were relatively quick to follow. There was quite a reluctance on behalf of the Prime Minister to instigate the lockdown, which was recommended by SAGE and other scientists. The CMO, Professor Whitty and CSO, Patrick Vallance, all entertained the idea that the British population would not put up with lockdown unnecessarily and that by delaying lockdown a degree of herd immunity could be built up. In early March, as it became clear that many people were getting symptomatic with Covid infection and that hospital admissions of such patients were soaring and the death rate was rising, SAGE advised an urgent, immediate lockdown. This was initially resisted with advice to avoid situations where viruses could spread and to execute social distancing but when it was thought to not be halting the spread of infection or lowering the death rate, a full lockdown eventually came into being on the 23ʳᵈ March, 2020.

Lockdown was associated with a continuously repeated slogan to stay home, protect the NHS and save lives. It appeared that Covid infection was overwhelming NHS resources and that the major problem was a severe respiratory-like illness, associated with shortness of breath, requiring oxygen and artificial ventilation. Repurposed drugs, usually used for viral infections, were either banned or seriously advised against.

Ventilators and Intensive Care Beds

It was deemed that there were not nearly enough ventilators available for the projected number of patients that would need them, nor were there enough intensive care beds. Tens of thousands of ventilators were therefore ordered and factories converted to produce ventilators. A number of emergency hospitals were constructed by the army and known as Nightingale Hospitals, and made available in a record time. Unfortunately the knee jerk measures were shown to be poorly thought through as it became apparent that artificial ventilation was not very helpful and that the majority of people on ventilators were not helped by them and were actually dying. The Nightingale hospitals, with all their resources, were of little use if there were not enough staff to run them and the majority were dismantled without ever being used.

It is bizarre that all this was being done without any thought as to how to prevent people who were clearly getting infected and experiencing symptoms from progressing to the point where they would need hospitalisation. Indeed, GP surgeries shut down and all advice was given on the phone or the patients were told to stay at home and basically suffer in silence and get over it and only call the ambulance and go to hospital if they were becoming seriously ill and short of breath.

Short Case Report
March 2020: A man, aged 35, caught Covid-19 whilst skiing in the Alps. He returned to the UK (no checks at the airports) and self-isolated in a flat in London. His condition considerably worsened over a few days such that he had no strength to walk down or up one flight of stairs, was severely breathless, plus numbness in his left side and tachycardia and cardiac dysrhythmia (irregular fast pulse). Fearing for his life he phoned 111 and was told that they would phone him back (....which they did, six days later). He telephoned his GP who told him that he was a hypochondriac. He finally telephoned 999 and, after some time, a team of paramedics in full protective gear arrived, measured his PaO2 level using a pulse oximeter, stated that he definitely had the Covid, pronounced his PaO2 to be normal and left. At no time was he given any useful advice or assistance. He had a further week of worsening symptoms, sleeping fitfully in a chair and unable to breathe when lying down, before gradually improving over a period of several months.

It was clear that the symptoms of this virus infection were those of an upper respiratory tract infection and very similar, initially, to those of cold and flu and that transmission was airborne, in droplets, and made worse with coughing and sneezing, but also could be transmitted from surfaces. This led to an obsession with hand washing and sanitisation, which probably made very little difference compared to dealing with the situation at hand, which was people getting suddenly very ill, with sore throats, headaches, fevers and shortness of breath.
Although we didn't initially know the nature of the virus it was clear that aerosol transmission involving the virus attacking the upper airways, would benefit from those medical expediencies known to greatly reduce this. The first of these, which was completely ignored in spite of advice from many experienced clinical physicians, was the association with low Vitamin D levels.[17] Indeed, there are studies showing that making sure healthy levels of Vitamin D are in place in a population renders the patients more resistant to flu infection than any flu vaccination programmes. As the action of the virus was very

similar to influenza it was obvious that Vitamin D supplementation should have been promoted but, despite advice to this effect, it was not acted on. Recent research has confirmed its efficacy.

The second issue was that the infection was in the throat and upper airways, where it attached to an ACE-receptor, which revealed that the virus was unusually equipped to adapt to human cell infection. Any such infection is accompanied by inflammation, which is what of course leads to the sore throat and other respiratory symptoms. Reducing the infection with simple measures, such as gargling with aspirin and taking other anti-inflammatory agents, particularly those that inhibit the COX-2 pathways, would help reduce the viral load. Another factor which was incredibly important, as it turned out, was the fact that aspirin is very useful at stopping blood clotting. As the disease became more understood, it was clear that the component that led to the majority of patients going to hospital involved the formation of small micro clots in the lung, serving as foci of inflammation. Therefore treatment upfront that reduced inflammation and clotting could clearly have reduced the number of patients progressing to having full blown lung infection or pneumonia, leading to hospitalisation and intensive care management.

The fact that no focus, no advice was issued by the Government and Department of Health or the NHS on this, must surely go down as an act of extreme negligence and dereliction of their duty of care. Once again, this highlights the recurring theme that all the UK government's reactions have been more interested in protecting the NHS than protecting the population from the disease. As the disease progressed it became evident that the initial symptoms of sore throat, dry cough, fever and shortness of breath were not the only ones that defined the infection. More and more cases of patients who claimed to have lost their sense of smell and/or taste, often with very little else in the way of symptoms, began to be recognised. Additional symptoms rapidly became evident, such as severe headache, fatigue and weakness. As the weeks wore on other symptoms began to be recognised, including severe muscle pain, muscle weakness, stomach cramps and bizarrely for upper respiratory spread infection, diarrhoea, which would appear to have been involved in up to a third of cases.

The clinical manifestation of diarrhoea has been of particular interest relative to the origin of this virus as it is not normally associated with other respiratory infections, such as influenza or, indeed, the common cold. It made editor AGD think back to work that had been published by the Wuhan laboratory where the WIV deliberately set out to manipulate the coronavirus so that it would be able to infect human intestinal cells and announced that they had successfully manipulated the virus in that way. AGD's first reaction to this mirrored that of most doctors when told about such work: '*Why on earth would anybody wish to make a very infectious virus even more virulent to cell lines that it does not normally infect?*' This highlighted that, in addition to the ACE 2 binding sites, these viruses were able to utilise secondary receptors much more efficiently than other coronaviruses. It helps to explain why the virus is so well adapted to infect a whole range of human cells and why this manifests in a whole gamut of clinical scenarios that one would not normally expect.

The clotting association with the formation of micro clots, particularly in the lung, is an essential step in the fatal aspect of the infection, where the clots become the centre of inflammation, which ends up with lungs secreting tacky mucus it cannot expel, so the patient starts to drown in their own secretions and the oxygen levels go down, which is why so many patients are extremely short of breath and have severe hypoxia, which is what they eventually die from. An understanding of this clinical pathology immediately explains why mechanical ventilation is unlikely to be helpful as all it will do is make the elimination of the mucous that is drowning the patient more difficult to expel, which is why the death rate of patients who are ventilated is so uncomfortably high. Indeed, this pneumonia, which has very specific abnormalities on a CT scan, as opposed to bacterial pneumonias and other infections, such as TB, is associated with widespread inflammation, which has been known for years to benefit from steroid administration to reduce this.

An obsession by the CMO not to use repurposed drugs led to a randomised study, known as RECOVERY, in which Dexamethasone, a standard anti-inflammatory treatment, was only given in a randomised manner and it is no surprise that this was one of the most successful treatments. We would argue that, as in the use of Vitamin D and aspirin, it was so obvious that corticosteroids would help that, even though the causative agent was not known, it should have been given to all patients admitted to hospital. There are two main questions here, how many lives were lost because a sensible first aid treatment of upper respiratory tract infection was not recommended to be given and how many patients died because they were put on a trial where they were denied standard anti-inflammatory treatment, unless randomised to it?

The Elderly and the Ethnic Groups at most risk from the virus

As the pandemic wore on it was increasingly noted that patients who required hospitalisation were mainly elderly and not too dissimilar to those who succumbed to seasonal flu, and it is worth remembering that only as recently as 2014/15, 30,000 patients died just of the flu, when no lockdown measures were put in place. Of the other patients, many were recognised to be very overweight and obese and had underlying health issues, such as diabetes and cardiac problems. Indeed, many other conditions have now been recognised as making someone far more likely to succumb to death if they get infected with Covid-19 than if they did not, and these include neurological problems, such as Parkinson's Disease and dementia.

However, another observation is that it appeared that patients who were from what was described at the time as "black and minority ethnic communities" (BAME) were much more likely to be hospitalised and die. This led to a commission being formed to investigate this, which clearly ignored two of the most important causes, mainly that they are far more likely to be seriously Vitamin D deficient and more likely to be overweight, with the other co-morbidities associated with this of hypertension and diabetes. Moreover a significant number may have had Sickle Cell Disease or Trait. We and others, such as the extremely experienced physicians who specialise in Vitamin D metabolism for decades, namely David Anderson and David Grimes,[17] advised that the administration of Vitamin D to at risk patients was an absolute urgency and that it even had a therapeutic role in patients who were ill with low levels. Again, rather than do something pragmatic, practical, cheap and useful, the Government seemed to be more intent on assuaging the BAME community, that their problem was all down to deprivation and racial discrimination issues.

In addition to the above, a pattern was emerging that elderly patients who by nature of their age are more likely to have other underlying co-morbidities are also more likely to die from Covid-19 than younger people and that it made sense to try to specifically protect them from the infections being brought into their environment by their relatives or care workers. This also highlighted the fact that many of these elderly patients were living in multi-generational accommodation and therefore were being exposed to the virus and becoming infected due to younger members of the household going out to work and other activities and thus bringing the infection back home.

This scenario can also be used to explain the very high levels of infection and death in Italy where many Italians in the northern towns also live in multi-generational accommodation, often with the younger members travelling some distance to other towns to work and hence increase the chances of bringing infection back home to the household. In Northern Italy there is a very close tie between the fashion industry and China and the large number of internationally mobile Chinese people explains why the pandemic struck Italy early. Quarantining the Chinese early on would almost certainly have been effective in slowing the spread of the virus.

It was argued that lockdown would help prevent the infection from spreading to the more elderly inhabitants in a household, who do not go out. However, we would argue that the effect would be very small compared with taking pragmatic measures within the house to prevent such transmission, especially since even with lockdown the majority of households still had someone going out to get essential food supplies, etcetera.

Within the United Kingdom the adherence to lockdown was much more effective than the Government initially expected and the constant Orwellian reiteration of '*stay home, protect the NHS, save lives*' along with constant parading of infection rates and the number of deaths, reduced a large percentage of the population into a state of permanent fear. Indeed, we are amazed at the number of people who have taken this advice extremely literally, boasting that they have successfully self-isolated for many months on end. Even when the first lockdown ended there were still many people who acted as if they could still easily be infected if they went outside, even when the virus infection levels had disappeared to virtually zero in August and September of 2020.

This highlighted a very important issue of lockdown, which had not been immediately evident at the time. The vulnerable patients, those considered particularly at risk, literally did not leave the house for months on end. Most of the public were not taking Vitamin D supplements because the Government did not have this in their official advice. The Vitamin D deficiency of the vulnerable was bound to get worse as they were not going outside! Similarly, they were doing less and less exercise and often eating more and increasing their alcohol and tobacco intake.

The constant media bombardment, and not being able to go out or socialise and meet family and friends, exacerbated stress. This is well known to be associated with a further depression of the immune response and inability to be able to handle new and other infections. In short, even those who did return to a more normal life after the lockdown were now in a situation where they were far more likely to be infected if they were exposed. If infected they were more likely to become symptomatic and ill and had an increased chance of dying.

The need for an analysis of the benefit and consequential negative effects of Lockdowns and other social measures

The proponents of lockdown have been very quick to point out the supposed benefits and point to countries, such as New Zealand and Australia, as prime examples, where lockdown has been supremely successful. We argue that this is nothing to do with lockdown but the effect of quarantine, which we previously pointed out are two extremely different instruments of preventing transmission. New Zealand banned all entry into the country during the lockdown, as did Australia, whilst we were allowing tens of thousands of people a day to land at Heathrow from areas with high infection. It was quarantine, not lockdown, that worked here and both countries were quick to implement quarantine on any new arrivals when lockdown was eased. Nearly every country throughout Europe instigated countrywide lockdown, with various degrees of severity, with one noticeable exception and that was Sweden, where the potential of inducing herd immunity, was taken very seriously by Anders Tegnell the Chief Medical Advisor. This action has been widely condemned and criticised by the majority of scientists and epidemiologists, all who censured his approach. However, it is important to defend his stratagem as he was actually strongly recommending a reduction in social interactions and activities likely to spread the virus. As opposed to making it compulsory like everywhere else, it relied on the trust that the Swedish citizens are more likely to act responsibly and could be trusted to do so. Although shopping malls, pubs and restaurants were allowed to remain open, they all took preventative measures to reduce the chances of transmission. When it transpired that Sweden had a much higher infection and death rate than its immediate neighbours, this was used to berate Sweden for being irresponsible in not introducing lockdown. However, their higher than expected death rate was for exactly the same reason as the UK in as much as both countries had sent infected patients from hospitals into care homes and this was the major source of an increased death rate. When it was pointed out that in spite of this Sweden still had a lower death rate than the UK, the apologists were quick to suggest that Sweden had a completely different population than the UK, that it was much less densely populated, with far fewer immigrants. As a frequent visitor to Sweden over the past several years, to the Karolinska Institute in particular, editor AGD would suggest that this is not the case. Most of the Swedish population live in towns and cities like Stockholm which are relatively densely populated and the country as a whole has a high population of immigrants, who would be perceived to be at increased risk for genetic, cultural and social behavioural reasons, compared to the indigenous population.

It was interesting that when the second wave started to hit Europe in October/November, the same observers were very quick to point out that Sweden was afflicted by this second wave. The implication was that the failure to have a solid lockdown in the first wave had led to a direct susceptibility to a second wave. However, we have seen no effort to put this into context, with the fact that countries that had the strictest lockdown in the first wave, such as Germany, Italy and Spain, have had just as bad, if not worse, second waves, which only leads us to the first bit of evidence that lockdowns do not work, on the grounds that if they did there should have been no second wave in Spain, Italy, Germany and the UK and it should only have affected Sweden.

We now know that the subsequent waves were driven by new variants, which were initially referred to by the countries in which they were first identified, such as Brazil, South Africa and the English/Kent strain. These strains would all seem to have acquired similar mutation, making them more infectious and more virulent than the first strain. These variants may have either evolved in different places at roughly the same time or have come from the same source as the original SARS-COV-2 agent that first appeared in Wuhan in the last quarter of 2019. It is important to note that the vaccines were trialled in the same places that variants appeared and it is a known fact that immunising people during a pandemic stimulates variants.

Whereas in Europe, and especially the UK, the lockdowns were instigated in order to preserve the NHS and other healthcare services from being overwhelmed, it was almost certainly introduced in Wuhan because they feared the virus was very similar to SARS and MERS, which were more infectious and having significant death rate, well above 10%. However, as the pandemic has rolled on it has become clear, in spite of the symptoms, the death rate of Covid-19 is much less than feared. Indeed, the death rate is overall thought to be less than 1%, compared to the over 10% of SARS and MERS and the 35% of other epidemic agents, such as the Spanish flu and Ebola. Moreover, the average age of death from Covid-19 has recently been calculated in the UK as 82, which is very similar to the average age of death from non-covid causes. Even then, the majority of elderly patients who died from the virus have underlying causes, which are associated with death in younger patients. As previously mentioned, these include obesity, diabetes, cardiac abnormalities, hypertension and neurological diseases, especially dementia.

Looking back, very few people under 65, without an underlying condition, have died and this is probably no more than the number of people under 65 who die of other infections without underlying disease. Indeed, over AGD's career as a general physician he has been amazed at the number of young, fit, healthy people that have been admitted to hospital and died of severe influenza or pneumonia, which should have been easily treatable. Their deaths are often put down to myocarditis.

When Covid19 began to surface in the UK and the death toll started to rise, it was noticeable that in the first two months of the pandemic there was an excess death rate but thereafter, the next two months, there was a reduced death rate, suggesting that the virus had basically brought forward the deaths of those who were susceptible and would have died shortly anyhow. The point of this is why would any rational government aware of these facts even contemplate introducing lockdown? It was always clear that the immediate costs of lockdown are catastrophic with regard to the impact on the economy and that the debt would be built up to an extent where many fear it will never be paid back.

Why did they instigate lockdown?

The management of the pandemic all appears to have been based on mathematical models from statisticians. This was speculation and not science. The advice from SAGE groups has a bent towards dealing with the worst possible predicted scenario. Were they not considering other possibilities, nor the impact of the action of the lockdown on the health and psychological wellbeing of the population, let alone the economy?

The Government has relied on the advice and figures from these people alone and justified their actions on the number of lives saved compared with the predictions. Given the fact that the death rate is so much lower than expected from similar viruses and that the people most at risk are those who would also be likely to die very soon with other infections it is staggering that the simple economic question as to whether the cost of the shutdown would pass a simple cost/benefit test, has not been done. It has been demanded by the Covid recovery group MPs here in the UK and others have demanded the same of other countries engaged in lockdown. Cost/benefit analysis is necessary to justify a policy which has caused untold harm to millions of people suffering from other conditions that could easily have been cured and treated successfully. This, in itself, is possibly unforgivable and that is before one considers the unbearable cost to the economy of lockdown and the destruction of a whole generation's education and wellbeing.

The only conclusion that one can come to is that nobody has done this analysis and nobody will even enter into the modelling of such cost/benefit analyses because they realise that such analyses would be devastating. We consider it likely that lockdown could not be justified on any one of the parameters mentioned at all.

Going back to the worldwide and indeed internal chastisement of the way Sweden has handled the pandemic, it is important to remember that whatever excuse critics like to give for the fact that the UK's death rate is still far worse than Sweden, the bottom line is that not a single day of schooling has been lost in Sweden. Normal education and development of children and young adults has been completely protected, whereas the negative consequences of the UK lockdown with regards to schooling and universities will have a knock-on effect for decades, which could be too severe to measure. Whereas it is clear that with online learning and parental help, the worst effects of closing schools has been mitigated in wealthy parents with good resources, the majority of children have not had this luxury and have fallen behind, not only in education but also in social maturity and behaviour and that this may never be regained. Either way, the goal of consecutive governments to reduce the social inequalities across the population has been destroyed at a stroke and will only widen because of the decision to close the schools, which we believe Sweden has shown to be completely unnecessary.

References: At the end of the book

Chapter 9

Social Interventions

Part 2: The harmful effects of social intervention on patients with cancer, cardiac and respiratory conditions: *The Editors*

Social intervention to forestall an infection had never previously been attempted on the scale of that brought in by governments all over the world at the beginning of the Covid-19 pandemic. Governments had instituted quarantine during bouts of Bubonic Plague, Ebola and other epidemics with mixed success[1] but never to the extent of the interventions of 2020.

The scientific basis for the policy was scanty, based on unreliable reports from the People's Republic of China. Were the lockdowns and other measures successful ? Were they justified ethically and what were the negative effects?

We shall now examine those questions more thoroughly.

The Horsemen of the Apocalypse

At the official start of the pandemic we, in the UK, saw on the TV people who had been repatriated from Wuhan ferried in four special Horseman coaches to a secure site for testing and isolation. At the time people made jokes about the Four Horsemen of the Apocalypse but after two hundred thousand deaths in the UK and over six million in the world, the joke does not seem funny any more.

Watching the paraphernalia on television we remarked that the passengers were all wearing protective gear but the drivers were not. This has turned out to be typical of the response to the pandemic with regard to travel: a bit of show but no real understanding of the principles of isolation and quarantine.

Did the repatriation and supposed isolation mean that the UK were putting people from China into quarantine? And later when it was clear that Italy and then the French ski resorts were having high rates of infection were returnees from there being quarantined? The answer on both accounts is a decisive NO!

In fact quarantine, the only measure that might have controlled the input of SARS-2, was not brought in until nearly a year later. Many people arrived into the UK in the meantime with barely a check at the border. How do we know this? Because, unlike many UK citizens, we have continued to travel completely legally and so have our relatives and friends.

In early February a friend returned from Italy, *no checks at the UK airport on return except the automatic passport machine*. A relative returned from skiing in Chamonix in March and was already suffering from Covid-19: *no checks at the UK airport on return except the automatic passport machine*. We travelled to Germany in June 2020, filled in a paper version of the passenger locator form: *no checks at the UK airport on return except the automatic passport machine*.

We travelled to Spain in October 2020, filled in a paper version of the passenger locator form: *no checks at the UK airport on return except the automatic passport machine*. Nobody phoned up to check if we were self-isolating.

We travelled to Barbados in December 2020 and the requirement was a negative PCR test before getting on the plane and quarantine in a government certified isolation site when arriving there. On the third day we had further PCR tests and only on the fourth day when the results came back as negative were we allowed out to see our relatives, who were living on the island. So they were doing quarantine properly. If we had tested positive we would have been taken from the quarantine hotel in a military ambulance to a detention centre in the north of the island, where we would have been detained for a minimum of ten days. This actually happened to people we met and they spent the whole of Christmas eating the M and S food which they had luckily taken over as Xmas presents. Did the quarantine system work? It did, very well indeed, until the prison guards broke the system by super-spreading at a huge beach party on Boxing Day.

We returned from Barbados in later January: *no checks at the UK airport on return except the automatic passport machine!* Nobody phoned up to check if we were self-isolating.

So until recently the UK's border was completely open. No quarantining, no checking on PCR tests, no thermometer guns to determine body temperature, no phone calls to check on self-isolation. True, all that is being done now but New Zealand, Australia and a host of other countries managed to administer quarantine procedures from the very beginning of the pandemic and have had a remarkably low death rate.

Instead, we relied on lockdowns and they signally failed to work.

Speaking in August 2022 to a colleague in New Zealand it is clear that they avoided the worst of the pandemic but are now trying rapidly to vaccinate against the virus and are using masks etcetera. Thus it would appear that by quarantining early they avoided the most lethal strains of the Covid-19 and the period of confusion when the most efficacious medical response to the virus was unknown

What were the negative effects of Lockdown?

At the beginning of the pandemic in March 2019, when the first lockdown was introduced, there was overwhelmingly complete support for lockdown from all the Government advisers, as being absolutely necessary to save the NHS. It was a copycat move, as this is what had been done to contain the virus outbreak in Wuhan and was repeated in Italy. It is amazing that there was such enthusiasm for maintaining the lockdown if the initial rationale was a short, sharp shock and delay to stop the overwhelming of the NHS. A lockdown was, perhaps reluctantly, decided and in retrospect many thought it had been introduced a little late at the end of March. Since this was a unique undertaking there should have been constant monitoring as to how long it should last, the degree of it and its consequences.

The shutting of the hospitality and travel sector, as well as preventing all but so called Key Workers from working, had a huge impact on the economy. The furlough scheme has cost hundreds of billions and whether it was worth it has never been carefully assessed. A group of MPs, known as the Covid Recovery Group have been demanding a simple cost/benefit test and these have been persistently ignored. The denial of such evaluations only has increased the lockdown scepticism, which is now growing stronger, three years plus into the pandemic.

Lockdown critics have been slapped down as 'grannie murderers' in an attempt to deny a logical and rational debate on the pros and cons. This shows disdain for evidence and virtue signalling coupled with abuse on the part of the lockdown enthusiasts. Another explanation put up in defence is that lockdown cost/benefit analysis is very difficult to do well and that it is hard to set the parameters of success. There is no doubt that much estimation would be needed to calculate the value of lives saved from lockdown, versus the enormous cost of shutting down businesses, schools and universities. It is worth repeating that lockdown was adopted because this is what China had done with the Wuhan outbreak, fearing that it was going to be just like SARS and kill indiscriminately up to 10% of the population. However, by the time it reached Italy and the dreadful impact was seen on the health services, it became apparent that it was not quite as virulent as feared and that people who were dying from it were older people with co-morbidities and that very few young people were getting seriously ill and those that were also had serious co-morbidities.

What plans were there for a pandemic?

We were meant to have a plan to prepare for a worse case scenario for a viral pandemic. This predicted a mortality rate of over 2%, (much higher than the actual figure for Covid-19) spreading over one or more waves and causing disruption to the economy. Apparently the plan was all focused on better hygiene, better protective equipment and the use of vaccines and treatments. This was planned for an influenza-like virus and a lockdown scenario was never even contemplated.

However, with the high number of deaths attributed to Covid-19 and even more predicted by computer simulations, the social interventions, including lockdown, will always be defended on the grounds that it prevented the National Health Service from being overwhelmed.

The National Health Service *was* overwhelmed because it stopped working for virtually everything, except dealing with some of the

Covid cases in hospitals. We maintain that the closing of GP surgeries and the failure to advise on how to cope with the symptoms, other than dialling 111 or 999 when it was too late, was a tragedy. We will discuss the effect on other routine procedures such as screening, diagnostic and early management, involving the tens of thousands of patients with cancer, ischaemic heart disease, neurological conditions and mental health. The impact of closing down services for these conditions was enormous and the knock-on effect will be with us for years to come.

The consequences for younger generations are beyond calculation. They have had their lives ruined by the adverse effects on education, social development and relationships and that they will end up having to the pay the enormous cost debt of the pandemic.

Sweden avoided locking-down its children and students by keeping open its schools, academies and universities. This will be a benchmark to measure the catastrophic damage the interventions have done and the outcomes will continue to unfold for years to come.

The initial delay

Apparently the first lockdown was delayed because it was felt that the British people would never accept such a draconian measure and it has, indeed, been somewhat surprising that the opposition to lockdown has been so muted. Some people have actually enjoyed being furloughed and having other working opportunities made available and many people have welcomed working full time from home without any loss of income. The lockdown was made easier by the fact that there was no shortage of food and we could even have it delivered directly to one's home, as well as no shortage of alcohol to purchase from supermarkets or, again, be delivered to the home.

Yet this overlooks a dreadful depredation of liberty where literally millions of people did stay in their houses, did not leave and did not have any physical contact with their immediate family and in the older generation, grandchildren. Elderly patients in care homes were completely denied all rights to see any of their friends and relatives for months on end. Many were kept in their rooms alone, much like the solitary confinement meted out on the worst behaving inmates of high security prisons.

Whereas there may have been a perverse logic for this at the beginning because of the dispersal of NHS patients to care homes taking the virus with them, there was no justification for continuing with this after the availability of rapid testing and the wholesale rollout of vaccination for all those in the 'at risk' population, which of course included people in care homes as prime targets. The concept of preventing people from meeting up with their family or friends in a mature, adult way, keeping social distance, with or without masks, being outside, was a draconian restriction, not even seen in the last two world wars. It was extremely patronising and clinically unnecessary to shutdown the hospitality industry, especially restaurants and hotels. There are very few examples of Covid being transmitted in a restaurant after the first lockdown and this surely had to be due to the fact that precautions were taken and the clientele acted in a mature way and abided by the advice. Even the larger pub chains had little evidence of infections and only a couple of hundred, or so, infections can be identified, which is a minute fraction of the number which were contracted in the hospitals or even supermarkets.

When restaurants were open the rule that you had to wear a mask when standing up but not when sitting down made no sense at all. Did the virus know that it was not allowed to attack you when you were seated?

The Fear

The effect of lockdown has an even more sinister side effect in that the constant bombardment of 'stay at home', 'protect the NHS', 'save lives', and similar such messages, has had an extreme effect on normally intelligent, sensible people. They became mortally afraid to go outside and socialise in a safe way because they had a sense of total fear and vulnerability, induced into them, which cannot be justified at all. Indeed, people meeting up, even outside in the garden whilst maintaining social distancing, was regarded as criminals and it is horrifying to hear how many perfectly innocent contacts were reported to the police by nosey neighbours. This is very reminiscent of Eastern Europe and the police state and it is a real worry that having induced these lockdowns and this draconian central government advice, being enforced by the police, that we have lost our sense of proportion and may never return to a proper normal existence.

The risk of infection and death due to Covid-19 was much lower than people were led to believe. We quote from Dr. Mercola [2] *"The real-world risk of dying from COVID-19 based on published data from the Irish census bureau and the central statistics office for 2020 and 2021 is as follows: For people under 70, the death rate was 0.014%; under 50 years of age, it was 0.002%, which equates to a 1 in 50,000 risk, or about the same as dying from fire or smoke inhalation. Under 25 years of age, the mortality rate was 0.00018%, or 1 in 500,000 risk of dying from COVID"*.

The number of people who have been paralysed by a state of fear and who will not engage in normal life, just to stay safe, is unprecedented. In oncology, this heightened fear is highlighted by patients cancelling operations for cancer at the last minute in case they get infected with an agent that has less than 1% chance of killing them, whereas not dealing with the cancer with surgical excision will, in their cases, ultimately lead to 100% chance of death. This is truly warped reasoning and highly irrational.

So why were they so affected by fear? The answer to this is in the book *State of Fear* [3]. The British Government purposely induced this fear in order to make people adhere to the rules of the social interventions. They used behavioural scientists to do this without any mandate to do so. This brainwashing and propaganda is continuing with attempts to persuade everybody to be vaccinated and vilifying people who do not wish to be jabbed. Similar experiments with psychological techniques are being used by other departments and are referred to euphemistically as "Nudge theory".

In the UK in 2020 over 640,000 people died of all causes, of which one in five was attributed to Covid. It must be reiterated that many of these deaths listed as due to the pandemic may not have been directly the result of the virus. It is estimated that approximately 600,000 people would have been expected to have died in that year so only 40,000 more perished, despite 130,000 being ascribed to Covid. This means that 90,000 of these patients would have died of something else within a short time anyway! Supporting this is the average age of death from Covid being 82 and the majority of these patients having co-morbidities. In the first two months of the pandemic, in March and April, there were excess deaths but in the subsequent months there were less deaths reported than normal, which is entirely consistent with the fact that the virus in 2020 brought forward deaths that would have occurred in the relatively near future and that many deaths were incorrectly ascribed to Covid-19.

Cinebuster March 24 2023   UK Health System Director Admits It Was All A Lie

24 Mar 2023 — Instead, a newly implemented **Medical** Examiner **System** for death certifications instructed **medical** personnel to categorize all pneumonia deaths as ...

Vilification of Dissenters

The media and especially the BBC liked to portray anybody who was anti-lockdown as a rebel rouser, a vaccine denier and plain stupid and they have plenty of fodder with the large mass protests, led by Piers Corbyn, that took place in London.   However, with a significant number of MPs being opposed to the lockdown, we note that one of the most senior Lords of the country, Lord Sumption, who was the supreme high court judge until his retirement, has written numerous articles with the overwhelming conclusion that lockdown just does not work.[4] He notes that at the start of the first lockdown, it was pushed by constant prophecies of doom from Professor Fergusson's team at Imperial College, which suggested 500,000 deaths would occur unless drastic action was taken. Such predictions were undoubtedly the worst case scenario and as such some people have suggested Ferguson should not be criticised[5] but they were purposely leaked to the public and most assuredly frightened people.

Many of the predictions and much of the advice were predicated on the view that it would take at least eighteen months for a vaccine to be produced but they were available in only six to nine months after the pandemic was admitted to be on our shores. Sumption argues that lockdowns cannot work, even temporarily, unless they are observed. He also argues that lockdowns are unenforceable without a degree of surveillance beyond the resources of the police and would provoke a backlash and depends on the public's willingness to comply. On this latter point, we would argue that it has been amazing that the public have been so compliant with this and the initial fears that there would be widespread disagreement did not materialise. In fact without the enforced lockdown people were already being sensible and taking preventative measures.

Different strategies in different countries

Lockdowns have not been uniform and in some cases not implemented at all, such as in Sweden and certain states of the USA. Although we think lockdown went over the top here in the UK there have been more severe and savage lockdowns, such as in Spain, where they put the army out on the streets and prevented people even going out for exercise.

There have been very many different versions, and, from our point of view, the biggest argument that lockdowns are relatively ineffective was the occurrence of the second wave, where countries locked down very severely, particularly Spain, Italy, Germany and France. Sweden, which had an advisory cautious and sensible approach only had similar first wave casualties. The fact that there started to be a second wave in Sweden was focussed on, by some commentators, with some glee stating that this was because they did not have a proper lockdown. However, the fact that the second wave was even worse in countries that had a more severe lockdown completely put paid to this argument. Lord Sumption notes that in London infections actually went up at the start of the second lockdown and he feels this is related to the basic instincts of humanity, which are fundamentally sociable and will assert themselves.

This is particularly so in the younger populations, which the Government tried to have confined to truly terrible, depressing student accommodation. No wonder there was a great rise in depression and suicides in this group. This is not just a practical problem but a moral problem, in that can the State impose the population to give up their humanity and the things that make life worth living, to achieve their objectives?

This particular pandemic rapidly made clear that Covid-19 was a serious threat to life for elderly people and those with clinical vulnerability and those of us against lockdown were encouraging the vulnerable to isolate themselves and to modify their lives so as to limit the risk.

Ordering young and healthy people to isolate was, we believe, ruinous. Since their death rate from Covid-19 is so very low they are the ones that should spread the virus to each other, helping create herd immunity. This would have been completely achieved without the vaccine programme.

The damage inflicted on the young by the lockdown policies will be with us for decades. As Lord Sumption put it, inflicting serious mental problems in children whose parents are precariously employed or inadequately housed and teaching them that they are killing their grandparents is worse than cruel. As is forcing talented graduates who cannot get jobs in their chosen field to take jobs as delivery drivers, not to mention destroying businesses that have taken a lifetime to build up. All of this was being done to relieve the Government of the consequences of years of underfunding the frontline services of the NHS whilst supporting a burgeoning management.

The crashing personal debt and higher taxes that the younger generations have been saddled with is basically inhumane. As the second lockdown in late 2020 continued to be in place, albeit lifted at an incredibly slow and unnecessary pace, Lord Sumption basically argued that the people making all these wrong decisions have invested too much to reverse out of the cul de sac, so they pressed on in order to avoid blame, rather than serve public interest. From analysis of the Hancock transcripts it is clear that this was the case.

It is worth pointing out that it is not just the UK but also applies to governments across Europe and the world. The classic response appears to be that as lockdowns haven't worked then they must have been implemented wrongly and not strictly enough. Even the opposition parties claim that there is nothing wrong with the concept of lockdowns and that the only solution is more of them! Einstein would have had something to say on this, relative to his remark that the definition of stupidity is somebody doing the same thing time after time, expecting a different result.

A change of heart from HART

In contrast to SAGE and numerous other Government committees there was a refreshing change in the attitude of the independent Health Advisory and Recovery Team (HART)[6], which has more than forty highly qualified relevant disciplines on it, overseeing and monitoring the evidence with regard to Covid-19. Their overview concludes that lockdowns must never be repeated, they serve no useful purpose and cause catastrophic society and economic qualms. It calls for a return to the pandemic plans prepared over a decade ago for just this sort of thing and endorsed by the WHO, who incidentally have also come down on the side that lockdowns did not work.

We reiterate that it is the failure of the WHO to deal with the outbreak in China that led to this pandemic and they have a lot to answer for. The

Chinese government instigated a very severe quarantine in Wuhan, China, when they should have quarantined the whole country and prevented it being spread all over the world and the WHO condoned this. The Government's reaction to Covid was labelled by HART as an untried experiment with neither time, nor research, to consider properly. HART recommend the following steps[7]:

1. *"Reinstate the existing pandemic planning policies from 2019, pending a detailed review of the policies adopted in 2020. Look to countries and states which did things differently. There should be a clear commitment from the Government that we will never again lockdown.*

2. *Stop mass testing healthy people. Return to the principles of respiratory disease diagnosis (the requirement of symptoms) that were well researched and accepted before 2020. Manufacturers' guidelines state that these tests are designed to assist the diagnosis of symptomatic patients, not to 'find' disease in otherwise healthy people.*

3. *Stop all mask mandates. They are psychologically and potentially physically harmful whilst being clinically unproven to stop disease spread in the community and may themselves be a transmission risk.*

4. *Vaccination. Abandon the notion that vaccine certification is desirable and that children should be vaccinated. There is no logical or ethical argument for either.*

5. *Devise a public education programme to help redress the severe distortions in beliefs around disease transmission, likelihood of dying and possible treatment options. A messaging style based on a calm presentation of facts is urgently needed.*

6. *Carry out a full public enquiry into the extent to which severe/fatal COVID-19 is spread in hospitals and care homes. There is stark recent evidence on this from Public Health Scotland and if true for the rest of the UK, there needs to be better segregation of COVID-19 patients and staff within these settings.*

7. *More funding and investigation of treatments for COVID-19, instead of only focusing on vaccination as a strategy. Given the high rates of hospital transmission, encourage a drive for more early treatment-at-home using some of the protocols discussed herein.*

8. *Divert funds. The not inconsiderable money saved from ceasing testing programmes can be diverted to much needed areas, such as*

mental health, treatment research and an increase in hospital capacity and staffing.

They also put forward three core points which proponents of lockdowns have never answered satisfactorily. Firstly, international comparisons show no correlation between severity of lockdown and level of infections and deaths. The example of Sweden has already been mentioned but in the U.S. there are extreme differences in neighbouring stages, such as North Dakota, which had implicated lockdowns, and South Dakota, which had no lockdown at all.

Economic Impact

The impact of Covid-19 on the world's economies has been severe. The disease itself did not cause most of the problem: the disease has mostly affected the elderly who are not particularly significant in the workplace and in many cases represent a cost to society. The younger adults have mainly had a mild illness which would not have affected their ability to work or spend.

It is clear that the main effect on the economy has been due to the introduction of government backed lockdowns. These have temporarily, or perhaps permanently, closed numerous businesses, curtailed freedom of movement and restricted commerce.

In 2020 the least affected economy was that of China, the very origin of the pandemic. Rather than lockdown they instituted a severe *quarantine* of the epicentre of the disease, Wuhan. Thus nobody was allowed out of Wuhan into China and, coupled with their access to Chinese vaccines already patented, the rest of China could continue to function. Their economy bounced back within a few weeks and had reached its normal level by the middle of 2020, when they were already vaccinating.

Notably the Chinese did permit people to fly out of Wuhan to the rest of the world. Rather than respond with quarantining China most of the countries instituted lockdown which they mistakenly led to believe was the main factor in bringing the disease under control in China. The countries instituting lockdowns were unable to keep the virus out and suffered because of this. Their economies only started to pick up once the vaccines were shown to be effective at the beginning of November 2020.

The stock markets reflect the economies in the larger countries and the bounce back in confidence after the advent of vaccines is quite obvious when graphs are examined.[8]

A few countries did quarantine arrivals rather than lockdown and some, very few, told their people to self-isolate but did not institute lockdown. So the response was:

1) Do nothing
2) Lockdown
3) Quarantine arrivals
4) Voluntary self-isolation and shielding.

Country	Approach	Deaths (by 16/4/2021)	population	deaths per million
Sweden	self-isolation	13,788	10,380,000	1328
UK	nothing then lockdown	127,000	68,169,000	1,860
China	quarantine	4636	1,408,000,000	3.3 (unreliable figures)
Australia	quarantine	910	25,880,000	35
New Zealand	quarantine	26	4,853,283	5.4
USA	lockdown	566,000	331,420,000	1,708
Brazil	nothing	372,000	210,000,000	1771
Belgium	Lockdown	23,718	11,629,525	2039

Quarantining of arrivals and careful track and trace can work. It is, however, clear that lockdown on its own is no better than voluntary self-isolation and shielding.

The vaccines on their own have not been very successful and the vaccines are not all equal. Chile had been heralded as a great success having vaccinated two-thirds of its population but the Chinese vaccine they used is not very effective with one dose, the country was not in lockdown and and the virus has recently surged catastrophically.

In the UK nearly 54 million have had at least one dose of vaccine. Israel, UAE and Chile have vaccinated more than UK . We do not really know how many people in China have been vaccinated and the trial data on their vaccines has not been adequately published. China has recently instituted lockdowns to combat the Omega strain with dire effects on their economy.

The Death of Science

Effect of Covid and Lockdown on individuals

It is clear from the graph below [1] that Covid-19 is more of a problem during the winter months and it is also possible, from the excess death data on the next page, to show that lockdowns and the concomitant actions were a major cause of death both from Covid-19 (the patients sent to the nursing homes) and from other illnesses (patients not presenting to the NHS or sent away inadequately treated).

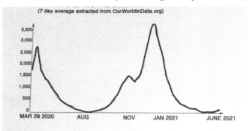

England : Daily Hospital Admissions for COVID-19

Analysis of Excess Deaths in England: March to July 2020

Analysis of the statistics of excess deaths[1] in the UK during the first lockdown of March to July 2020 is revealing. In particular we focussed on three areas, London, the North West and the South West.

A large number of cases of deaths from Covid-19 were being reported in London, somewhat fewer in the North West and far fewer in the South West. The *excess* death statistics bear this out with around 6000 excess deaths attributed to Covid-19 in London, 5,000 in the North West and only 1,500 in the South West. The populations are 9.3 million, 7.3 million and 5.6 million respectively. Correcting this per million puts the North West as the worst affected at 684, London next at 645 but the South West way behind at 268 per million - less than half the number of cases.

Looking at the place of death is interesting. There are four main places: home, care homes, hospice and hospital.

In all three districts there were fewer deaths than usual in the hospices. In London most excess deaths occurred in hospital and were due entirely to covid. Half the excess deaths in care homes were Covid-19 related and a third of those at home were due to Covid.

In the North West the majority of the excess deaths from any cause occurred in care homes and two thirds of these were Covid related. The excess deaths in hospital were all Covid related and were equal in number to the Covid deaths in care homes. One eighth of the excess deaths at home were Covid related.

Excess Deaths in 3 areas of England 20 March 2020 to 31 July 2020

LONDON	Care home	1,386	1,395	2,781
	Home (and other)	2,015	680 159 (other)	2854
	Hospital	3859		3859
	Hospice	-188		-188

NORTH WEST	Care home	1,230	2,318	3,548
	Home (and other)	2,327	314 168 (other)	2809
	Hospital	2,368		2,368
	Hospice	-333		-333

SOUTH WEST	Care home	591	1,324	1915
	Home (and other)	1,779	147 28(other)	1954
	Hospital	-380		-380
	Hospice	-232		-232

Source: Public Health England analysis of ONS death registration data

Excess deaths, Covid-19 not on death certificate

Excess deaths with Covid-19 mentioned on death certificate

Fewer deaths than expected

In contrast in the South West nearly all the deaths from Covid-19 were in care homes with 70% of the excess deaths in care homes due to Covid but 30% to other causes. Only one thirteenth (1/13) of the excess deaths at home were Covid related. In the South West of England overall the excess deaths at home and in care homes due to causes *other* than Covid-19 significantly outnumbered deaths from Covid-19 whilst the hospitals had considerably fewer deaths than normal.

What can we make of all this? It looks as if the London hospitals held on to a lot of the patients with Covid-19 but at the other extreme the South West hospitals, as directed by the Department of Health, got rid of them to the care homes (where many died from the Covid), and actively discouraged admissions (hence excess deaths at home from non-Covid related conditions).

This is all a matter of surmising from statistics but we believe it shows that the management of the hospitals in the South West were over zealous in "protecting the NHS" with the obvious result that they under-treated the population. In the South West the Lockdown and other interventions were killing more people than the Covid-19 even at the peak of the first wave!

The statistics are based on death certificates and they are notoriously inaccurate. It is possible that many of the deaths at home which were not diagnosed as Covid related may have actually have been misdiagnosed and the Covid missed. It does however suggest that assiduously emptying the hospitals does lead to excess morbidity and mortality in the community. This is to be expected and could have been predicted. It is to be hoped that in the future hospitals will continue to treat conditions other than just coronavirus. Otherwise we will not have been clapping the ongoing efforts of the National Health Service Health but applauding the inception of solely a National Covid Service.

We ask again when did the emphasis of the NHS change from one in which they protect us, the public, to one in which we protect the NHS? One question remains. Why were the hospitals emptied and the Nightingale hospitals not used? One answer is that they did not have enough staff. In Bristol at the time of writing this chapter there was a shortage of nursing staff in the hospitals due to an increase in patients (due to Covid-19) and many nurses were off work with the Covid or self-isolating. At the Bristol Royal Infirmary notices placed around the building instructed the nurses that they would each have to look after more patients. There was apparently no consultation with unions or with the Royal College of Nursing.

Why are there too few nurses? The simple answer is that they are not paid enough. Looking after sick people is a very hard job, especially when it endangers your own health, and a qualified nurse can usually get a better paid job working as a representative of a drug company or moving into a managerial role in the health service. Pay the frontline staff five times as much money and the staff would miraculously appear. But the latest reviews have only recommended a very modest rise.[9] The same applies to "junior" doctors who earn about the same as a novice bus driver and right now we are to seeing strikes as a result of this parsimony.

The climate of fear was also a reason that people did not want to see their doctors. Some GPs have been afraid to see patients and, vice versa, patients have been afraid to see the doctors, either in general practice or in the hospitals. In some ways this is not surprising since these days a hospital is a prime place to pick up infection.

Short Case Reports

Case 1

Patient A, aged 71, had been on dialysis for over ten years and had managed very successfully. He was wary of going to the dialysis unit but was obliged to do so as his electrolyte balance was becoming difficult. He caught Covid-19 at the unit, was very ill for two weeks and eventually died from the disease.

Case 2

Patient B, 70, had suffered from carcinoma of the breast ten years previously. During the lockdown she telephoned her GP three times complaining of back pain. She was prescribed paracetamol on each occasion with a presumptive diagnosis of sciatica. Eventually at the end of lockdown, presenting in great pain at the local A and E, she was found to have advanced metastatic disease in her spine. She was put on palliative care and has subsequently died.

Case 3

Patient C was suffering from loss off appetite, general weakness and a small amount of blood loss per rectum. He was too ill to visit the surgery and had been reluctant to do so when he was initially ill. The GP initially refused a home visit. The patient died without a full diagnosis but a probably diagnosis of bowel cancer was made.

Case 4

Patient D knew he had sickle cell disease and was admitted to a ward suffering from probable Covid-19. He asked for oxygen but this was refused by the nurse. He quickly died from complete organ failure due to a sickling crisis.

Harmful effects of Lockdown (Oncologists's report February 2021)

"As an oncologist I was immediately aware of the effect of the pandemic on the diagnosis and management of patients presenting with cancer as more and more patients with covid were admitted, resulting in having to reduce provision for non-covid patients. Normal activity was altered immediately with trials being halted to all new recruitment and therapies withdrawn from patients, except those with urgent, proven treatments. The worse effect appears to be on the frontline, dealing with early symptoms. Although there are many reported exceptions, the majority of patients and people I have dealt with, have complained bitterly of not being able to see a GP with urgent and worrying symptoms and when they do get an appointment, it has been on the telephone, with a prescription for an antibiotic for a sore throat, lumps in the neck, etc., with repeat different antibiotics when the symptoms have progressed. Normally these patients would be seen and examined and the fact that the lump in the neck was not that normally associated with a sore throat would have been picked up and the patient referred for the relevant diagnostic procedures, etc. Because of the pandemic there are many such patients who have progressed to the point where they are admitted to hospital very ill, having tried to stay away from what is known as a major source of Covid infection (i.e. the hospitals). When they are finally diagnosed they have malignant disease that is too far advanced to cure, whereas had they been managed as before the pandemic, they would have had a diagnosis of a condition that was completely curable when diagnosed and treated in time. We have no idea how many patients have suffered from this and will die much earlier than had they been treated in time. However, we do know that the number of patients presenting for the diagnosis and treatment of cancer has fallen significantly during lockdown, suggesting that the deaths caused indirectly by the Covid pandemic are not by infection directly and is likely to be many tens of thousands.

A major problem that has emerged is that patients have been reluctant to go to hospital when they normally would and this would appear to be associated with the fact that the Government's propaganda has been so successful that they are frightened to go to hospital for fear of catching Covid. I am aware of several patients who have cancelled operations for malignancy at the last minute because they are frightened of catching Covid if they come into hospital for the procedure which, given the chances of dying from the infection, is in the order of 1-2%. The chance of dying from the malignancy remaining untreated is many fold higher and this is an example of the skewing of rational decision making, which I believe is a direct by-product of an overzealous and unnecessary fear and subjugation and control programme by the Government." *(This and the legal justification for these decisions will also be discussed elsewhere in this book, Ed.)*

"Cancer Screening shut down:

When the original national lockdown was introduced across the UK in March 2020, the focus was on dealing with the overwhelming demands of patients with Covid who were being referred to hospital, requiring urgent attention and intensive care. In response to this many hospitals shut down all other activity or reduced it to a bare minimum. Nationally, cancer screening was suspended and routine diagnostic work deferred, with solely the urgent symptomatic cases prioritised for diagnostic intervention. Only patients who were on chemotherapy, which was likely to cure the patient, were able to continue. All others, including adjuvant treatments, were ceased. Overnight the NHS rapidly became the national covid service and the population was expected to protect the NHS.

"As I write this it is now a year since the first lockdown was introduced and the death rate from Covid stands at just under 130,000. However, this, unlike many countries, is likely to be higher than reality as many patients have been recorded as dying with Covid based on a positive test within a month of dying. Many doctors have remarked that many patients have died of something completely different and their deaths are nothing to do with covid but have basically boosted the figures. Indeed, I have been informed that there is a further bias as doctors have been encouraged to consider whether covid was the cause and have often put this down, even when there is no antigen or antibody evidence."

"The actual figure of patients dying directly from Covid is far less than the 130,0000 plus already recorded and has to be borne in mind with the not unusual annual deaths of flu of up to 30,000 per year. Very few flu deaths have been recorded, perhaps because they have been put down as Covid. Exactly how many deaths have been prevented by lockdown cannot accurately be estimated, especially as the waves of infection seemed to reduce long before lockdown was imposed, making the effect of lockdown very hard to assess. However, in complete contrast, the number of deaths that have been *caused* by lockdown in several major conditions can reliably estimated. They have not been adequately screened, diagnosed and treated, as they would have been in the absence of a lockdown."

"The number of additional deaths has been estimated by several sources, from cancer alone, at over 35,000 and this was early on in the pandemic and is likely to be much higher. Whereas the average age of the patients dying from Covid-19 was not much different from the average age of death from non-Covid causes, the tragedy of the failure to screen, diagnose and treat cancer has had a major impact on younger patients. My own experience involves the classic presentation of a young person with a lump in their neck, a sore throat and fever, treated remotely with different antibiotics, with the classic symptoms of a lymphoma, involving night sweats and weight loss, ignored until the patient was too ill to continue and had to be admitted to hospital where his aggressive lymphoma had been diagnosed too late and he died early in his mid-thirties. I am aware of several other cases of patients with abdominal and bowel symptoms who have been given all sorts of symptomatic treatments remotely, without being seen by their GP, who eventually have been found to have advanced bowel cancer. The conditions were no longer curable, which they would likely have been, had they been seen and assessed in the normal manner, prior to the lockdown."

"All my colleagues have many such examples and the situation has been made worse by patients fearing to come into hospital for operations, which would prevent their cancer spreading, terrified that they may contract and die of covid, which has a far less serious outcome than the cancers that we know the patients have."

"To try and put this all into perspective, the English National Health Service Cancer Registration and Hospital Administration data sets for adults with breast, colorectal oesophageal cancer and lung cancer were used to estimate the impact of diagnostic delays and to model the subsequent effect of these delays on survival. The authors published their predictions in *The Lancet* in July 2020.[10] They collected data for 32,000+ patients with breast cancer, 25,000 with colorectal cancer, nearly 7,000 with oesophageal cancer and 29,000 with lung cancer. Just for the delays in diagnosis alone, they estimated the best or worse case scenarios and estimated the impact on net survival on one, three and five years after diagnosis to calculate the additional deaths that could be attributed to cancer and total years of life lost (YLs), compared with pre-pandemic data.

For the described population, the estimated additional deaths were over 300 for breast cancer, 1500 for colorectal cancer, 1300 for lung cancer and up to 340 for oesophageal cancer. For these four tumour types the data corresponded with approximately 3,500 additional deaths across the scenarios within five years but the total additional years of lost life across these patients is estimated to be well over 60,000 years.

It is important to appreciate that these figures are just as a result of a delay in diagnosis and are only focused on four cancers with available data in the UK. It does not take into account patients who had already been diagnosed whose treatment was delayed, nor the many thousands of patients who were on treatment who had it ceased on the grounds that there was no proof that it was curative, which could be argued is the case for the majority of solid tumours. Early treatment, if properly implemented and monitored, has greatly increased the survival of many of the common cancers and this may have been denied during lockdown. This is particularly true with the impact of immunotherapy, which has revolutionised the frontline treatment of melanoma and lung cancer and has made a significant difference in over twenty other cancer types.

A further study published in March of this year, analysing data up to October 2020, prior to the second lockdown and second wave, by Morris et al in *The Lancet*,[11] just focussing on patients with colorectal cancer, had concluded that by April 2020 there was a 63% reduction in the monthly number of referrals for suspected cancer and a reduction in the number of colonoscopies, from 46,000+ to less than 3,500. These numbers just recovered by October 2020. This meant that over 3,500 fewer people have been diagnosed and treated for colon cancer in England than would have been expected, with a 31% relative reduction in the numbers receiving surgery and a lower proportion of laparoscopic surgery and a greater proportion of those requiring stoma-forming procedures."

"There were two major issues at play here, the first with regards to diagnosis and early treatment, which was due to the fact that staff were redeployed and intensive care capacity became very limited and therefore fewer procedures could be performed, due to the requirement for full PPE and robust cleaning protocols between patients. All this was done with no formal quantification of the potential impact of treatment delays across most cancer types and treatments, including radiotherapy."

"The second major impact was the fear of patients of having any contact with hospitals and having procedures, having been made aware that hospitals were the main source of covid infection in some areas. Therefore the patients deliberately delayed presenting their symptoms to GPs and getting the early, necessary diagnosis and treatment."

In another systemic review of this topic, published in November 2020,[12] the researchers studied the effect of delay across all treatments for seven different types of cancer. The malignancies investigated included bladder, breast, colorectal, lung, cervix, and head and neck treated by surgery, radiotherapy, systemic chemotherapy and immunotherapy. Delays of only four weeks were associated with greater mortality impact. In the UK alone, a twelve week surgery delay over a year of lockdown, backlog recovery for breast cancer alone, translated to approximately 1,400 additional (and unnecessary) deaths, not counting the downstream effects of any systemic therapy or radiotherapy delay, leading to further mortality or disease recurrence."

"The simple stark conclusion from this is that there is an urgent need to address the enormous cancer backlog, which has been built up and made worse by the second wave.

During the lockdowns the majority of the National Health Service essentially shut down from dealing with cancer patients in a normal manner and delayed and rationed treatments. A few hospitals, usually led by clinicians, took steps to preserve the cancer management and separate it from the tremendous pressure of covid infected patients. However, the need to redeploy staff, including doctors and nurses, to frontline covid management made these initiatives difficult to

maintain."
Cardiac Management and Covid 19

In all countries studied to date there has been a clear pattern of Covid-19 on heart failure, hospitalisation and management. Hospitalisation of patients with acute pulmonary syndromes other than Covid-19 showed a dramatic drop of approximately 40% and even more pronounced in patients with chronic coronary syndromes, with unknown effect on cardiovascular mortality.

Essentially, there was a significant reduction in the number of procedures being carried out in interventional cardiology, which could mean the difference between being stabilised with coronary catheterisation and stents and coronary artery replacement, or no treatment and a much higher likelihood of a poorer outcome.

In a one month survey in Germany, the proportion of cardiovascular deaths increased by 7.6%.[13] In this study there was a 35% reduction in catheterisation activities, which led to an 8% increase in cardiovascular mortality, which included strokes and a 12% increase in cardiac mortality.

The factors leading to this were very similar to those previously noted in cancer. They were mainly twofold:

- A reduced ability of doctors to perform these procedures due to redeployment and the need for PPE and other precautions, reducing the capacity to treat patients,
- A reluctance on the behalf of patients to present with acute chest pain because of the pressure on hospitals [13].

There are numerous studies of the impact of covid-19 on care and outcome of hospitalised myocardial infarction across Europe and in the UK. After the implication of lockdown, there was a substantial decline in admission of acute myocardial infarction, those presenting being younger, with less co-morbidities and a higher thirty day mortality. It is noteworthy that the number of deaths of those dying at home from non-covid causes greatly increased over this time.

The Respiratory System: Effects of the Covid-19 Pandemic

In January 2020 the WHO announced to the world that the novel coronavirus infection could be transmitted person to person and we were told that it was a respiratory infection. The symptoms to look out for were dry cough and high fever.

But the virus can attack a large number of different areas in the human body in two ways:

- By attaching with its spike proteins to angiotensin converting enzyme (ACE 2) receptors. These are part of the renin/angiotensin system that controls blood pressure and other functions around the body.
- There is an abnormally high positive charge on the surface of the Covid-19 virus which can thus easily be attracted to the negative charge on the surface of almost any human cells.

The virus is usually spread via inhalation as droplets and hence the initial information about cough and fever as the condition is characteristically a disease of the respiratory system. Many other signs, symptoms and complaints have, however, been added to that list and will be mentioned here.

In adults general symptoms initially include fever, tiredness, lethargy, loss of appetite and loss of weight. In the upper respiratory tract it can cause sore throat and an itchy nose. The new variants have more effect on the nose and this leads to more sneezing which may, indeed, be part of the reason that the variants are more easily transmissible.

In the respiratory system the virus attaches to the ACE2 receptors on the lung cells (or pneumocytes) that usually produce surfactant. This is a substance that reduces surface tension much in a similar way to a detergent. The virus gets into the lung cells and takes over the function in order to reproduce more virus. The production of surfactant is prevented and without surfactant the alveoli collapse due to surface tension. Chest symptoms include a continuous non-productive dry cough or, less commonly, a productive cough. Shortness of breath and difficulty in breathing may predominate but in a significant proportion silent anoxia can develop. A pulse oximeter may show very low oxygen levels whilst the patient is barely noticing breathlessness.

Chest CT shows areas of ground-glass opacification, mainly at the mid-zones and bases, peripherally. In the later stages the opacification can spread throughout the lungs. Collapse, consolidation and pneumothorax may occur.

Unfortunately the lockdown led to some general practitioners in the UK self-shielding and refusing to see patients. Signs outside surgeries still tell patients that they should not enter if they have any of the symptoms of Covid-19.

Effects of the Lockdown on access for Respiratory Medicine

The routine clinics for respiratory patients were all cancelled and patients became very reluctant to seek medical attention. The latter was partly because they were afraid of catching the Covid-19 virus in the hospital and partly because they did not want to overburden the NHS when they were being asked to protect it. A report from the Office for National Statistics (ONS) regarding the first lockdown suggested that 41% of the excess deaths in England were the result of missed medical care rather than the virus itself [14]. As many as 16,000 extra people died because of the lockdown.

According to the British Lung Foundation[15] one in five of the deaths in the UK are due to lung diseases, including asthma, chronic obstructive pulmonary disease or other long term respiratory illness. About 10,000 people in the UK are newly diagnosed with a lung disease every week and at least half of these need to be put on treatment. During the initial lockdown the NHS closed the clinics and emptied the wards, mostly into nursing homes. Patients found it very hard to access their GPs and diagnoses were made over the telephone. Whilst this can sometimes be a useful way to proceed little or no research has been done to confirm that it is equivalent to direct consultation. James le Fanu, writing in the *Daily Telegraph*[16], had been informed of a case where a patient received two different, erroneous, diagnoses and treatment without seeing a doctor. Only after a neighbour's intervention was the patient admitted to hospital *'moribund with a lung abscess'*.

The Office of National Statistics[17] stated that Non-Covid deaths in March and April 2020 were 15.3% above the 5 year average but between May and July were 6% below, presumably due to deaths 'brought forward' in March and April. Tellingly, however, deaths in private homes were still above average. The deaths in hospital had fallen to below average at this time suggesting that too few patients were being treated in hospital.

The medical staff saw referrals of patients needing urgent care for lung conditions drop by as much as 70% during lockdown. An average of 3,399 patients per week missed out on urgent and routine referrals during lockdown, according to the Taskforce for Lung Health[18, 19] and, due to long waiting lists, the access has continued to be poor. The data from NHS England, analysed by the Taskforce, also showed that nearly 2 in 5 (39%) of CCGs in England did not see a single appointment booking for respiratory conditions in May, and 65% of CCGs had 5 or less bookings. As 1500 people are typically newly diagnosed with lung disease each day in the UK, this would suggest that the number of people who are now waiting to be diagnosed is likely to be in the thousands.[20]

Conditions such as fibrosing alveolitis can cause a very short life expectancy and a delay in diagnosis can result in the patient missing out on significant treatment and support in the short period that they have to live.

Respiratory function studies can induce coughing so their use was suspended during the pandemic. Sleep apnoea patients are often treated with CPAP devices and initial concerns that these may spread the Covid disease caused a drop in their use in March and April 2020. Subsequently the patients realised that this was only very rarely a problem and that CPAP may, in fact, help protect them, thus they continued to carefully follow their treatment regimes[21]. The major concern now is the delay in diagnosing the conditions and thus delays in starting treatment

Increased smoking and alcohol intake

"The first Covid-19 lockdown in England in March-July 2020 was associated with increased smoking prevalence among younger adults, and increased prevalence of high-risk drinking among all sociodemographic groups"[22]

This bodes badly for the future as the smoking is likely to lead to an increased incidence of chronic obstructive pulmonary disease, lung cancer and a variety of other diseases including heart disease, stroke, emphysema and asthma (to name but a few of the adverse effects). The increased alcohol intake will have a myriad of effects including an increase in liver disease, neurological problems, cardiomyopathy, obesity and cancer.

References at the end of the book

Social Interventions

**Part 3: The harmful effects of social intervention on Mental Health, Education, Obesity, and Diabetes : ** *The Editors*

The Covid-19 pandemic has affected mental health in a myriad of ways. There has been the direct effect on health due to infection, the effects on people forcibly kept away from work and from friends and family by lockdowns, shielding and self-isolation, the uncertainty about future employment and the possibility or not of returning to work. The propaganda that created a deliberate climate of fear will not be forgotten and will have ongoing effects.

In addition the effects of the pandemic on the mental health of clinical staff and frontline workers should not be ignored and is likely to be very significant.

The Public

The climate of fear was generated in order to coerce people into following new regulations that curtailed their freedom in ways that had not been experienced in peacetime in the western democracies in the modern era. This fear added enormously to the harmful effects of the regulations themselves. Even when initially writing this in Autumn 2022, with all restrictions lifted, it was not uncommon to speak to someone who was going out of their house for the first time in more than two years. Moreover a foray to the local supermarket will permit you to spot people who are still wearing masks.

In the UK the first lockdown resulted in large numbers of people having uncertainty over their jobs, losing daytime activity, and either being socially isolated or having to spend protracted periods of time with their family. These problems were exacerbated in the subsequent lockdowns. All of these factors are associated with increased mental morbidity.

A recent study has shown that separation anxiety is an important factor in assessing suicide risk[1]. Pini et al found that their study *'indicates a substantial role of separation anxiety in predicting suicidal thoughts, both as state-related symptoms (evaluated by HDRS item 3) and as longitudinal dimensional symptoms (as evaluated by MOODS-SR). Greater understanding of the influence of separation anxiety in patients with affective disorders may encourage personalized interventions for reducing suicide risk.'*

Previous studies have cited separation anxiety in children and adolescents as a risk factor for suicide[2] but this study highlighted its importance in adults

The study was undertaken before the advent of the Covid-19 pandemic but does bring strongly into question the wisdom of the punitive level of separation brought in by the lockdowns in many countries.

In the UK adherence to the policy of self-isolation has been high (data from the Office of National Statistics discussed in Medscape [3]. But with the reported 82% adherence the survey also stated that the self-isolation had worsened wellbeing and mental health in 35% and 28% had lost income.

The stress of the pandemic and the restrictions has worsened the nation's smoking habits[3] with 30% of smokers smoking more regularly and 10% of those who had given up starting again!

In Japan an initial small drop in suicide rates of 14% during the first wave of the pandemic was followed by a small rise of 16% during the second wave[4]. Whilst the first lockdown was bearable (and some people actually enjoyed it) subsequent restrictions were very disturbing and the way in which they had been instituted seemed arbitrary and nonsensical. In England a big fuss was made as to whether a scotch egg constituted a substantial meal (in which case you could be served a drink in a pub) or did not (in which case you couldn't!). When the restrictions were loosened if you went for a meal in a restaurant you had to wear a mask as you walked in but could take it off as soon as you sat down…. Clearly the "powers that be" believed that the virus only attacked you when you were ambulant.

Covid-19 itself can have severe effects on the neurological system and difficulty in thinking, known as 'brain fogging', is a common symptom during Covid infection and a symptom of "long Covid"[5]. Brain fog and headache have also been reported as relatively common side-effects following vaccination.[6]

Lockdowns have increased anxiety amongst all age groups. Some 20%

of people were worried about going back to work at the end of lockdown and 23% worried about travelling on public transport[7] .

The climate of fear engendered to persuade people to self-isolate, lockdown and submit themselves to vaccination has continued to create a heightened level of anxiety.

Many people in England have welcomed the end of lockdown and the chance of returning to a restaurant or pubs but a substantial minority are worried about resuming social contact.

All of the harmful effects of lockdown have been far worse for people on low income and living in inadequate housing. It is one thing for the privileged few to self-isolate whilst on a decent pension and living in a large detached house with a garden and quite another to be forced to work due to lack of income yet finding that this is almost impossible because the children are at home in a one bedroomed flat. Add to that not being allowed to even sit down on a bench in the local park and after all this getting symptoms of Covid-19 and not being allowed to see the family practitioner because she is shielding herself! Is this a true scenario? In lockdowns you bet it is!

Short Case Report

A man aged 21, working as a heating engineer, has suffered from anxiety in the past. 'The lockdowns have made it a million times worse. A friend committed suicide in the first lockdown and I sat on the same bridge wondering whether it was worth going on. I didn't have the nerve to kill myself but I understood why he did it. I just felt that I couldn't inflict my suicide on my parents and brother. I get some relief now by going to the gym, putting on my headphones and getting into the zone. I'm not going out at all apart from working. I have to work as there would be no money coming in otherwise and my work is considered as an essential service. I'm afraid of meeting people in a social situation.'

Children and adolescents

The Covid-19 pandemic has only very rarely caused severe infection in children and the main cause of concern has been the effects of lockdown and isolation on their mental health. After several weeks of the first lockdown in April 2020 one of the authors overheard a child of infant school age plaintively enquire: *'Mummy, why don't I have any friends anymore?'*

The playgrounds in the park were barred and the swings padlocked. Adolescents climbed over to use the remaining equipment and adults with young children stood impotently around with younger children who were complaining that it was unfair: *'Why can the old children use the playground and we can't?'*

Back at school the children had to remain in 'bubbles' and wear masks. As soon as they left school they all played together in the park showing that the wearing of masks was not to protect themselves but perhaps to pacify the teachers.

The long period away from school means that the youngest children have not had the important socialisation effects of pre-school and the infants school. Schools help to teach children what is expected of them as they mature and become full members of society. Older children have missed significant education and the opportunity of doing their best in examinations and talk of a 'lost generation' has only served to make them even more anxious about their future..

Home schooling has at best been very patchy and the worst affected have been children of the families with the lowest incomes.

Significantly the essential workers who were obliged to keep working throughout the pandemic and its social interventions were also the people on the lowest salaries.

Globally the lockdowns and concomitant school closures have impacted more than 1.5 billion children. According to the WHO: *'Movement restrictions, loss of income, isolation, overcrowding and high levels of stress and anxiety are increasing the likelihood that children experience and observe physical, psychological and sexual abuse at home – particularly those children already living in violent or dysfunctional family situations.'* [8]

In the UK reports are circulating that 20,000 pupils are missing from the roll call now that the students are back at school. There is no official register of children being homeschooled and it is not known how many of the missing children are having schooling or have simply stopped being taught. [9,10]

The "madness" of constantly testing and isolating children has sparked considerable concern [11]. Why was the testing and isolation being done and who were the authorities trying to protect? Clearly if the Covid-19 only mildly affects children this was not being done to protect them, thus it must have been introduced to protect adults such as teachers, parents and relatives. This was at considerable cost to the children. One parent described how her child had seven times been sent home to isolate along with all the other members of the "bubble" because one child tested positive. A friend told us that her child and ninety other children had been barred from a school walk because one child tested positive on a lateral flow test. The PCR test proved negative so the entire outing had been cancelled due to a false positive test.

The Daily Telegraph reports that mental health referrals for children rose considerably in 2020 with 1 in 9 experiencing mental health problems in 2017 rising to 1 in 6 by mid 2020.

The schemes to reduce spread of Covid-19 in schools have included keeping within socially distanced hoops, sanitising books, surrounding desks with black and yellow tape and constant mask-wearing, cancellation of exams and avoidance of practical subjects such as work in science laboratories. The mask-wearing can lead to physical problems such as skin, mouth, throat and chest infections and the social isolation is like a very tough punishment. In addition wearing most types of mask leads to an increased level of carbon dioxide since the expired air is not completely dissipated when the mask wearer inhales. This is akin to respiratory acidosis seen, for example, in patients with chronic lung diseases such as chronic bronchitis and also observed in people with sleep apnoea. [12]

Schoolchildren are being forced to wear masks for hours on end and this is causing unacceptable levels of CO_2. According to Wallach et al writing in JAMA Pediatrics [13]: *"The normal content of carbon dioxide in the open is about 0.04% by volume (ie, 400 ppm). A level of 0.2% by volume or 2000 ppm is the limit for closed rooms according to the German Federal Environmental Office, and everything beyond this level is unacceptable."* When wearing masks *"the value of the child with the lowest carbon dioxide level was 3-fold greater than the limit of 0.2 % by volume. The youngest children had the highest values, with one 7-year-old child's carbon dioxide level measured at 25 000 ppm."*

It is, in any case, totally ineffective since as soon as they are out of school the children meet up in the parks and play areas with no thought of isolating or mask-wearing.......and why should they isolate? The measures were not brought in to help the children and many of them are fully aware of this.

University

The useful experience of University has always included the effect of meeting and socialising with the peer group and one-to-one discussions with the lecturers. In the UK the only courses that have permitted such interaction have been those with a practical element. All social events for new students starting in October 2020 were cancelled and for theoretical subjects only distance learning was permitted. An increase in students asking for help due to mental problems has occurred over the last few years and the Covid restrictions have exacerbated the problems.

Health Workers and other frontline staff

Whilst many of the public have been furloughed and only working intermittently during the pandemic the experience of the health workers and frontline staff in essential jobs has been very different. Many of these people, such as care assistants in nursing homes and shop assistants, are amongst the lowest paid people in our society but are essential for its continuance. They have had to endure long working hours dressed in cumbersome, uncomfortable and often ineffective personal protective equipment (PPE).

In addition to this health workers have to daily face the threat of infection which, due to the potentially high viral load, may prove fatal. Also many health workers have co-morbidities, such as obesity, chronically low vitamin D and sickle cell trait, that make them susceptible to Covid-19.

In the first lockdown the uncertainties over treatment protocols, the shortage of PPE and the absence of nearly all the usual patients, led to considerable anxiety amongst hospital and nursing home staff. Patients were discharged into nursing homes in the UK without proper testing and the staff receiving them were soon in great difficulties. Throughout the healthcare sector staff levels have been historically low because of staff, by necessity, self-isolating every time they had a slight cold or sniffle. Lack of testing initially was a factor in worsening the anxiety levels and some have rejected vaccination due to concerns over the safety of the vaccines,

The lockdowns decreased the number of patients with complaints other than Covid-19 being seen and treated in the hospitals. Now the NHS staff have to cope with the enormous backlog of 4.7 million people waiting to start treatment on the NHS in England alone. That was the figure at the end of February 2021 and is the highest figure since records began in 2007. [14] The President of the Royal College of Physicians (RCP), Professor Andrew Goddard, in 2020 called for a doubling of the number of doctors in the UK. The RCP stated that *"Globally, more than 300,000 health-care workers have been infected with COVID-19 in 79 countries, over 7,000 have died, and many more have suffered as a result of stress, burnout, and moral injury."*[15]

Dementia , Learning Difficulties and Disablements

Patients with dementia and people with learning difficulties have been shown to be particularly at risk during the lockdowns. Their life expectancy has worsened due not only to the Covid-19 but also due to isolation. According to one care home owner: '*Without the visits from family and friends and the hands-on support from the care home staff many of the dementia sufferers have lost the will to live and simply died.*' Dementia sufferers in the community and those with learning disabilities find it very hard to cope with the new restrictions and are bewildered by the lack of interaction from family and friends. They also find the more stringent hygiene regimes difficult to follow. This may, in turn make them more liable to infection.

The deaf find it impossible to lip-read when people are wearing masks and blind people are unable to read many of the new notices about restrictions in shops, such as a refusal to take cash (card only sales). Speaking to one disabled person who has very restricted mobility we were told: '*When the first lockdown came I was inexplicably not classed as vulnerable despite my disabilities. I was at the back of the queue when trying to get a delivery slot for food online and, when I was almost out of food in my flat, the delivery man refused to carry the items up to my landing due to fear of catching the Covid. My physical health deteriorated because I was not allowed to visit the swimming pool for aquatic therapy. The overall effect of lockdown was very detrimental.*'

UK Politicians

Perhaps bravado informed the UK politicians in the first few weeks of the pandemic when they did nothing and assumed we would simply avoid being affected as had been the case with SARS1, MERS and Ebola. By 2021 fear of new variants, fear of being too lenient and fear of incriminations appeared to be the dominant feature in Downing Street. As the Daily Telegraph stated *'If a fear of vaccine-resistant variants is now driving policy it is hard to see how normal life can resume.'*[16]

There was no effective opposition to the draconian measures brought in by the UK government. The official leader of the opposition, Labour leader Sir Kier Starmer, has shown his true colours by consistently asking Boris Johnson and subsequent governments to make the restrictions more severe. His point has been that most people agree with the lockdowns and restrictions. As an article by Jonathan Sumption states: *'When democracy becomes a mechanism for mass coercion, with the approval of the opposition, it is surely heading towards its end.'* [17]

Many people have been shocked by a recent revelation that many of the top civil servants have appointments with industry that surely provide a conflict of interest. Already on very high salaries they have taken up these jobs whilst still employed in the civil service![18] Bureaucratic dictatorship really is taking over the UK.

General comments about socialisation

The longterm detrimental effects of the lockdowns can presently only be guessed but the health benefits of socialisation are well known and include the following [19]:

- Mental Health. Being social decreases depression.
- Confidence and self-esteem. People who are lonely often have low confidence and esteem
- Increased quality of life. Loneliness correlates with functional decline.
- Reduced blood pressure. Loneliness is a risk factor for high blood pressure
- Reduced risk of Alzheimer's. "Risk of Alzheimer's Disease was more than doubled in lonely persons compared with persons who

were not lonely."[20]

- Boost immunity and other physical health benefits. Socialisation can reduce the risk for cardiovascular disease, cancer, osteoporosis, and rheumatoid arthritis.
- Increased brain health. Socialisation boosts cognitive function
- Promotes purpose. Spending time with others helps us feel useful and that our life has a greater purpose

If socialisation has these major benefits preventing people from meeting and interacting will do exactly the opposite

Conclusion

The pandemic has resulted in multiple causes of concern with regard to mental health and these have been compounded by the draconian lockdowns and their enforcement, and the unethical use of behavioural science to create a climate of fear.

Covid-19 infection can cause long term brain fog and depression and these effects are worsened by the lockdowns. Human beings are social animals and being forced into isolation is used in prison as a very severe form of punishment. Now, however, completely innocent people have been put into nursing homes and denied contact with their families for extended periods. During lockdowns people cannot visit theatres, cinemas, taverns, churches and even the accommodation of friends. The general misery this has created will be transferred into an increased incidence of mental and physical illness. Indeed recent research, widely reported in the media[21] shows the incidence of significant depression in adults more than doubling over the past year and affecting nearly a quarter of the population. Lockdown and self-isolation may cause separation anxiety and the vaccines, despite claims to the contrary, do have a high incidence of side-effects including headache and confusion. Suicide has shown an upswing in the second wave and subsequent lockdowns.

Healthcare staff are at considerable risk of stress, burnout and injury.

Dementia sufferers have had their lives shortened by Covid-19 but more so by the lockdowns.

UK politicians seem to be making decisions based on fear and the civil servants have given up their right to claim impartiality by taking on appointments with industry. To add insult to injury it is clear that at the highest level in the UK politicians and civil servants were ignoring the lockdown rules and enjoying illicit parties.

The harmful effects of social intervention on Obesity and Diabetes

Morbid obesity, the condition of being considerably overweight, carries considerable health risks and major costs for the NHS and social services. The table on page 48 (Chapter 3) lists some of the health risks ranging from coronary heart disease to cancer, mental illness to high blood pressure [22].

There is almost no common cause of death in the developed world which is not more frequent in morbidly obese people compared with those of normal weight. Unfortunately the UK was seeing a major increase in obesity before the Covid-19 pandemic. Due to the lockdown this problem has markedly worsened. A study published in October 2020 looked at the eating behaviour and physical activity during COVID-19 lockdown [23]. Over two thousand adults completed a survey and this showed that a large number showed worsening of eating habits and exercise behaviour during the first lockdown. For example well over half the respondents reported snacking more frequently. People who were already overweight or obese reported even lower levels of physical activity and diet quality, and a greater reported frequency of overeating.

People on a low income are at a greater risk of obesity, eat worse food and exercise less. This has worsened due to lockdowns that impact their income and thus the quality of their food and prevents them from doing inexpensive exercise.

In fact the double whammy of closing businesses and public facilities such as parks and swimming pools particularly affects those who are the most socially deprived. Obesity doubles the risk of dying from Covid-19 so preventing people from doing the things that might have reduced that risk does seem absurd,

This problem does not just affect the adult population. In the UK one in three children are leaving primary school overweight and one in five are living with obesity.[24]

Cancer

Obesity has now overtaken smoking as the most common predisposing factor for cancer as shown in the table below.[25]

Type of Cancer	Increased risk
Endometrial cancer	x 2 to x 7
Oesophageal adenocarcinoma	x 2
Gastric cardia cancer:	nearly x 2
Kidney cancer	nearly x 2
Multiple myeloma	10% to 20% increase
Meningioma	50% increase
Pancreatic cancer	x 1.5
Colorectal cancer	30% increase
Gallbladder cancer	60% increase.
Breast cancer: postmenopausal women	20% to 40% increase
Ovarian cancer:	5-unit increase in BMI = 10% increase
Thyroid cancer	5-unit increase in BMI = 10%
Liver cancer	up to x 2

Table 1 Increased Risk of Cancer due to Obesity [25]

The economic effects of closing businesses are obvious but need repeating. The government's furlough scheme was exceedingly expensive but incomplete. Many of the self-employed fell through the net and received no support. Some people who had been on higher incomes received no support. Many people were made redundant just before the furlough scheme started or were made redundant during the scheme because of the costs of the part that their employers had to bear. It has been suggested that the unemployment figures in the UK, which have been reported as 5%, do not reflect the true state of affairs. Almost two million people are in hidden unemployment: *"They are out of work and eager to find jobs but are classified as economically inactive rather than unemployed"* [26]. Clearly when children were not allowed to go to school one of the parents was very likely to have become "economically inactive".

The poorer people had a far worse experience of lockdown and many took to snacking, greater alcohol intake and increased smoking.

Type 2 Diabetes

Ninety percent of the cases of Type 2 Diabetes are related to obesity. According to reports from the virtual Diabetes UK Professional Conference the lockdown has been a disaster with regard to the diagnosis and treatment of diabetes [27]. This is not surprising since only a third of patients could access the NHS in the first wave [28]. Matthew Carr Research Fellow, University of Manchester, presenting at the virtual conference, stated that in the first wave of Covid-19 the diagnosis rate of type 2 diabetes and new prescriptions for the preferred treatment, metformin, fell by 70% in April [29]. Given that obesity levels are soaring with two thirds of adults already overweight or obese and the levels rising during lockdown, this represents a frighteningly serious figure. Over the period March to December more than a quarter of the diabetes cases were missed. Carr reported that "our estimate of 60,000 missed or delayed diagnoses may well be an underestimate if changes in lifestyle during the pandemics and lockdowns have increased obesity rates of other risk factors for diabetes in the general population."

Delayed diagnosis leads to the condition of the patients deteriorating before they are finally treated thus increasing the burden on the patients and the health service.

Table 2 Symptoms of Untreated Type 2 Diabetes

Increased thirst
Frequent urination
Increased hunger
Unintended weight loss
Fatigue
Blurred vision
Slow-healing sores
Frequent infections
Numbness or tingling in the hands or feet
Areas of darkened skin, usually in the armpits and neck

Richard Batterham Professor of Obesity, Diabetes and Endocrinology, University College London and Steve Bain Professor of Medicine (Diabetes), Swansea University, speaking at the same conference, referred to the enormous backlog problem in the world of Covid and lockdowns, and the barriers facing overweight patients with regard to treatment. These barriers included lack of services in deprived areas, stigma, impact of COVID, and patient psychology/empowerment to navigate NHS systems. All the problems had been made worse by lockdowns.

According to the Mayo clinic [30] the symptoms of untreated type 2 diabetes are myriad. They are listed in table 2 on the previous page.

Diabetes commonly affects many major organs. In the cardiovascular system it causes heart disease, stroke and high blood pressure. Nerve damage, kidney disease, eye damage, hearing impairment and dementia are also increased in incidence. Diabetes increases susceptibility to skin infections and low healing of cuts and blisters. Severe damage may require toe, foot or leg amputation.

Early treatment reduces the risks associated with diabetes and delayed diagnosis is therefore a major problem. The supposed benefits of lockdowns should have been weighed against the major drawbacks and safeguards put in place to ensure that conditions such as diabetes did not go undiagnosed. This was not done.

Most observers on all sides of the political divide would now agree that the costs of lockdown were too high. Many would also say that the experience should never be repeated.

The Guardian
https://www.theguardian.com › business › jun › the

Reference 31

the costs of lockdown are too high

Daily Mail
https://www.dailymail.co.uk › news › article-9386889 ⋮

Reference 32

The shattering price of lockdown on our health

Stop Press: If you are still in doubt as to whether lockdowns were useful do check out the report from the Institute of Economic Affairs which states that they were a costly failure.[33]

References: At the end of the book

Chapter 11

Vaccination and Gene Therapy

The Editors

Vaccination Against Covid-19

Having misguidedly discounted any intervention using repurposed drugs the leading medical authorities put their faith in novel "vaccines" and perhaps the potential of new drugs in the more distant future. They chose the Big Pharma approach.

Contrary to public perception the UK population was not the first in the world to receive a vaccine against SARS-CoV-2. The Chinese scientist Yusen Zhou filed a patent for Covid vaccine on February 24th 2020. This work had been underway well before the Covid-19 pandemic had occurred. It was certainly part of the work performed with Shi Zhengli in conjunction with Peter Daszak funded by the USA which Daszak referred to in a video made in the Autumn (Fall) of 2019 when he stated that it was easy to add spike proteins to coronaviruses but making vaccines was difficult. Yusen Zhou died mysteriously within three months of filing the patent. Scarlett Yan, the Hong Kong virologist who escaped to the USA makes a good case that the Chinese military virologists had already proven that the COVID-19 could infect humanised mice and that they were trying it out on prisoners when it escaped.[1] This is further substantiated by an article in the Christian newspaper *Good News*.[2] The article details the torture meted out to Ovalbeck Joseph Turdakun in the notorious Xinjiang prison....

"Jospeh and his fellow inmates were injected with a vaccine that was said to prevent colds. They felt pain in their ears, hands and feet; yellow fluid came out of their ears; some had difficulty walking. When he was finally released, Jospeh still had difficulty walking."

Right now as we write this chapter China is in a mess. According to the

BMJ there are so many Covid-19 fatalities that *"China has effectively stopped counting covid cases and deaths, abandoning mass testing and adopting new criteria for counting deaths that will exclude most fatalities from being reported."*[3]

The enormous upsurge in cases is said to be due to the Omicron variant. If this is true why are the Chinese vaccines not working? Given the low death toll from Omicron elsewhere in the world have the earliest vaccines sensitised the Chinese populous and are the deaths the result?

The UK and vaccines

In the UK the government were offered a variety of vaccines. These included Dalgleish and Sorensen's vaccine against the conserved non-humanlike parts of the virus. The government chose not to support that vaccine but rather to promote the Astra-Zeneca (Oxford), Pfizer and Moderna…all of which target humanlike spike proteins.
The initial results were good. Very few people who had been vaccinated were hospitalised.
Lately (2022/23) the results are different. At this point it is important to plea for a nuanced argument rather than the usual vaxxers versus anti-vaxxers diatribe.

Anti-Covid Vaccines

So what is the story with regards to the "vaccines" against Covid-19?
The Chinese vaccines fit the description of earlier vaccines in that they are killed virus that acts as an antigen and stimulates antibody production when injected into a person.
The Astra-Zeneca, Pfizer and Moderna do not meet that description. They are really gene therapy rather than vaccines.
In a paper in 2020 [4] Sorensen, Susrud and Dalgleish suggested that mistaken assumptions about SARS-CoV-2's aetiology risked creating ineffective or actively harmful vaccines, including the risk of antibody-dependent enhancement. Their own vaccine, Biovacc-19, had a method of operation acting solely upon nonhuman-like (NHL) epitopes which are 21.6% of the composition of this coronavirus's spike protein. Moreover they proposed that an adjuvant, IMM-101 be used with Biovacc-19.

Unfortunately this was not chosen as the preferred vaccine and the UK and other governments went ahead with the "big pharma" offerings.

The Pfizer and Moderna vaccines use a lipid shell to surround the mRNA and this is injected into the arm where it is supposed to stay within the muscles cells, causing the cells to produce spike proteins which then act as the antigen. Oxford/AstraZeneca, Sputnik V (the Russian vaccine) and Johnson and Johnson each use a weakened "harmless" virus as the vector with the genetic code of the harmless adenovirus engineered to produce spike proteins.

The Response to Vaccines

The initial response to the vaccines was better than expected when introduced to the UK populous in December and January 2021. The number of cases of Covid-19 dropped remarkably and it appeared that the vaccinated people were not spreading the virus.

Later in the same year the story was rather different. By that time the vaccinated persons were at least as likely if not more likely to spread the virus. [5.]

In addition the vaccine was no longer stopping the vaccinated from catching the virus. The authorities clung on to the idea that it was reducing the severity of the disease but no real evidence was provided to substantiate that claim.

Meanwhile the age groups being vaccinated dropped right down such that the vaccine was even being offered to children aged twelve or over. In the USA younger children were being vaccinated. There was no justification for this. (See chapters 12 and 13)

The first company to report adverse reactions was AstraZeneca, whose vaccine was causing a small percentage of patients to suffer venous thrombosis. Using that as an excuse President Macron of France banned the use of the AZ vaccine in the elderly although similar problems occurred with the Pfizer and Moderna vaccines but were not reported.

The severe reactions to the other vaccines were not being made public by Pfizer and Moderna. Pfizer demanded that their adverse reactions should be kept secret for many decades. However it became clear that there were a significant number of severe reactions including some cardiac events.

In January 2022 we (the editors) felt obliged to send a rapid response

to the BMJ.[5]
"Vaccinating young people is not justified moreover banning unvaccinated staff from working in health services is not based on science and is a serious "own goal.""

The UK Government Reported Covid Vaccine Reactions

In March 2022 the UK Government reported [7] :-
" As of 16 February 2022, there have been 721 reports of myocarditis and 483 reports of pericarditis following the use of the Pfizer vaccine" and
"206 reports of myocarditis and 115 reports of pericarditis following the use of the Moderna vaccine. Some cases have been reported following the use of the AstraZeneca vaccine, but given the extensive use of AstraZeneca in the UK, these are thought to reflect the expected background incidence rate of myocarditis and pericarditis conditions."
According to the UK Government these cardiac complications occurred about 1 in 60,000 overall and had a higher rate in children and young adults (around 1 in 40,000). In comparison the usual rate of reactions to other vaccines is about 1 in a million! The cardiac reactions to the Covid vaccines are thus, according to the Government, roughly twenty times more common. The reactions to the Pfizer and Moderna Covid vaccines should not be considered as rare events. It is wrong to compare vaccine adverse reactions with drug reactions since the drugs are not given to the whole population of healthy people.
Other reported side effects to the Covid vaccines include a headache along with blurred vision, feeling or being sick, problems speaking, weakness, drowsiness or seizures (fits) a rash that looks like small bruises or bleeding under the skin, shortness of breath, chest pain, leg swelling or persistent abdominal pain.[8] Arthritis and blistering of the skin have also been reported.
These reactions occur more frequently after the second dose of the vaccine and are increasingly troublesome with boosters.
These are the UK Government's figures and it is clear that there is considerable under reporting of the side effects.

Non-Mainstream Reports of Covid Vaccine Reactions

Although the evidence is not yet clear it is likely that some of the excess deaths being reported now that are not due to Covid-19 may be due to side-effects from the vaccines. Some people have suggested that vaccine boosters are killing as many as one person for every 800 doses administered![9]

Dr. Schetters, who is a recipient of the Medal of Honour of the Faculty of Pharmacy at the University of Montpellier in France, told Dr. Robert Malone, an inventor of mRNA vaccine technology, that medical doctors are currently seeing "all sorts of symptoms that they do not know what it is" and that "in the Netherlands now it's very clear that there is a good correlation between the number of vaccinations that are given to people and the number of people that die within a week after that". It is essential to look at all-cause mortality, he said, as the vaccine "potentially affects all organs".

The rate of myocarditis following Covid vaccination has variously been reported as considerably higher than that assessed by the UK Government.

Recently the Florida Department of Health suspended inoculations for the 18-35 years group stating:[10] *"This analysis found that there is an 84% increase in the relative incidence of cardiac-related death among males 18-39 years old within 28 days following mRNA vaccination."*

Oncologists and pathologists around the world have become aware of an association between covid vaccination and aggressive unusual tumours.

Dr Ute Kruger states:[11] *"Covid-19 vaccines appear to cause fast-growing cancers or porocarcinoma (a type of skin cancer) and also inflammatory conditions in the body, so-called autoimmune diseases,"* said Dr Krueger. *"Perhaps this cancer development is linked to inflammatory conditions. I've talked to other doctors who are seeing an increased number of tumors that were almost never seen before. I mean rare tumors and that the number of cancer cases has increased in different organs."*

These findings have all been heavily contested but certainly there is anxiety about the number of excess deaths in the UK and various reports have tried to link this to lockdowns or to Covid-19 infections.

Comment

For the "vaccines" to be good science they should be testable. The test of a vaccine must include the cost/benefit analysis. The benefits are usually obvious: the recipient should no longer be susceptible to the infection and they should not pass it on to other people. The costs include the monetary expense incurred but also the potential harm to the person who is vaccinated.

In the case of the Covid vaccinations the benefits have become blurred. Initially it was hoped that the vaccine would convey protection for a long period of time but even the official UK Health Security Agency states that the protection wanes very quickly. [12] The figures are incomplete and vague but Pfizer and AstraZeneca appear to have waned in protecting against symptomatic infection down to about 20% by four months and at six months the protection becomes negative, the recipient becoming more likely to be infected than the controls! The agency provide no information about mortality or transmission citing insufficient data. The UK is usually a frontrunner with information of this nature due to its nature as a nationalised health system. Do other countries have better information? The Florida administration has been condemned by pundits for suspending inoculations for the 18-35 years group.[10] But given the lack of information about efficacy and in the light of the knowledge of side-effects the Florida Department of Health would appear to be taking a sensible position.

The vast majority of people in the UK have come in contact with Covid-19 and have some natural immunity. Adding extra boosters increases the risk of developing reactions and interfering with the natural immunity whilst pushing the emergence of new variants. The time has come in the UK for a moratorium on the Covid-19 vaccine programme until a vaccine such as that suggested by Sorensen et al has been tested and shown to be safer and more effective than the present offerings.

The debate is difficult. Doctors against vaccination have been struck off or suspended when they have spoken out or refused to take part in the vaccination programme whilst those in favour have received vitriol online. That is not how science can progress. [13]

Pfizer wanted the data on reactions to be kept secret for many decades. If the vaccines cannot be tested they are not science, they are simply untested and potentially dangerous technology.

Other Vaccinations

We believe that used properly vaccines are one of the greatest benefits that science has bestowed on humankind. Before Jenner in 1796 started vaccinating patients against smallpox the best that could be hoped for was a mild form of the disease. In fact 'variolation' was in vogue. This was the inoculation of material from a mild case of smallpox into a fit and healthy recipient and had a death rate of around 1 in 25. Moreover it was a good way of starting an epidemic ![14]

Certainly the eradication of smallpox has saved many millions of lives and possibly billions of people from hideously deforming scars. It was by far the most successful intervention of medical science. Ever!

Jenner's success led to a search for vaccines against many common infectious diseases. Pasteur was next when he discovered a vaccine against anthrax and an attenuated live vaccine against rabies.

Vaccines against twenty-six different infections (and multiple versions of each) are available and used in the USA ranging from Adenovirus to Yellow Fever. Many other vaccines exist but are not on the commonly used list. But vaccination and all types of immunisation have a very chequered history.

The proponents of vaccination against smallpox claimed throughout the 19th century that it was harmless, safe and gave lifelong immunity against smallpox. In fact there are many people who needed to avoid vaccination (for example, people with eczema) and the immunity probably lasts ten years, not a lifetime, then a booster is required to maintain the immunity.

Syphilisation in the 19th century was an example of extremely poor science and poor medical practice with doctors carrying out prolonged and repeated inoculation of supposedly attenuated syphilitic matter into patients who already were suffering from the disease. By all accounts it only served to make matters worse.

There are occasions in which the vaccines have been contaminated or harmful in other ways and the longterm effects of modern vaccines are only now being determined.

Overall for the human race vaccines have been an amazing boon but for an individual they have sometimes been disastrous.

The Wakefield Affair

It is very difficult to write about this without upsetting one side or other on this debate but it is important to include the Wakefield Affair in a book about the death of science. Putting people off having their children vaccinated risks major epidemics that can otherwise be avoided but, and it is a big but, vaccination does carry some risk whatever the vaccinators may say to the contrary.

The Death of Science

So what happened? In 1998 Andrew Wakefield presented a paper in *The Lancet* purporting to show the MMR vaccine (measles, mumps and rubella) causing a new syndrome of autism and bowel disease. This was later retracted and Wakefield was struck off the by the General Medical Council.

Was there any truth in the assertion? Research has now shown that there is a *reduced* chance of autism in vaccinated children compared with children who are not vaccinated which appears to suggest that *The Lancet* paper was completely incorrect.

The argument is rather more nuanced than this. Yes, overall it is safer to be vaccinated but an individual could still suffer from having an immunisation and it is the individual cases that make the news.

Combined MMR vaccines have been in trouble from the very beginning. In September 1992 the Department of Health withdrew two brands of MMR vaccine after research suggested they were associated with a raised incidence of transient mumps meningitis, although much lower than with natural disease.

Wakefield has never suggested that vaccination should stop...he has always called for the introduction of separate vaccines for each of measles, mumps and rubella. Whether they would be safer than the joint vaccine is not known.

In 2004 it was revealed that the Legal Aid Board funded Wakefield's research and that many of the children in the report were litigants. This was clearly a vested interest and in March of 2004 ten of the thirteen authors withdrew their support for Wakefield's paper.

A measles outbreak occurred in the UK in 2006 and one child died, the first for 14 years. In 2010 the paper was withdrawn by *The Lancet* and Wakefield was struck off.

But is it possible that vaccinations could cause the syndrome Wakefield described? Well, a muted yes. Even the makers of the vaccines never say they are completely safe....just that they are safer than catching the disease. That much is definitely true and it is possible that they could be made even safer but, as with antibiotics, we come across cost/benefit analysis and lack of profit as a reason for not creating new versions of the vaccines.

"Public confidence in MMR and vaccination has never fully recovered, at least not in developed countries. This was made evident by recent news that the number of measles cases in Europe increased by 400 per cent in

2017, with more than 20,000 cases and 35 needless deaths." [15]

Reports published by the Centers for Disease Control (CDC) and the National Center for Biotechnology Information (NCBI) state that the following vaccines have been linked to encephalitis: [16]

- MMR vaccine – Measles, Mumps and Rubella
- DTP or DTaP vaccine – Diphtheria, Tetanus, and Pertussis (whooping cough).
- Influenza (flu) vaccine

Some of these vaccines have also been associated with conditions similar to secondary encephalitis, such as acute disseminated encephalomyelitis (ADEM) and measles inclusion body encephalitis.

There have been more than 1,100 cases of encephalitis (including brain stem encephalitis) reported to the Vaccine Adverse Event Reporting System (VAERS). [16]

If everybody in the USA is being vaccinated that makes encephalitis an event that occurs in about 1 in 300,000 people. Many are vaccinated multiple times bringing this down to the ballpark figure of one in a million per vaccination event.

Note that the chance of dying from a measles epidemic is somewhere between one in six hundred and one in a thousand. Clearly it is safer to be vaccinated against measles than to suffer from an epidemic…maybe as much as one thousand times safer.

But we have always known that it is better to be vaccinated and before there were vaccination programs careful parents tried to make sure that their children had the childhood illnesses when they were fit, healthy children.

So what is the advice to parents? If your child is ill, wait until he or she is better before having a vaccination. Who else should not be vaccinated? That depends on the vaccine concerned and the guidelines are too long and detailed to be included here. They can be found online. [17] The type of advice is to avoid vaccination if they are the wrong age or if there was a previous allergic reaction, recent coma, seizures, active eczema etc.

Some people will not want their children to be vaccinated at all. They are then relying on the herd immunity provided by other people's children being vaccinated and this could result in some hostility if the parents of the other children get to hear about the decision, though they are probably not putting vaccinated children at greater risk.

Moreover it is possible that lack of vaccination could debar a person from travelling abroad or working in certain health care occupations. The appearance of multiple variants which vaccinated people can catch means that total herd immunity is unlikely to be achieved by vaccination.

The subject of vaccination for COVID-19 was discussed earlier in this chapter.

Comment

We agree with Schneider et al that postmortem examination with additional investigations is a necessity for every fatality following vaccination. That is the only way to advance the science.[18]

Vaccines are a great boon to society when created and administered correctly but draconian mandates, vested interests and poor science run the risk of putting them in disrepute.

Stop press: At the time of writing Dr. José Luis Domingo, the editor of *Food and Chemical Toxicology* has been obliged to resign because he allowed the publication of an important research article showing that the mRNA vaccines suppress the innate immune system.[19] Moreover a more recent detailed paper from Cleveland clinic shows full Covid vaccination *increases* the risk of catching Covid-19. [20]

Vaccines push variants?

In New Scientist this week[21] Carissa Wong states: *"High levels of immunity due to vaccination or from previous infection are creating a selection pressure towards immune-evading varieties."*

It is well known that vaccines exert strong selective pressure on pathogenic viruses[22,23] In the light of this knowledge consider the first three waves of Covid-19 in the UK as shown in the graph of hospital admissions repeated below.

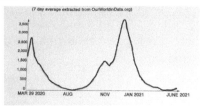

England : Daily Hospital Admissions for COVID-19

Coronaviruses tend to have a peak in the winter and the same virus returns with a considerably smaller peak the following autumn. The first peak of the novel coronavirus was delayed and appeared in the spring of 2020 due to the time it took to spread from its point of inception in China. It then had a double peak in the winter of 2020/2021. The November peak was a little higher than expected and the January peak was very high indeed. It seems reasonable to assume that the November peak was due to variants pushed by the vaccination programme in China, a country from which the UK government mysteriously did not quarantine people. The January peak was due to the so-called Kent variant (re-named Alpha) which was more transmissible due to its tendency to make people sneeze. It is likely that the Kent variant actually came from Continental Europe and spread up from the port of entry, Dover. Was it the result of the Pfizer trials which had started in July 2020? Were subsequent variants the result of vaccine trials in South America, South Africa and India?

These questions need to be asked because the subsequent production of booster doses has not reduced the overall number of cases. Some people have caught the Covid infection multiple times, presumably with a different variant each time.

The Omicron variant seems to have been the least harmful but now booster doses have been given against it. Whilst this may reduce the infections with Omicron will it inadvertently push a newer variant or, as suggested in New Scientist, a whole soup of variants?[20]

Co-editor PRG has suggested that with the present vaccines only the very vulnerable should be vaccinated. They should then be quarantined for two weeks to prevent spillover of new variants. A Sorensen/Dalgleish type of vaccine should be made available that only attacks those parts that are preserved and nonhuman-like.[4]

A recent study[24] has shown that the bivalent Covid-19 vaccine was very below par in protecting against infection. *"Among 51,011 working-aged Cleveland Clinic employees, the bivalent COVID-19 vaccine booster was 30% effective in preventing infection, during the time when the virus strains dominant in the community were represented in the vaccine."* Such a low level of effectiveness would normally preclude a vaccine from being used. The WHO usually demands at leat 50% efficacy.

And we ask again: Why are post mortems and full enquiries not being carried out on people who have died within 30 days of receiving a Covid shot? When they *have* been done the vaccines was implicated in 74%. [25]

References: At the end of the book

A Closer Look at Covid-19 Vaccines

Rosamond Jones

Background:

In March 2020, at the time of the first UK lockdown, both the Chief Medical Officer, Professor Chris Whitty, and the Chief Scientific Adviser, Sir Patrick Vallance, were quite sanguine that new Covid-19 vaccines would take at least 1-2 years to produce (bear in mind a new drug commonly takes 5-10 years from concept to authorisation).[1] The stated purpose of the lockdown was to 'flatten the curve' to ensure the NHS did not collapse. Indeed the WHO stated that the only justification for lockdowns were as a short term measure while building up capacity and stocks of PPE and other equipment.[2] Had the damning report on Pandemic preparedness (or lack of) been acted on rather than buried,[3] there might have been less excuse for panic.

It was suggested that the elderly and high risk would self-isolate for twelve weeks whereas the young and healthy would emerge after three weeks once it was clear the hospital service could manage, and they would presumably catch covid and establish reasonable levels of herd immunity making it safer for the vulnerable groups to emerge.[4]

But a huge amount of public money was poured into vaccine research, with an unholy race between manufacturers as to who could get a successful vaccine to market the quickest. 'Herd immunity' became dirty words.

Early concerns:

Coronaviruses have been a notoriously difficult target for vaccines. The Common Cold Unit in Salisbury worked for around 30 years before abandoning its attempts.[5] At that stage, coronaviruses were generally considered to be mild, so unlimited funding was not an option.

However, the SARS outbreak in the Far East in 2003 with an Infection Fatality Rate (IFR) of around 30%, ended the complacency abruptly and much effort went, unsuccessfully, into making a safe vaccine for this disease. One early promising candidate produced an excellent antibody response in mice, only for them to die when subsequently exposed to the virus - a condition named Antibody Dependent Enhancement (ADE).[6] Further studies were undertaken after MERS (Middle Eastern Respiratory Syndrome) but again without success.

In 2020 when the hunt for a Covid vaccine was on, a number of warnings were voiced around potential risks,[7,8,9] but were largely ignored. Interestingly however, the recent Lockdown Files (personal messages from the UK Health secretary, Matt Hancock, leaked to the Telegraph newspaper) included a statement from Professor Whitty that the IFR for Covid-19 at less than 1% was too low to justify abridged testing or fast track authorisation,[10] so he was at least thinking straight early on, though he seemed to have completely forgotten his cautious approach by Summer 2021 when he was pushing the Joint Committee on Vaccination and Immunisation (JCVI) to recommend vaccinating healthy children.[11]

The trials & authorisation process:

The public have been repeatedly told that no corners were cut in the vaccine research, but this was patently not the case. New vaccines have a fast-track system, on the basis that the technology has been tested over decades and it is simply a matter of inserting a different organism e.g. a meningococcal vaccine following on from a pneumococcal one. But as outlined in the previous chapter, most of the Covid-19 vaccines in use in UK and Europe, involve either mRNA technology (Pfizer & Moderna) or viral-vector-DNA technology (AstraZeneca and Johnson & Johnson), both of which would be more accurately described as gene therapy. Moderna were certainly expecting a tough regulatory process appropriate to a novel technology and in their June 2020 submission to the US Securities and Exchange Commission stated, *'No mRNA drug has been approved in this new potential class of medicines, and may never be approved as a result of efforts by others or us. mRNA drug development has substantial clinical development and regulatory risks due to the novel and unprecedented nature of this new class of medicines.*[12] Later in 2020 the WHO set up a series of meetings and produced a first draft for a new regulatory process,[13] but they were already behind the curve with both the manufacturers and the politicians, leading to acceptance of the standard vaccine paperwork. Thus, although some animal studies were done, they were hugely curtailed and also remained unpublished until long after rollout, only to be released following legal challenge.[14]

One obvious shortcoming was the lack of basic pharmacology. Studies of pharmacokinetics (drug clearance rates) and biodistribution (where a drug is concentrated), were never performed in humans. Pfizer for example, studied a small number of rats but only using the lipid nanoparticles rather than the complete vaccine and only ran the studies for 48 hours despite the test material still accumulating in liver, spleen, adrenal glands and ovaries. The following table was extracted from the Non-Clinical Evaluation report, only obtained via a Freedom of Information Request. [15]

Sample	Total Lipid Concentration (µg lipid equiv/g (or mL))						
	0.25 min	1 h	2 h	4 h	8 h	24 h	48 h
Adipose tissue	0.057	0.100	0.126	0.128	0.093	0.084	0.181
Adrenal glands	0.27	1.48	2.72	2.89	6.80	13.77	18.21
Bladder	0.041	0.130	0.146	0.167	0.148	0.247	0.365
Bone (femur)	0.091	0.195	0.266	0.276	0.340	0.342	0.687
Bone marrow (femur)	0.48	0.96	1.24	1.24	1.84	2.49	3.77
Brain	0.045	0.100	0.138	0.115	0.073	0.069	0.068
Eyes	0.010	0.035	0.052	0.067	0.059	0.091	0.112
Heart	0.28	1.03	1.40	0.99	0.79	0.45	0.55
Injection site	128.3	393.8	311.2	338.0	212.8	194.9	164.9
Kidneys	0.39	1.16	2.05	0.92	0.59	0.43	0.42
Large intestine	0.013	0.048	0.09	0.29	0.65	1.10	1.34
Liver	0.74	4.62	10.97	16.55	26.54	19.24	24.29
Lung	0.49	1.21	1.83	1.50	1.15	1.04	1.09
Lymph node (mandibular)	0.064	0.189	0.290	0.408	0.534	0.554	0.727
Lymph node (mesenteric)	0.050	0.146	0.530	0.489	0.689	0.985	1.366
Muscle	0.021	0.061	0.084	0.103	0.096	0.095	0.192
Ovaries (females)	0.104	1.34	1.64	2.34	3.09	5.24	12.26
Pancreas	0.081	0.207	0.414	0.380	0.294	0.358	0.599
Pituitary gland	0.339	0.645	0.868	0.854	0.405	0.478	0.694
Prostate (males)	0.061	0.091	0.128	0.157	0.150	0.183	0.170
Salivary glands	0.084	0.193	0.255	0.220	0.135	0.170	0.264
Skin	0.013	0.208	0.159	0.145	0.119	0.157	0.253
Small intestine	0.030	0.221	0.476	0.879	1.279	1.302	1.472
Spinal cord	0.043	0.097	0.169	0.250	0.106	0.085	0.112
Spleen	0.33	2.47	7.73	10.30	22.09	20.08	23.35
Stomach	0.017	0.065	0.115	0.144	0.268	0.152	0.215
Testes (males)	0.031	0.042	0.079	0.129	0.146	0.304	0.320
Thymus	0.088	0.243	0.340	0.335	0.196	0.207	0.331
Thyroid	0.155	0.536	0.842	0.851	0.544	0.578	1.000
Uterus (females)	0.043	0.203	0.305	0.140	0.287	0.289	0.456
Whole blood	1.97	4.37	5.40	3.05	1.31	0.91	0.42
Plasma	3.96	8.13	8.90	6.50	2.36	1.78	0.81
Blood:plasma ratio	0.815	0.515	0.550	0.510	0.555	0.530	0.540

Table 1. Mean concentration of radioactivity (sexes combined) in tissue and blood following a single IM dose of 50 µg mRNA/rat

In the authorisation paperwork, items such as 'genotoxicity' (effect on fertility), teratogenicity (potential damage to the unborn baby) and carcinogenicity (increasing cancer risk) were all simply marked N/A.[16] The first two might be considered 'not applicable' if designing a vaccine for use in the elderly, or indeed if treating a patient with a potentially fatal condition but are clearly highly relevant if designing a vaccine to give to a healthy population including children.

Statements from so-called experts affirming that there is absolutely no risk from taking the vaccines in pregnancy, should have more honestly said, 'we have no idea about the safety of the vaccines in pregnancy, as pregnant women were specifically excluded from all the trials, so the best we can say is that we hope it's safe and we will do extremely careful follow-up for anyone who chooses to get vaccinated'.

The Phase 3 human trials were also cut short, with a decision taken early on to allow the codes to be broken and the control group to receive the vaccine after only a few months. This was in clear breach of international guidance which recommends at least one year of follow-up.[17] The lack of a control group has made the detection of medium to long term adverse events much more problematic, as potential side-effects can be dismissed as coincidental. The gold standard double-blind randomised controlled trial is gold standard for a reason. It requires the researchers to be in so-called 'equipoise' i.e. with an open mind as to whether their proposed treatment is better or worse than no (or an existing established) treatment. The trial investigators argued that if they showed the vaccines to be 'effective' then it would be unethical to withhold them but that assumes they had already made up their minds that the products were totally safe. As for children, the trials were even smaller, with efficacy largely assumed from antibody studies, a so-called 'immuno-bridging' methodology. The Pfizer trial which allowed the rollout to millions of primary school children was based on 1,518 vaccinated children followed for just one month post their second dose[18] - you don't need to be a scientist to know that is not evidence of 'Safe & Effective'.

There is another fundamental rule for a gold standard study design which was ignored and that is that the primary endpoint should be all cause mortality (or severe morbidity for a condition with a very low death rate) rather than just mortality or morbidity from the disease under investigation. It is noteworthy that in the original Pfizer trial, there was one more death in the vaccinated group than the placebo group but this was buried in the supplementary tables. It is true that there were less deaths from Covid-19 but this was offset by more cardiovascular deaths in the vaccine arm.[19] All-cause mortality or morbidity as the primary trial outcome becomes especially important if giving a vaccine to a broad spectrum of people with a very different risk from Covid-19 and a different risk of adverse events. The Covid-19 vaccine adverse events are somewhat perverse in that some of the serious side effects are more frequent in younger age groups, the very groups for whom a SARS-CoV-2 infection causes least problems. This is the case for Vaccine Induced Thrombotic Thrombocytopaenia (VITT), a serious blood-clotting problem linked to viral-vector-DNA vaccines, which particularly affected younger women,[20] or for myocarditis which is most prevalent after a second mRNA vaccine dose in young men aged 15-25.[21] It is easy to see how the benefit ratio may be completely different when offering vaccination to an 80 year old with co-morbidities for whom a SARS-CoV-2 infection might carry a 3% mortality risk compared with an 8-year-old boy whose risk of death from Covid-19 is around 1 in 1-2 million.

Trials should also be analysed on an 'intention to treat' basis. The Pfizer trial excluded participants who developed covid-like symptoms until 7 days after their second dose,[22] on the basis you wouldn't expect a vaccine to provide instant protection, but these were not counted as adverse events either, as if this unexpected increase was of no importance. Similar findings of an initial increase in cases were shown by Public Health England[23] and also by data from Israel.[24] This may have had a serious impact in care homes in December 2020, when staff and residents were all vaccinated in a single session. Several care homes who had avoided any deaths in the whole of 2020, reported a cluster of deaths in that first week.[25] Around the world, spikes in cases following vaccine rollout have never been fully explained. Many of the subsequent 'real world' estimates of efficacy have used a model which was even more confusing: rather than excluding cases occurring in the first 21 days, they included them as 'unvaccinated'. Some studies even counted people as unvaccinated until two weeks after their second dose.

Another problem was the overuse of relative risk reduction rather than absolute risk reduction, contrary to the code of practice of the

Association of the British Pharmaceutical Industry (ABPI), the pharmaceutical industry's regulator.[26] Take the early promise of 90% efficacy: for the 80 year old, a 3% risk of death would be reduced to 0.3% giving an absolute risk reduction of 2.7%, which doesn't sound nearly as impressive as the 90% but still might seem worth having if the side effects were say 1 in 10,000. But for the 8-year-old their risk goes from 0.0001% to 0.00001% so the absolute benefit is only 0.00009%. Throw into the mix a 1 in 1,000 risk for a serious adverse event and the child is 1,000 times more likely to suffer an adverse event than to be prevented from dying of Covid-19. Indeed Iceland, which has a child population of only 60,000, had no child die of covid, but when rolling the vaccination programme out to healthy children, saw 100 significant adverse events, eleven of which were severe enough to result in a hospital admission.[27] The MRHA (The Medicines and Healthcare products Regulatory Agency) in its own 'Blue Guide'[28] says *"Advertising which states or implies that a product is "safe" is unacceptable. All medicines have the potential for side-effects and no medicine is completely risk-free..."*. However, the MHRA, the UKHSA and the NHS have all frequently used this term when promoting the use of Covid-19 vaccines. The mantra '*Safe and Effective*' would appear to be less about science and more about propaganda (see chapter 2).

NHS
https://www.nhs.uk › ... › COVID-19 vaccination ⋮

About the COVID-19 vaccine

COVID-19 vaccination is safe and effective. It gives you the best protection against COVID-19.

NHS Propaganda.

Many claims of safety have been based on the billions of doses given worldwide with the assumption that all was well. But the regulatory post-marketing safety signals are largely derived from voluntary reporting systems such as Yellow Cards in the UK, and VAERS in the US. These systems are known to have significant under-reporting.[29] A study from Israel, where diary cards were given out and side-effects actively sought, produced a 1,000 times higher reporting rate than that published by the Israeli Department of Health[30] and similarly high adverse events have been found from health insurance data in Germany.[31] In the US, as many as 1 in 12 children sought medical attention in the 48 hours post vaccination.[32]

Estimations of the risk of myocarditis have been particularly wide, ranging from 1 in 10,000 for young males based on voluntary reporting, up to 1 in 43 for teenagers given diary cards and undergoing blood testing and electrocardiographs on days 1, 3 and 7.[33] The UKHSA has repeatedly described myocarditis post vaccination as 'rare and mild, with recovery in a few days. However, they have made no attempt to verify these claims - routine cardiac MRI scanning of children presenting with palpitations or chest pain has shown significant scarring in the heart muscle in 88% of those studied,[34] a feature known to be a predictor of poor long-term outcomes.[35] Follow-up studies on these children are still not complete, yet the vaccination programme for this age-group was allowed to go ahead.[36]

Natural immunity:

Another aspect of the vaccine rollout which ran counter to basic understanding of immunology, was the question of naturally acquired immunity. In 2020, many statements were made expressing uncertainty about whether or how long natural immunity would last - but of course these questions were all even more applicable to the vaccines. Israel followed a similar vaccine rollout as the UK in terms of starting with the oldest and working downwards but giving priority also to those with specific co-morbidities. One major difference was that initially they excluded those who had already had proven SARS-CoV-2 infection, only giving them a single dose of vaccine once the infection naive members of the population had received their first two doses. This allowed an excellent opportunity to compare subsequent infection rates of those post infection and those following vaccination.[37] A similar study from the US,[38] confirmed that a previous SARS-CoV-2 infection provided excellent immunity, as shown in Figure 1.

As can be seen from the chart, the group most clearly at risk are those whose were neither 'convalescent' nor vaccinated. The next highest rate of infection was seen in those who had never had Covid but who had been vaccinated and the lowest infection rate was in those who had already been infected regardless of their vaccination status. Thus, it is clearly a waste of public money and health service time to vaccinate everyone regardless of their immune status.

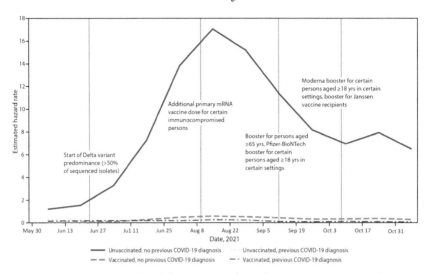

Figure 1. Incident laboratory-confirmed COVID-19–associated hospitalizations among immunologic cohorts defined by vaccination and previous diagnosis histories — California, May 30–November 13, 2021

Moreover, there have been several papers showing that adverse events are higher when vaccinating post infection and this dangerous practice may have contributed to staffing shortages in the health and care sector.[39,40]

Prevention of infection and transmission:

Much of the push to vaccinate children, stemmed from the suggestion that this would help protect older more vulnerable members of their family and the wider community. This is where not only science but also ethics collapsed. When involving children in research, it is required by international law that the treatment or procedure must be potentially for the child's benefit.[41] Moreover, the trials were never designed to look at reduction in infection and it was soon apparent that those with break-through infections had a similar viral load regardless of their vaccination status.[42] Whereas vaccination may give a short term reduction in viral load, this wanes rapidly by 70 days post-dose, but for the unvaccinated and recovered there is a more prolonged effect.[43] But long after it was obvious that the vaccinated were still catching Covid, shrill calls continued for the unvaccinated to be either mandated as in the care and health sector (no jab, no job) or excluded from civilised society, being barred in many countries from theatres, shops or travel or even entering the house of a friend or relative. In Austria, a law was passed to force vaccination on the entire adult population, non-compliance punishable by hefty fines or even imprisonment. At the time of writing, the US will still not allow unvaccinated travellers to enter the country.

For children, NHS advertisements such as this one, are particularly unethical, and reminiscent of the 'Don't Kill Your Granny' calls for masks and distancing.

Figure 2. NHS Kernow advertising for the children's vaccine – Summer 2022

Waning vaccine efficacy and boosters:

As time has gone by, the SARS-CoV-2 virus has undergone innumerable small mutations and new variants have arisen. As with most previous pandemics, the trend has been for new mutations to be more contagious but less virulent - more catching but less severe. The new mRNA technology was much vaunted as allowing easy update to cover new variants but unfortunately for their proponents, immune imprinting has meant that even with a new bivalent vaccine, a more robust antibody response against the original Wuhan strain has occurred with only a lesser response to the new component.[44] One of the vaccines in early production, Valneva, which used an attenuated whole virus i.e. a standard vaccine technology, was hoped to give a broader immunity more akin to naturally acquired immunity, and therefore with more sustained efficacy against new variants. However, whether this promise would have been fulfilled is not known for UK citizens, since the contract was abruptly cancelled with a bizarre statement by the then Health Secretary, Sajid Javid, that it would not have been approved by the MHRA.[45] This was denied by the MHRA, which proceeded to authorise Valneva a few months later but no doses have ever been purchased.

Immune degradation:

It has also been apparent that infection rates are higher in the multiply vaccinated than the unvaccinated.[46,47]

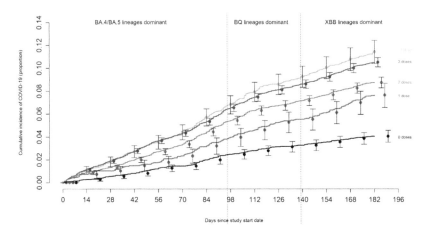

Figure 3. Cumulative incidence of Covid-19 for subjects stratified by the number of Covid-19 vaccine doses previously received.

Waning back to baseline would be disappointing but waning to below baseline, i.e. to a situation where the vaccine appears to have negative efficacy, is much more concerning. This has been accompanied by research on immune response to vaccination, showing a class switch from IgG1 to IgG4.[48,49] It is this immune dysregulation which has been linked to a reported increase in aggressive cancers following repeated doses of vaccine.[50]

Excess deaths:

One area where 'science' seems to be asleep at the wheel, is that of non-covid excess deaths across many countries and most age groups. This phenomenon was first noted in teenage boys in summer 2021 both in the UK[51] and in Austria[52]. The issue was raised in the High Court[53] where a spokesperson for the Office of National Statistics (ONS) agreed that there had been a statistically significant rise in deaths in young men but stated that they were not intending to investigate unless the signal became stronger. They refused to share the raw data as they said it would be 'disclosive'.

Questions have been asked in the House of Commons as long ago as March 2021[54] but have still not received a clear answer. Since that time there have been numerous countries with excess deaths, greater in 2022 than in 2020[55] and a correlation with vaccination uptake particularly of booster doses has been demonstrated.[56,57] Similar trends have been shown between regions in Germany.[58] In UK the deaths are mainly in the category cardiovascular and it was suggested by the Chief Medical Officer that these excess deaths are due to lack of access to health screening and statins. Whilst the likely explanation will be multifactorial, there appears to be no scientific curiosity as to whether vaccines have any role. Indeed, an inquiry into excess neonatal deaths in Scotland, has specifically said that the vaccination status of mothers has not and will not be looked at.[59] Public Health Scotland stated, "Any link to Covid vaccines has been ruled out on the basis of international evidence demonstrating their safety in pregnancy, but PHS confirmed that it had not checked the vaccination status of any of the mothers affected." It stressed that there was no public health basis to do so, and that such an analysis "whilst being uninformative for public health decision making, had the potential to be used to harm vaccine confidence".

The suggestion that an investigation of any role of vaccines might increase 'vaccine hesitancy' is clearly a non-argument. If the outcome of such an investigation showed no link to vaccination status, then surely that should reduce vaccine hesitancy. But if by any chance the vaccines do turn out to have a role in these deaths, then it would be negligent not to act upon such information.

Conclusion:

It has been apparent from early on that there was a concerted international effort to rollout these vaccines, come what may. Drug trials are never large enough to exclude rare but serious side effects and post-marketing surveillance is an essential part of so-called pharmacovigilance. Drugs rushed to market are known to have a greater risk of unexpected adverse outcomes leading to later withdrawal.[60] The Pandemrix vaccine, produced in haste in 2009 for the Swine Flu outbreak, was given to several thousand children in Finland before they observed an increase in the brain injury, narcolepsy, and the drug was withdrawn in Scandinavia. Yet the European Medicines Agency (EMA) continued to recommend its use for several more years before it was finally withdrawn.[61]

Dengerix, under research for prevention of Dengue fever, had promising results in the initial trials, but the Philippines Health Minister decided to roll it out without waiting for the trials 2-year follow-up. Unfortunately for the children of the Philippines, this vaccine caused Antibody Dependent Enhancement (ADE) such that in the next Dengue season, those children who were Dengue-naive and had been vaccinated had a higher death rate than those who were unvaccinated. Six hundred child deaths were investigated although not all would have been vaccine-induced and vaccine confidence plummeted.[62]

The experience with the thrombotic complications seen with AstraZeneca vaccine is another example where the UK regulators were well behind their Scandinavian counterparts. Denmark suspended the vaccine after one death while they investigated. The decision in the UK to limit its use to the over 40s followed two months later, with several more lives lost unnecessarily.

It is thus very concerning to hear Dame June Raine, CEO of the MHRA, stating her pride at transforming the organisation from 'watchdog to enabler'.[63] An aim to get drugs from authorisation application to market in 100 days should fill any scientist with horror. The last three years have not only seen the death of science, but in my view also a terminal decline in medical ethics and humanity.

References: At the end of the book

The Erosion of Trust:
Science in the Age of Covid

Clare Craig

The covid years have impacted dramatically on the public's perception of science and contributed to an erosion of trust in experts and scientists. Various factors have contributed to this decline in trust, including the manipulation of evidence, industry influence, and silencing of particular views. It is important to address these issues to restore faith in the scientific enterprise and promote a more transparent, open, and accountable approach to research. By understanding the root causes of this decline in trust, we can work towards re-establishing a healthier relationship between the scientific community and the public, ultimately fostering a renewed commitment to the pursuit of knowledge.

The scientific method is a systematic process used to investigate, acquire, and expand knowledge through the formulation of a question, followed by the collection of data, analysis, and interpretation of results. The decline of the scientific method has become increasingly apparent as various fields have been plagued by manipulation and political interference. Science is dependent on objectivity, scepticism, and the willingness to change one's mind based on new evidence. It is not compatible with a culture which is politicised or which has faith in certain beliefs regardless of the evidence. In recent years politics and religious-like beliefs have both contributed to the death of science.

The politicisation of science is not a new phenomenon, as evidenced by the historical debate surrounding germ theory 150 years ago. If the debate between germ theorists and miasma proponents had been purely based on the evidence, then passions would not have been raised the way they were. When germ theorists struggled to be heard, they ended up exaggerating their case to the point of denying the possibility of any airborne transmission.[1] A belief was born that all

The Death of Science

infectious disease spread occurs only through close contact. They had evidence that disease was caused by microorganisms. They did not have evidence that disproved the idea that spread could occur through the air – but in their fight to be heard firmly adopted that belief. The consequences of that extreme belief was still impacting public health policy in recent years. Evidence of airborne spread of SARS-CoV-2 was labelled as "misinformation" by the WHO[2] and they did not concede that spread was possible over a long distance until December 2021.[3] By that time the message that risk would be reduced by keeping two metres apart was firmly embedded in the public psyche. This example underscores the danger of allowing political interests to dictate the course of scientific research and the potential damaging and long lasting consequences of doing so.

Furthermore, covid has highlighted how political and religious interests can undermine the integrity of scientific discourse. In many cases, politicians have presented their positions with exaggerated certainty, stifling debate and inquiry. Science relies on a healthy exchange of ideas, challenges, and open discussion, but the highly politicised environment surrounding covid has hindered such discourse. As a result, many scientists have faced attempts to discredit, shame, and even terminate their careers for questioning the wisdom of policy.

Carl Sagan's quote highlights the difference between scientific inquiry and religious dogma[4]: *"In science it often happens that scientists say, 'You know that's a really good argument; my position is mistaken,' and then they would actually change their minds and you never hear that old view from them again. They really do it. It doesn't happen as often as it should, because scientists are human and change is sometimes painful. But it happens every day. I cannot recall the last time something like that happened in politics or religion."*

Religion often promotes unshakeable beliefs with exaggerated certainty, which can impede the pursuit of knowledge. The culture of fear around covid cultivated by government propaganda led many to cling to the comfort of certain beliefs, avoiding any questioning of authority or the need to restructure their thinking. These beliefs included myths that actually increased the fear such as a mistaken understanding of the risk of death and the belief that numerous healthy people could be spreading the infection. As with religions,

181

people adopted ritualised behaviours to afford protection. These created a feedback loop whereby individuals believed that obsessively avoiding touching objects in public, frequent hand sanitising, and mask-wearing were the reasons they had avoided covid infection, even though those living a more normal life also had a low risk of infection. No amount of evidence could shift certain people's beliefs on certain topics. This mentality is antithetical to the spirit of scientific inquiry, which thrives on uncertainty and the willingness to confront and revise one's own beliefs.

Within the field of epidemiology there lies a core belief that the public is ignorant and reckless, unable to comprehend the dangers of exponential spread and prone to alter their behaviour based on reassurance. However, with covid the public demonstrated a willingness to restrict their behaviour well before any official mandates, debunking this long-held assumption. Public health officials are tasked with bridging the gap between science and politics. With covid they ultimately leaned heavily into political narratives, presented to the public with misplaced certainty and undermined the spirit of scientific inquiry.

The credibility of peer-reviewed scientific articles has come under scrutiny in recent years. In 2015, *Lancet* editor Richard Horton stated that perhaps half of the scientific literature might be untrue, suggesting that science had taken a dark turn.[5] Additionally, *Nature* reported that over half of researchers were unwilling or unable to provide raw data supporting their work.[6] This decline in standards was exemplified by the *New England Journal of Medicine's* series arguing that rules about declaring conflicts of interest to stop drug companies influencing doctors were overly strict. This stance led to criticism from three former senior editors, who were shocked by the journal's *"seriously flawed and inflammatory attack"* on dissenting opinions. One of them, Dr. Marcia Angell, said in 2009 *"It is simply no longer possible to believe much of the clinical research that is published, or to rely on the judgment of trusted physicians or authoritative medical guidelines. I take no pleasure in this conclusion, which I reached slowly and reluctantly over my two decades as an editor of the New England Journal of Medicine."*[7]

The result of the conflicts of interests, politicisation and cult-like belief systems on scientific work regarding covid was stark. Not only were certain voices unable to break through the gatekeeping of the editors of scientific journals but some were even prevented from publishing their work in places that are meant to be open to all comers, prior to the peer review process. One such website, medRxiv states that they do not publish *"Works that challenge or could compromise accepted public health measures and advice regarding infectious disease transmission, immunization, and therapy."*[8] Others had work accepted and then removed without explanation or recourse. For example, a paper on the risk of myocarditis in teenage boys by Jessica Rose, a computational biologist experienced in data analytics and Dr Peter McCullough, an eminent US cardiologist was published by *Current Problems in Cardiology* and subsequently withdrawn.[9] There was no scientific basis for this withdrawal and the authors were not even notified.[10] The atmosphere was such that, in order to pass through this gatekeeping, researchers would quote from the scriptures in their conclusions even while what they said contradicted their own results. An almost identical paper was later published reporting the same risk written by other authors more willing to quote the scriptures, saying about the risk to adolescent males, *"This risk should be considered in the context of the benefits of COVID-19 vaccination."*[11]

The most politicised science was that regarding the covid vaccines. The very word "vaccine" has immense power attached to it. Anyone who criticises vaccines is immediately smeared as an "anti-vaxxer," implying both ignorance and being a danger to the public with all the reputational and career damage that comes with that. The covid vaccine was therefore politicised before it even came into existence. There was a binary choice to be an anti-vaxxer or be pro-vaccine. Furthermore, the covid vaccines were introduced in an atmosphere of fear as our only potential for salvation. They were therefore given a messiah-like status. People sang songs about how excited they were to have their appointment, wept as they received it and gave thanks, declaring their allegiance to the new faith through social media banners and branded earrings or even tattoos.

The scientific community failed to remain objective when faced with this onslaught. Whichever way data was presented the outcome could be guessed from the start. One paper on care home vaccination showed that the infection rates fell more in the unvaccinated than the vaccinated and yet concluded that the vaccines were protecting the unvaccinated more than the vaccinated.[12]

A significant factor contributing to the decline of scientific integrity is the pressure to produce positive and groundbreaking results, driven by a desire for academic prestige and media attention and to help compete for funding. This pressure can lead to detrimental practices, such as cherry-picking data, analysing increasingly smaller subgroups to find a desired result, and suppressing negative findings. These practices degrade scientific literature, as they prioritise sensationalism and career advancement over the pursuit of knowledge. This distortion of scientific research is further exacerbated by multiple tactics employed to produce favourable outcomes in vaccine and drug studies, such as selectively reporting results, choosing endpoints that favour positive outcomes, and altering trial designs. The manipulation of scientific research has significant ramifications for public trust and the pursuit of knowledge.

Methods Employed to Manipulate Data in Covid Vaccine Studies

1. Carry out the study when cases are falling

A common tactic employed in covid vaccine studies involves the manipulation of study cohorts to make vaccines appear more effective. By enrolling all participants as unvaccinated at the beginning of a study and transitioning them to the vaccinated group over time, the unvaccinated are exposed to higher prevalence periods and for a longer duration. In contrast, the vaccinated group is only exposed later on, making them less likely to contract covid and giving the illusion that the vaccine is highly effective.

The ONS used this approach to claim a 32-fold lower mortality rate among the vaccinated.[13] This case of extreme data manipulation involved comparing winter disease prevalence in the unvaccinated to summer disease prevalence in the vaccinated, rather than a fairer comparison starting from spring. The Office for Statistics Regulation upheld a complaint regarding the ONS's data manipulation in this instance.[14]

2. Don't include meaningful outcome measures like death

The vaccine clinical trials did not focus on meaningful outcome measures like death. Due to the rarity of death with covid, trials were unable to demonstrate a significant effect on mortality. For instance, in the Pfizer trial with 44,000 participants, only 29 deaths were reported up to the point when the placebo group were themselves vaccinated.[15] Of these 29 deaths, 15 were in the vaccinated group including one of the three covid deaths. There were only 20 severe covid cases reported in the Pfizer submission to the FDA for Emergency Use Authorisation, including those that did not need hospital care.[16] Instead of using outcomes which are hard to distort, the trials relied on test results as the primary outcome measure.

3. Only measure outcomes for part of the time after vaccination

During the initial two weeks following vaccination, individuals may experience an increased risk of covid infection.[17] After infection a person is protected from their naturally acquired immunity. There is therefore potential for a serious bias. Given that only a fraction of the population was susceptible to each variant, the increased risk of infection in the first two weeks after vaccination will lead to many of those who were susceptible being infected and acquiring natural immunity. However, because this period was ignored, the increased infection risk was ignored and the period of protection from acquired immunity was instead measured and described as a success of vaccination.[18]
Scientists repeatedly redefined what "unvaccinated" meant to include the period two weeks or even three weeks after injection.[19] Rather than analysing this period separately it was included as part of the control. There is therefore a double whammy of making the vaccinated appear healthier by removing the period of increased infection risk and making the unvaccinated appear sicker by attributing this period to them. To accurately assess any benefits, it is essential to consider the entire period from the date of injection, including instances where vaccines may cause susceptible individuals to experience infections earlier.

4. Use modelled data

The most reliable scientific papers ensure that the population being studied is representative of the population as a whole. Sometimes that is hard to achieve and adjustments need to be made afterwards to account for any differences e.g. the sample may be younger than the population as a whole. These adjustments are a reasonable thing to do to correct for small problems in the sample.

However, if the sample is so different to the general population that massive adjustments need to be made then effectively the study is no longer based on real world evidence. Instead it has become yet another prediction based on modelled data.

For example, the CDC claimed, contrary to all other evidence, that people with a prior infection were 5 times more likely to become infected than those who had been double vaccinated.[20] The actual results from the study showed a 70% higher rate but their adjustments made this into 500%. There were other serious flaws in the study which makes even the 70% claim highly dubious.

5. Analysing or ignoring subgroups

A classic way to manipulate research results is to divide the population into various subgroups until a subgroup with an interesting finding is discovered. Because there are numerous ways to create these groups eventually a spurious result that was due only to chance will be inevitable.

A conflicting subgroup can be intentionally excluded from analysis. For instance, when assessing vaccination's impact on transmission, heavily vaccinated care home residents were omitted without justification from a PHE study.[21] Real-world household transmission rates[22] were much higher than those reported in the study. The PHE study claimed that only 6% of contacts of the vaccinated were infected and 10% of the unvaccinated whereas the overall figure for the whole population was 12%. That implies that the rates must have been particularly high among the groups who were omitted, especially heavily vaccinated care home residents who were all excluded from the study and for whom understanding transmission rates was highly relevant.

6. Use the wrong dose of the drug

A drug can be discredited in a trial where the protocol is deliberately designed to give a drug at an inappropriate time or dose. For example, the RECOVERY trial was said to show that hydroxychloroquine treatment was not helpful for treating covid[23]. The trial design used a dose of hydroxychloroquine that was in the toxic range and may well have been responsible for the deaths of participants in the treatment arm of the trial. Hydroxychloroquine doses over 1500mg are associated with cardiovascular and neurological side effects, and can be potentially fatal.[24] The trial used a dose of 2000mg in the first 18 hours and 400mg every 12 hours thereafter, meaning the toxic threshold was reached.

Conclusion

The manipulation of evidence during the covid years highlights the need for scientific vigilance, transparency, and integrity. Across research fields, unreliable studies have led to public confusion and diminished trust. The pressure to produce groundbreaking results, industry influence and silencing of particular views contributed to this decline in trust. One important factor was that peer review has taken place in open forums using social media.

The important question is whether this result is necessarily a bad thing. Given that much of the harm that resulted from covid policy had its roots in misplaced trust in scientific authority, a decline in trust in science should be seen as a healthy outcome. Less trust will mean more questioning and more personal responsibility both of which would be beneficial for avoiding errors and making good decisions.

However, a balance needs to be struck. More openness about uncertainty and the challenging of ideas that are inherent in scientific progress will lead to a better public understanding of the scientific process and its limitations. On the other hand, losing too much trust could lead to genuine advances in knowledge being utterly disregarded.

To address these issues, the scientific community should prioritise transparency with open public review, address conflicts of interest and gatekeeping, insist on publishing pre-registration and pre-analysis plans to prevent later manipulation, and encourage replication studies. Scientists and experts should engage with the public more actively, both to dispel misconceptions and to foster an appreciation for the complexities and uncertainties inherent in scientific research. This might involve participating in public forums, contributing to popular media, and working to improve science communication skills within the scientific community.

The decline of trust in science is a multifaceted problem that demands a co-ordinated and concerted effort from researchers, policymakers, and the public alike. By addressing the issues of manipulation, political interference, lack of transparency, and industry influence, the scientific community can work to reestablish a new relationship with the public and reaffirm its commitment to the pursuit of knowledge. Only through a reinvigorated scientific enterprise can we continue to advance our understanding of the world and address the myriad challenges that lie ahead.

References: At the end of the book

Chapter 14

Other medical services
suffering from a lack of science

The Editors

The NHS in the UK suffers from a lack of finance at the provision level and this is reflected in the service provided. Most areas are suffering but several have been in the news recently. As to be expected the science suffers along with the service.

Maternity Services

The recent obstetrics scandal in Shrewsbury is another medical scandal. Catastrophic failures at the NHS trust may have led to the deaths of more than 200 babies, nine mothers and left other infants with life-changing injuries.[1]

There has nationally been a mistaken belief that midwives should be in charge of deliveries until there is an emergency, at which point the obstetrician might be called in. This is a cheaper way of providing obstetric services but does result in an infant mortality rate twice that of Sweden. Obviously putting obstetricians in charge of every delivery would be more expensive but that is the price of progress. Even normal deliveries are hazardous and waiting until the last minute, cutting down on ultrasound scans and relying on under-trained midwives will always lead to a bad result.

Co-editor PRG's own experiences with obstetric services some forty years ago in the South West showed him that the Shrewsbury scandal is not an isolated problem. Recently he spoke to someone who had the same problems in maternity services locally that PRG had noted all those decades ago. There had been no discernible improvement.

"Senior midwife Donna Ockenden examined maternity practices at Shrewsbury and Telford NHS Trust (SaTH) over 20 years."

Ockenden's report was precisely what was needed in contradistinction to that of Ian Kennedy, who had no clinical experience but plenty of prejudice. (See Chapter 3).

Ockenden reported:[2]

- A culture where mistakes were not investigated and a failure of external scrutiny
- Parents were not listened to when they raised concerns about the care they received
- Where cases were examined, responses were described as lacking "transparency and honesty"
- The trust failed to learn from its mistakes, leading to repeated and almost identical failures
- A culture of bullying, anxiety and fear of speaking out among staff at the trust "that persisted to the current time"
- Caesarean sections were discouraged, often leading to poor outcomes

All except the last point could be levelled at any or all of the recent problems in the NHS. Like a psychopath the NHS does not learn from its mistakes and has no desire to do so.

Similar problems with maternity services have recently surfaced at East Kent hospitals University NHS trust.[3]

'This cannot go on': NHS maternity care report's author calls for fresh approach

Expert behind study into East Kent hospitals university NHS trust speaks out ahead of publication

Search | The Guardian | UK edition | News website of the year

The Daily Telegraph[4] on 20/10/22 reported on the Care Quality Commission (CQC) findings that more than half the maternity units in England failed on safety. The CQC had deep concern about the quality of care. Here is a bit more from the BBC's coverage of the Ockenden report: *"Ms Ockenden had earlier said staff were frightened to speak out about failings amid "a culture of undermining and bullying", with staff advised by trust managers not to take part in a "staff voices" initiative set up to assist the investigation into what went wrong."*

Why is the NHS in a parlous state?

In 2008 PRG wrote a book about the NHS[5]: *The history of medicine, money and politics.* It was subtitled *Riding the rollercoaster of state medicine.* In the book he detailed the rise and fall of the NHS and why it is in such a parlous condition. In particular he drew attention to the

Salmon report (implementation in Wilsons' era) which shifted experienced nurses off the wards into unnecessary management roles, the burgeoning of management under Thatcher and the sell-off to the private sector via Private Finance Initiatives (PFIs) under Blair and Brown. Subsequent governments have failed to reverse this decline mostly because the power of the managers has become entrenched and the clinical staff, previously able to control their own work pattern, have lost the ability to manage the system.

When PRG's book was published it hit a chord with the public. On a radio phone-in programme numerous NHS staff put in their say, agreeing with him, but would not give their names in case they were disciplined *"For bringing the NHS into disrepute."* As if it is not the NHS's own actions that are bringing it into disrepute!

A letter in the Daily Telegraph from Dr Hilary Aitken[6] highlights the problem of burgeoning management and the fact that nobody on the clinical side can understand what the managers have been employed to do: *"....unintelligible job titles such as "Hard FM Commissioning Manager" or "Portfolio Lead for People-Led care.."*

A colleague remembers the time when he was invited to a research meeting on colorectal cancer. He, as a radiologist, had been instrumental in diagnosing such cancer for decades and ran the very frequent multi-disciplinary meetings involving the surgeons, pathologists, radiologists, nurses and other team members on the same subject. At the new meeting a young woman introduced herself as being the manager in charge of diagnosis and treatment of colorectal cancer for the colleague's Trust. Needless to say the colleague had never seen this woman at any of the many multi-disciplinary meetings but it turned out that she had been in post for over a year but *"had not really started the research yet"*.

It is even worse now as many such managers are permitted to work from home. Many managers have been appointed to sinecure posts, do no useful work and take significant salaries. Meanwhile the number of clinical posts is carefully restricted and the clinical staff are overworked.

As Dr Hilary Aitken continued in his letter:

"The NHS could save a lot of money by recruiting a group of averagely intelligent 12-year-olds. If you can't explain to them in a sentence or two what your job entails, you are out."

Psychology, Psychotherapy, Psychiatry, Neurology and Neurosurgery

Mental Health Services from the NHS are in trouble. The Care Quality Commission (CQC) has just published its annual report (27/10/2022). According to Medscape: [7] *'This year's survey includes responses from 13,418 people who received treatment for a mental health condition in England between September 1 and November 30, 2021, using NHS community mental health services. The results showed just under one quarter (22%) of people did not get the help they needed from crisis care services, 4 in 10 (40%) said they had not had a care review meeting in the past 12 months, and less than half (47%) reported that they 'definitely' got the help they needed.'*

Just as we have argued that obstetrics and midwifery are just one subject and should be combined it is also possible to contend that Psychology, Psychotherapy, Psychiatry, Neurosciences, Neurology and Neurosurgery are all part of a continuity. The mind exists within the brain and the brain is a physical object made of elements and functioning due to movement of electrical waves and chemical transmitters. Advanced electrophysiology and imaging using CT, MRI MRS and PET scanning are enabling the functioning of the brain to be examined in increasingly complex detail.

Some of the ingrained ideas of each of the overlapping specialties have been shown to be highly inaccurate. It is now possible to say that all psychiatrists should have training in neurology and all neurologists require instruction in psychiatry. Moreover it is clear that many of the older practices in psychotherapy are not based on science. Recently some of the newer techniques, such as mindfulness and and cognitive behavioural therapy, have been taken away from their clinical context and are being taught to schoolchildren. The rationale behind this has been that it will make the children more resilient against mental illness, a very laudable aim. In practice it seems, sometimes, to do the opposite. Focussing on negative thoughts can be harmful and psychotherapeutic techniques taken out of clinical control need careful monitoring to check whether they are doing more harm than good.[8]

The next chapter looks at psychopharmacology through the eyes of Professor Nutt. We shall let him take up the story.

References: At the end of the book

Chapter 15

Drugs and drug policy

How politics trumped science to the detriment of patients

Professor David Nutt

Background

I am a psychiatrist and currently professor of Neuropsycho-pharmacology at Imperial College London where I have worked for the past 14 years. In 2016, having run a national centre for psychopharmacology for some years I retired from the NHS. This was largely due to the burden of administration and bureaucracy that limited my ability to treat my patients with optimal – as opposed to licensed – medicines. I vividly recall one chief executive asking me why my pharmacy bill was so high. I replied that I was a psychopharmacologist i.e. I used drugs to treat my patients. He asked why couldn't I ask the GPs to do the prescribing and I replied "Because most of what I prescribe is off-licence". He went pale and asked if that was allowed to which I replied "I believe the role of an academic doctor is to prescribe off-licence as that is the only way we can get new ideas of how to treat other disorders".

In my professional career I have made significant insights from off-label prescribing that have changed medical practice. For example, when at the university of Bristol I pioneered the use of SSRIs that had just been introduced as antidepressants to treat anxiety disorders. These are now the NICE-preferred medicine for these disorders, supplanting the benzodiazepines for reasons of efficacy and safety. Also when at Bristol we pioneered the use of the benzodiazepine antagonist flumazenil to treat withdrawal from alcohol and other drugs, a use then commercialised by the company Hythiam. I also when at Bristol conducted the first UK trial of the opioid mu receptor agonist buprenorphine as a safer alternative to methadone.

Retiring from the NHS I was re-employed half-time at Imperial College but this freed me up to explore other pharmacological avenues and now I have part-time appointments as a research officer in two companies – GABA Labs that is developing a less-harmful alternative to alcohol and Awakn Life Sciences that is developing new treatments for addiction and depression and currently proving ketamine therapy for these disorders. I also set up a UK charity Drug Science for which I am still a trustee and head of research, that tells the truth about drugs – and chair a European psychedelic policy group called PAREA - but more on these later.

Research career

You will by now have guessed that the main focus of my interest is pharmacology. I used to use drugs as medicines to treat my patients and also to use drugs to explore the actions of the brain (note - I am no longer clinically registered). The latter has often fed back into clinical utility. My tongue-in-cheek claim to fame is that I have given more different classes of drugs to humans than anyone else ever. As yet this claim has not been contested, though perhaps the fact is more due to having been in the field for nearly 50 years than a special ability.

At 10 I knew I was going to be a scientist and by 15 I wanted to be a brain researcher. To pursue this career plan I studied medicine at Cambridge and then Guy's hospital largely because I saw it as a useful step in my desired career path of human research. It turned out to be necessary rather than useful as I would not have been able to take responsibility for all the hundreds of studies I have done since without that medical oversight. But also and rather unexpectedly I discovered that I really enjoyed being a doctor as well as a researcher. My patients taught me a lot about the human condition and of course raised important questions about how we might improve their treatments. The interplay between research and clinical treatment is critical to develop ideas and evaluate theories. Sadly as described in other chapters in this book it has been largely eroded, to everyone's detriment.

My move into psychiatry came after a couple of terms as a neurology SHO at Guys and St Mary's hospitals which made it clear to me that the psychological side of brain function was considerably more interesting than the neuro side. So I switched to psychiatry first at Guys then to Oxford where I was extraordinarily lucky to obtain a research position at the MRC unit of clinical pharmacology under Prof David Grahame-

The Death of Science

Smith and Dr Richard Green. In those days the current animal research regulations were not so bureaucratic and delaying so we were able to change research directions quickly and with agility to follow up new avenues. My goal was to use rodent models to find a less invasive alternative treatment to ECT. This led me to using gamma-aminobutyric acid (GABA) receptor antagonists to produce therapeutic seizures, but as part of this process I had to validate their efficacy. In doing this I used them against a series of GABA agonist drugs including benzodiazepines and alcohol.

These studies led to several *Nature* papers and also my discovering that the GABA receptor antagonist bicuculline could sober-up a rat intoxicated with ethanol. I clearly remember rushing into Prof Grahame-Smith telling him I had made this earth-shattering discovery – an alcohol antidote. My flight to Stockholm to collect the Nobel prize was in my mind when he said "What's the use of that?".

"Er," I stuttered "Well perhaps you could find your way home when drunk more easily, remember what you did on a night out – etc."

"Yes," he replied. "But the alcohol will still rot your liver heart and brain – and it might be that it would encourage people to even drink more?" The dream of fame and greatness popped and I went back to proper research.

However this was the first discovery that a selective GABA antagonist could reverse the effects of alcohol, and fuelled others research into alcohol and GABA. Now forty years later my company GABA Labs has turned this research into products. We are using GABA promoting drugs and botanicals to mimic the relaxing and sociability effects of alcohol in drinks like Sentia that offer a safer alternative to ethanol.

Policy engagement

It was my psychopharmacology research portfolio that got me into the policy arena, that eventually twenty years later led to my becoming chair of the Advisory Council on the Misuse of Drugs (ACMD) and then being the first chair of this committee to be sacked! In the late 1980s I returned from a two year stint in the USA running their in-patient alcohol research ward at the NIH in Washington DC and started my research unit at Bristol university. We worked on opioids and antidepressants and related drugs so when the first wave of concerns regarding MDMA [ecstasy] developed I was asked to join the

195

Home Office expert group led by Prof Grahame-Smith. Strangely that group probably did more good to reduce drug harms than any I have served on subsequently. When it became clear that MDMA deaths were being caused by dehydration-induced hyperthermia we recommended that all venues must serve water for free. The government made this a law which is why today you can get fresh tap water in all hospitality venues. We also recommended all dance clubs had chill-out rooms and though this was not made a legal requirement many did set them up. Together these two simple measures virtually eliminated deaths from MDMA in the UK. All was well until the 2000s when the UN decided that as MDMA use hadn't declined since they banned it they tried to reduce its supply by stepping in with a ban on safrole – a natural product that is the main precursor of MDMA . This led to a massive increase in deaths for two reasons. The first was that the underground chemists switched from safrole to anethole. This didn't make MDMA instead it made PMA a chemically similar but much more toxic compound that was sold as MDMA and killed hundreds of people in the UK. Then after a few years the underground chemists worked out how to make a synthetic alternative to safrole, which turned out to be a lot cheaper so allowing 200-400 mg MDMA pills to be made for the same price as the older 50mg ones. Now we even have 1gm bags of crystal MDMA being sold. These super strength products now dominate the market, and are more toxic, which is why deaths from MDMA have now risen to record levels.

I think this gentle sortie into the policy arena led to my being co-opted on the Runciman committee as the clinical expert. This first systematic and independent review of drug laws since the first Misuse of Drugs Act was put into place in 1971. This committee was full of remarkably talented people such as Simon Jenkins and the philosopher Bernard Williams but not least was Ruth Runciman the chair, who was an exceptional woman. Ruth had served on the ACMD when the AIDS epidemic was fulminating and was the person who had persuaded the Prime Minister Margaret Thatcher to allow needle exchange programmes in the UK. This changed the whole trajectory of HIV infections in the UK and as result of needle exchange we became a world leader in AIDS harm reduction. Our report was ground-breaking in suggesting major reforms to the drug laws with a focus on treatment rather than punishment. We also recommended the downgrading of all cannabis products to Class C. It received lots of favourable press, even from the right wing media, and a couple of years later cannabis was indeed downgraded – though for just a few years. From being the clinician on the Runciman committee I was invited to join the ACMD as chair of their technical committee, the group that decides on the harms of drugs, if these are sufficient to warrant control under the Misuse of Drugs Act (MDAct)1971 and if so what Class or Schedule they should be put in. At my introductory meeting I had been horrified by the lack of systematic analysis of the harms of drugs that were being discussed so I made it a condition of my taking in the role that we would use a new 9 point scale of harm that I had developed for the Runciman review. The Home Office agreed and the civil servants in the section were enthusiastic. Over the next 15 or so meetings spanning 5 years we slowly worked our way through most of the major drugs of concern, including legal ones such as alcohol, tobacco, nitrous oxide and solvents. Then we asked the addiction psychiatry section of the Royal College of Psychiatrists to do the same by a written questionnaire. The results were very concordant so, after a great deal of hostility from referees, the editor agreed it was important so it was published in *The Lancet* in 2007. The results are shown in figure 1.

Figure 1. *The 2007 Lancet paper on drug harms Nutt King Blakemore: Developing a rational scale to assess the harms of drugs.*[1]

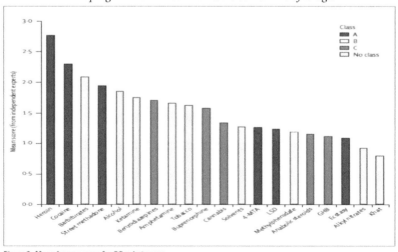

Figure 1: Mean harm scores for 20 substances
Classification under the Misuse of Drugs Act, where appropriate, is shown by the colour of each bar

It received a lot of press especially as it showed no relationship between the harms of a drug and its position – or not – in the MDAct1971. The anti-tobacco brigade complained that tobacco should have been rated the most harmful because it killed the most people. We argued that deaths were not the only harms and drugs like alcohol and heroin scored higher because of their much larger social and familial impact. The most important input came from Prof Larry Phillips of the LSE who wrote to me saying that we had done a good job but could do a better one if we used a new technique called MCDA - multi-criteria decision analysis. This approach had been used by the government with success in determining the best way to deal with the complex issue of nuclear waste where social concerns as well as scientific issues had to be taken into account. Drug harm assessment was similarly complex as it includes harm to people who use drugs and harm to their families and wider society. Larry and I (on behalf of the ACMD of which I was by then the Chair) had a meeting with the head of the MRC – Colin Blakemore and it was agreed to do this. Funds were pooled from MRC and the Home Office and a decision conference was held over one weekend in an isolated country hotel using the full complement of the ACMD committee – experts ranging from forensic scientists to schoolteachers by way of addiction specialists, lawyers, police and sociologists.

At the meeting we agreed that there were 16 ways drugs could do harm. Nine of these were to the user and seven to other people or society – see table 1. We then defined each of these for consistency of decision making in future assessments.

Table 1 – the sixteen harms of drugs

Harms to users

1. Drug-specific mortality
2. Drug-related mortality
3. Drug-specific harms
4. Drug-related harms
5. Dependence
6. Drug-specific impairment of mental functioning
7. Drug-related impairment of mental functioning
8. Loss of tangibles
9. Loss of relationships

Harms to others

1. Injury
2. Crime
3. Economic cost
4. Impact on family life
5. International damage
6. Environmental damage
7. Decline in reputation of the community

But the ACMD never put them into practice because I was sacked shortly after the meeting. This came as a result of a lecture I gave at Kings College London in which I argued the drug laws were not only **not** evidence based but in many cases did more harm than good. The BBC picked up my comments and on the Today programme I was grilled about this. When I said that alcohol was the most harmful drug in the UK and was definitely more harmful than cannabis or LSD the world went mad. I was all over the newspapers in the UK and globally and was viciously attacked by most of the right-wing media. The next day the Home Secretary Alan Johnson sacked me. He said as the chief advisor on drugs I should not lobby against government policies. I replied that, as a scientist contracted to advise the government on the harmful effects of drugs, not to tell them the truth about comparative drug harms would be unethical. Of course the real reason he sacked me was that the 2010 election was looming and New Labour wanted to appear tougher on drugs than the Tory opposition.

Luckily my replacement as ACMD chair – a previous tutor of mine from Cambridge – Prof Les Iverson was able to persuade the Home Office to make the MCDA process available on the government websites and it is now used by the ACMD as the backbone of their decision making processes. [2]

Within a few days of my sacking a philanthropist Toby Jackson had emailed and offered to fund me to set up an independent version of the ACMD to tell the truth about drugs free from political interference or threat. I accepted with delight and alacrity and formed the charity that is now called Drug Science. This has grown from strength to strength over the past decade and now is self-funded and has huge international following due to our prodigious scientific output. The most significant of our many publications is *The Lancet* 2010 assessment of drug harms, see fig 2. [3] This has now been cited over 2000 times and has become a meme for drug harms. Since then similar reviews of the same twenty drugs using an identical MCDA process by independent experts from Europe and Australia found almost identical results. They all came to the result that alcohol was the most harmful drug of all, largely because of the massive social harms in all these western jurisdictions. In terms of harms to users alcohol isn't the most harmful – that's either crack cocaine or methamphetamine. One clear conclusion is that the drug laws and the UN Conventions on intoxication drug control bear no relation to the actual harms of drugs. This means they are unjust and, given that in many countries the death penalty can be applied for some drugs less harmful than alcohol, immoral. In fact the clear conclusion from this research is that drug laws are largely based on moral opinions or political machinations and not on estimates of true harms.

Figure 2 MCDA analysis of drug harm

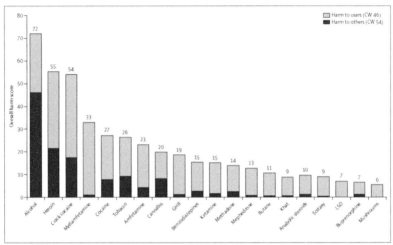

Figure 2: Drugs ordered by their overall harm scores, showing the separate contributions to the overall scores of harms to users and harm to others
The weights after normalisation (0–100) are shown in the key (cumulative in the sense of the sum of all the normalised weights for all the criteria to users, 46; and for all the criteria to others, 54). CW=cumulative weight. GHB=γ hydroxybutyric acid. LSD=lysergic acid diethylamide.

Nutt DJ King LA Phillips LD (2010) Drug harms in the UK: a multicriteria decision analysis Lancet 376: 1558-66 DOI: 10.1016/S0140-6736(10)61462-6

One lesser discussed aspect of this fundamental flaw in drug control policies is that it has dramatically impeded research, especially with psychedelics such as LSD and psilocybin. These were put into the most severely controlled Schedules of the UN Conventions along with drugs such as crack cocaine on the grounds that they were very harmful (the graph above shows they are not) addictive (they can be used to treat addictions) and of no medical value (which given that over 40,000 patients had been treated with them before the ban was a deliberate falsehood). Schedule 1 drugs are almost impossible to research because government's will not fund research with them on the claim that this might encourage recreational use. And if you were able to get philanthropic funding the national regulatory authorities such as the

DEA in the USA and Home Office in the UK made it very difficult to get permissions to use them. This led to a massive fall off in research - (see figure 3) making it the worse censorship of research in the history of the modern world.[4]

Figure 3

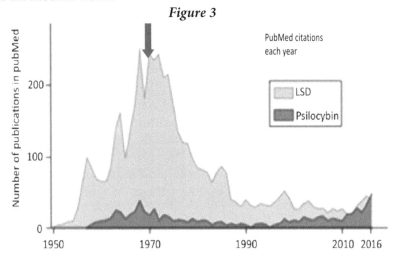

Kyzar et al 2017 TIPS

Impact of the 1971 UN Psychotropics Convention on psychedelic research

In the past decade this censorship has been reversed by research groups in the UK and USA with remarkable outcomes. Our team has explored the brain mechanisms of a range of psychedelics and discovered that they all produce a state of disorganised brain activity that has been called the entropic brain state. This state explains the hallucinations and altered consciousness produced by psychedelics. It also led us to trial psilocybin for the treatment of depression because we believed the trip could disrupt the ruminative thought processes that characterise this mental illness. We found that a single psilocybin trip markedly improved depressed mood in people with treatment-resistant depression who had failed on at least 2 antidepressant medicines and also on CBT. This paper spawned a massive surge of interest in this approach and a large number of small pharmaceutical companies were set up to pursue this approach with psilocybin and other psychedelics. Our findings have now been replicated by a multi-centre dose-finding clinical trial run by COMPASSPathways and they are now moving into a phase 3 trial. [5]

Smaller trials have also revealed psychedelics to have therapeutic utility in alcohol and tobacco addictions, OCD and anorexia. The common thread in these disorders is a state of inwardly focused thinking loops that the patient often knows are maladaptive but which they cannot stop. Psychedelics disrupt these loops and make the brain more flexible after just a single trip. This is a totally new paradigm in mental illness treatments, that we predict will invigorate the field of psychiatry because there has been so little innovation in treatment for half a century. The drugs we use today all work in the same way as the first ones discovered by serendipity in the 1950s, though they have less adverse effects and are less toxic in overdose. Psychedelics work in a totally different way so offering the many patients who fail on conventional treatments new hope. The pity is that these could have been used since their first introduction in the 1950s if only our drug laws had been based on evidence not politics.

References at the end of the book

Nutrition

The Editors

There are few areas that promote themselves as scientific yet show little adherence to science that are quite so blatant as that of nutrition. We are afflicted with advice about our diets coming at us from a multitude of directions. The fact that the advice is so conflicting does tend to undermine the outstanding claims that are made.

The history of nutritional science

People with curiosity must have realised that food and drink are essential for health and growth way back in the mists of time but nutritional science did not really get underway until the alchemists became chemists and started doing some useful research.

The 'chemical revolution' partly occurred just before the French Revolution near the end of the 18th century. For example Claude Berthollet in 1785 found that the vapour that came from decomposing animal matter was ammonia, and that this gas was composed of three volumes of hydrogen and one volume of nitrogen, or around 17% hydrogen and 83% nitrogen by weight. [1]

Antoine Lavoisier, also had an interest in metabolism. With the help of his assistant Armand Seguin, he measured human respiratory output of carbon dioxide both at rest and when lifting weights, and showed how it increased with activity.

François Magendie went on to discover, via experiments on dogs, that a diet consisting of a single component such as sugar, olive oil, gum or butter, could not sustain life for more than a few weeks.[2] Magendie realised that a diversity of foods was a necessity for health.

The dogma was that proteins, carbohydrates, fats, and minerals were the only necessities in the diet. This was shown to be incorrect by the discovery of vitamins. *"Clinicians soon recognized scurvy, beriberi, rickets, pellagra, and xerophthalmia as specific vitamin deficiencies."* [3]

The need for an anti-scurvy component had been identified by James Lind as far back as 1746 *"He took 12 sailors, all with a similar severity of the disease, divided them into pairs and, for 2 wk, gave each pair one of the many treatments that had been recommended for the condition. …. the pair receiving lemons and oranges were almost recovered after only 6 d, whereas those receiving either dilute sulfuric acid or vinegar had shown no improvement after 2 wk."* [1,4]

Other vitamins were discovered during the 19th and early 20th centuries.

One hundred years ago fat was considered to be useful only as an alternative to carbohydrates for the provision of energy. However in 1929 and 1930 George and Mildred Burr demonstrated that some of the fatty acids were necessary for health[5]. The Burr's work *"led them to identify polyunsaturated fatty acids"* [6] as essential components of the diet of rats, (and later, the diet of human beings). These are called the essential fatty acids.

Norman Salem Jr. says *"that modern nutritional biochemists can learn a lesson from the Burrs' experimental procedures. By keeping the diet very simple and repurifying the proteins and sugars, the Burrs invented the whole approach of how to exclude fat from the diet. It is a mistake people still make today."* [6]

Peculiar Diets

There is still important work to do in nutritional science. For example Philip Cowen (Oxford University)[7] has been doing good work showing that altering the relative amino acid balance in proteins can alter the mood of patients. He does, however, point out that such diets are not particularly palatable.

John Tarlton, Bristol,[8] has shown that increasing the proportion of omega-3 (n-3) polyunsaturated fatty acids compared with omega-6 can slow the development of osteoarthritis. The work was done in guinea pigs but is highly likely to be applicable to human beings explaining the benefit of oily fish in one's diet!

However many peculiar diets are being suggested all the time without any reference to good science. There is a very strong vegetarian lobby on the grounds of cruelty to animals and the argument that it has a "lower carbon footprint". Even more extreme is the vegan diet that eschews any animal product, such as milk, butter, or eggs. Some vegans even refuse honey because it has been stolen from the bees.

A vegan diet usually does, however, necessitate the addition of supplements since such diets are not natural for human beings, a species which evolved on an omnivorous diet. Vitamins must be added, particularly D3 and B12, and omega-3 fatty acids. Vitamin D3 can be extracted from fish oils but the *synthesis* of Vitamin D is a multistage process, usually starting with lanolin from greasy sheep's wool! The alternative more vegan approach is to start with extracts from lichen. Vitamin D2, found in plants, is not so useful.

An alternative touted for the future is that of lab grown meat. Apart from being an exceedingly expensive and time consuming method of creating food there is no evidence that it is really safe in the long term. Growing animal cells to create fake meat does require the slaughter of animals in the first place and the "meat" is grown in foetal bovine serum. The cells grown have to be abnormal, pre-cancerous or cancerous or they will not divide sufficiently.

In contrast "meat only" diets are also being pushed. It is possible to live on such diets although undercooked (i.e. rare) meat is necessary with a "meat only" diet in order to obtain vitamin C. Some meats, such as rabbit, do not contain sufficient fats and a "rabbit only" diet would rapidly lead to death. Similarly caribou (reindeer) at certain times of year are too lean and the Inuit people in Canada knew that they had to have a store of fat-laden caribou to get them through the winter as the starving caribou would not provide enough fat.

The drive for a low fat diet was pushed in the 1980s and 1990s by the sugar lobby in the USA and UK rather than cutting back on sugar and other carbohydrate intake. In reality it is easier to limit intake of calories if fat is included since it appears to satisfy the hunger drive where carbohydrates do not. So eating fat does not necessarily make you fat since it can reduce your desire to eat more food.

Recently there has been a very big drive to reduce sugar in drinks. This has been accomplished by replacing the sugar and additives that contain sugars (such as apple extract added to cranberry juice) with artificial sweeteners. The most common of these sweeteners is aspartame. This substance has been shown by research to be linked to serious health problems including cancer, cardiovascular disease and neurological problems.[9,10] It can also, by altering the gut flora, lead to weight gain and diabetes making it highly dubious for it to be included in products labelled as "diet" drinks.

Another similar product is Erythritol. This is an alcohol based sugar substitute found, in small amounts, in natural foods such as pears and grapes. It is used as a 'natural sweetener' and sugar replacement in foods and drinks. Unfortunately it increases stickiness of platelets leading to an increased risk of heart attacks and strokes.[11]

The significance of trace elements has not been completely elucidated but research does show that people living in areas supplied by "hard" water have better cardiovascular health than people in areas with "soft" water. This may be related to calcium and magnesium levels.[12] Yet a search on the internet for the health benefits of water filters will immediately yield many advertisements suggesting that they are beneficial. Who is right?

Body Mass Index

The dangers of obesity were discussed earlier in the book. Whilst it is clear that morbid obesity is highly dangerous it is not so clear where to draw the line with slightly overweight people. The Body Mass Index, (BMI) is defined as the body mass divided by the square of the body height, and is expressed in units of kg/m2, resulting from mass in kilograms and height in metres. Major adult BMI classifications are underweight (under 18.5 kg/m2), normal weight (18.5 to 24.9), overweight (25 to 29.9), and obese (30 or more).[13]

However, though this is frequently used by physicians, it is highly inaccurate. A very muscly man might easily exceed a BMI of 30 and be classified as obese when he is healthy and has little fat. Certainly the range of 25 to 30, classified as overweight, does not seem to relate to any good research. Clare Wilson[14] states it was *"cemented into medical orthodoxy by a report of the WHO in 1997"*. In fact research since then has shown that in people over eighty years of age it is healthier to be in the 25 to 30 range than in the 18.5 to 24 range. Being underweight can be far more dangerous than being slightly overweight. Elderly men who lose more than 10% of their bodyweight are almost three times more likely to die in the next few years than those who do not lose weight and similarly women who lose the same percentage of body mass are more than twice as likely to perish.[15]

Chapter 17

Medical Training and the NHS

The value of research in Medical Training (and recent loss of this experience)   *Dr. Nabil Jarad*

Editorial Comment: *The Editors*
Dr Jarad, the author of this chapter, is a very esteemed respiratory physician. In the chapter he looks at the way in which research during medical training helped his progress and considerably aided the patients. He describes how this has changed in recent years such that it is no longer *de rigeur* for consultants to do research. He explains how being an active researcher helped him, helped the NHS and helped the patients. He also discusses how the latest training does not encourage research and talks about the inevitable lack of understanding of the techniques involved, the diminishment of the medical staff and the sad loss to the science of medicine.

Medical Training
Dr. Nabil Jarad

Summary:
In my consultant interview, I was asked whether doing research in more than one area in respiratory medicine was *"A strength or a weakness?"*. I regarded it as a strength. I had worked for and with people of many intellectual capabilities, but with different clinical interests. I decided to make the most of the fields I worked in.

The majority of the specialist trainee registrars (SpRs) in the South West region of England do not aspire to do an academic degree. At one point, training committees even tried to put a break on the number of SpRs wishing to have an out of programme experience for research, for the fear of this creating gaps in the service rotas.

Training committees are nowadays populated by consultants who are research inactive. In the present day it is not unusual that, even in central hospitals, academic medicine does not exist.

The reason I have always been confronted with is *"lack of time for research."* This is partially true but does not represent all the facts.

The Death of Science

There are many disincentives to doing academic work. I did not advance my academic status beyond the level of honorary senior lecturer. However I was the only person in a large department in a major teaching hospital who put in the kind of academic effort which I shall now describe. In this chapter I seek to present my own research experience in several areas of respiratory medicine while being a clinician. Doing, presenting, and writing up research was a source of satisfaction and a source of fun. To ignore academic endeavour and not do any research is, in my view, a loss of intellectual capabilities inherent in being doctors in an advanced civilisation.

Opportunities and tools:

This is how it came to pass! My career took me to know and to work in many areas in respiratory medicine at a great depth. In July 1987, I received the Diploma in Respiratory Medicine from London University after spending a year at the Brompton Hospital and the London Chest Hospital. [figure 1].

Figure 1
Dr. Jarad Receiving a Diploma in Respiratory Medicine in 1988 from Professor Margaret Turner Warwick and Professor Margaret Hodson

The diploma course was a stimulating mixture of tutorials, ward rounds, outpatient clinics, and joining radiology sessions and physiology sessions. The teachers in the course were worldwide renowned respiratory physicians. Their teaching, their clinics and their ward rounds were remarkably interesting.

However, the highlight of the course was in attending the weekly teaching grand round which used to be held at the surprisingly modest tutorial room of the Brompton Hospital. The one-hour session was divided into case presentations and a plenary session including a rendition of research projects which were presented ahead of their publication.

I had decided to go into formal research to achieve an academic degree. I was guided by the late Professor Margaret Turner-Warwick, Professor Duncan Empey and particularly by the guidance of Dr Robin Rudd to do my research at the East London Part of the Hospital (London Chest Hospital) under the supervision of Dr Rudd.

Ahead of this step, I had asked for a guidance meeting from the Dean of the institute. In my longer than planned meetings with her, Professor Turner-Warwick was clear that striving for a PhD would be far preferable than doing an MD owing to the international grandeur of the PhD degree. MD, which is a postgraduate academic degree in the UK, is in fact the graduation medical degree in most countries in the world including the United States. Professor Turner-Warwick had done an MD, but noticing the less than impressive reaction to her degree, especially from American counterparts, she felt that she had to do a PhD also. So she did! In 1993, I was awarded a Doctor of Philosophy (PhD) from London University for a thesis prepared at the Cardiothoracic Institute (now Imperial College). The topic of thesis was *"Structural and Immunogenetic Aspects of Asbestos-Induced Lung Disease"*. The research was done under the guidance and supervision of Dr Robin Rudd. In preparation for the PhD I met, studied, and cared for a large population of asbestos workers attending clinics and wards at the London Chest Hospital in East London. I also needed to know the British approach to respiratory medicine. So, I was engaged in many general respiratory clinics.

I now realise that completing the PhD was only one benefit from doing research. Getting the skills in designing clinical research, getting proficiency in clinical statistics and obtaining boldness in trialling new drugs and new medical devices were the main benefits which have lasted throughout my career. Understanding the pitfalls and problems in preparing, undertaking and writing research enabled me to better appreciate and critique other researchers' published works.

Adding to that, spending three and a half years at the London Chest Hospital and the Brompton Hospital working with outstanding mentors and colleagues offered another once in a lifetime experience, and helped forging personal and professional relationships with international figures that has continued.

Figure 2
The London Chest Hospital

Collateral Benefits of Research

During my work on the thesis, I became interested and proficient in other related areas:

Lung sound analysis

I contributed to the development of a system to visualise and analyse lung sounds. I did so in collaboration with a biochemical engineer, Mr Ronald Logan Sinclair, and in particular under the guidance of Dr Robin Rudd. Visualising lung sound waves gave the opportunity to expand understanding of how changes in lung structures would result in changes of lung sounds.

Over the intervening years, I was asked to write a multimedia editorial on lung sound analysis in different lung diseases. I also supervised the production of an online tutorial for medical students at Bristol University. Latterly, BBC-Bristol invited me to take part with a group of scientists focussing on the effect of the sounds around us (not only in medicine) in our day to day life. This culminated in the production of the series *"The Listeners"* (Figure 3).

Figure 3. The advert for "The Listener" on BBC 4 (2016). Lung sounds being representers of lung pathology was highlighted, side by side as the sounds of high waves in troubled sea environments, birds sounds and other ambient sounds...

https://www.bbc.co.uk/programmes/b04dgrbc

210

The reward from my research was extensive. I had attained a PhD from one of the best UK institutions. Every chapter written in the PhD thesis was published in *Thorax, Respiratory Medicine* and the *British Journal of Industrial Medicine.*

I made friends with notable colleagues and consultants who have remained friends for life. Research and PhD thesis are not only a scientific exercise. The degree was also a social experience as it was necessary to work, to get on with and to help other people.

The respiratory reputation of the London Chest Hospital was enhanced as a result of the work undertaken by the clinical researchers under the supervision of Dr Wisia Wedzicha, Dr Neil Barnes, Dr Duncan Empey and Dr Robin Rudd.

Sadly, the departure of this great host of doctors resulted in the demise of respiratory research at the London Chest Hospital.

Lung Imaging:

I became proficient at looking at the (then) modern chest imaging, in particular chest CT scans having looked at hundreds of images analytically as part of my thesis.

We compared CT features of asbestos-related disease and idiopathic lung fibrosis. We found many differences that might help a medical expert to favour one condition from the other during asbestos claims.

We had fun. We found that lung fibrosis in many asbestos workers clump in a similar shaper to the vegetable broccoli. This appearance was jokingly dubbed by the juniors at the time as *'Jarad's Broccoli Sign'* *(See figure 4).*

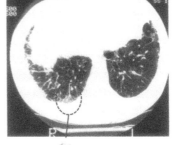

Figure 4

The broccoli sign. This is seen in asbestosis and not in lung fibrosis

Tuberculosis (TB):

After finishing my PhD research, I was appointed as a lecturer at the London Chest Hospital and continued to research in several different aspects of chest medicine including tuberculosis.

Unlike the media hype, the incidence of drug resistant tuberculosis even in this high prevalence area was found to be low (6.8% of all cases). Most of these patients were resistant to just a single drug – isoniazid. This posed no clinical significance as there were many other effective anti -TB antibiotics.

A small number of patients (1.2 %) of patients were resistant to more than one drug including isoniazid and rifampicin. Out of those (0.6 %) were regarded to have extended drug resistance.

The country of origin of patients with drug resistant TB varied. It included patients from Somalia, Bangladesh, Hong Kong, and the UK. Patients with drug resistant tuberculosis had a higher frequency of having bilateral TB opacities on their chest X rays.

The low incidence of patients with drug resistant TB was also reflected on regional and national surveys. However, presentations in hospital grand rounds and other educational meetings exaggerated that picture. These gave (and still do give) the impression that the prevalence of multiple drug resistant TB is high. To gain unjustified funding, they portray these small number of patients as a threat to the health of the nation.

It was noteworthy that none of the patients we treated who had single or multiple drug resistant TB died of tuberculosis. In fact, to our knowledge all responded to treatment, quickly became sputum-negative and cured after TB treatment using the drugs that they were resistant to *in vitro* or by addition of second line drugs.

Chronic Obstructive Pulmonary Disease (COPD)

The second half of my work as a lecturer was to recruit and to conduct work on the ISLODE (inhaled Steroids in Obstructive Lung Disease in Europe) at the London Chest Hospital. This was the first national clinical trial looking at the value of an inhaled steroid, fluticasone, for reducing the decline in lung function tests in COPD. This was a three-year trial.

My interest in COPD was carried into my appointment as a consultant and undoubtedly helped me to be appointed.

As a new consultant at Bristol Royal Infirmary, and in collaboration with E-San (an Oxford IT company) we developed the first remote monitoring system for early detection of exacerbations.

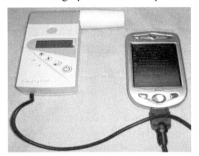 

Figure 5 *The remote monitoring device designed by E-San. It consisted of a handheld computer (similar to a smart phone) and a spirometer.*

The work started on Cystic Fibrosis (CF) exacerbations and was extended to patients with COPD. Patients needed to report their daily symptoms and to measure FEV1 using the spirometer. Exacerbations were defined according to nationally set criteria.

Two parallel studies were running: one on CF patients and the other on COPD. Unlike our initial expectations, COPD patients took to the device more than CF patients. They recorded more days and uncovered more exacerbations than CF patients.

CF patients had a lot more gaps in their daily recordings. Because of this, the object of this study was defeated in this group. In contrast, the modest number of COPD patients gained benefits at the end of the study.

CF patients were quick to accept contributing to the research and receiving the device, but a significant number did not record their symptoms or lung function tests enough to allow early detection of exacerbations. Their ease and privileged access to healthcare would enable them to contact the CF team when they felt unwell rather than recording their symptoms. This was the real reason for lack of success of remote monitoring of exacerbations in CF.

Unfortunately, it was noted by members of the CF team that many CF patients had used the device for applications other than the study itself.

Some lost it and one patient offered it for sale on their Facebook pages. This was seen by our CF nurses.

In contrast, COPD patients did not have the same support. They considered being part of the study and getting the device to be a privilege. They recorded frequently and they received exacerbation treatment.

Unlike initial assumptions the COPD patients did not struggle with the technology. For all these reasons, this small study revealed benefits from early intervention for exacerbations.

Bronchoscopic volume-reduction therapies:

The idea developed out of the practice of volume reduction surgery. The concept is based on the assumption that removing a part of the lungs which has been destroyed with emphysema would help other parts of the lungs, the diaphragm, and the chest wall to function. The aim is to reduce breathlessness, improve quality of life and extend survival.

The clinical needs in breathless patient with emphysema was obvious. The surgical risks, however, were great and made surgeons, patients, anaesthetists, and respiratory physicians all very wary about proceeding. Very few operations were taking place nationally.

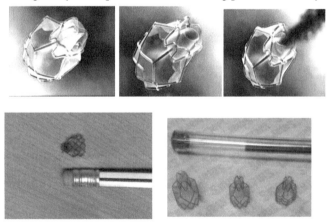

Figure 6 The zephyr endobronchial valve. Top a schematic presentation of the valve on inspiration (duckbill is closed) and on expiration (duckbill open) thus releasing air and secretions. Bottom The actual sizes of the valves (the size of a peanut) compared to a pencil and a ballpoint pen

Therefore, introducing endobronchial valves (Figure 6) as a minimally invasive solution was very attractive.

Getting a new procedure done in the NHS is not easy. We were assisted by a fortunate event. On a cold September day in 2014 a thin 72-year-old lady with emphysema stepped into the respiratory HOT clinic. She was very breathless at rest and was pushed in a wheelchair by her daughter.

Her images showed rapidly expanding emphysema of the left lung. Her cardiac area and mediastinum were pushed to the right hemithorax (Figure 7).

The patient was hospitalised but could not be discharged for eight weeks because of her breathlessness. She was bed bound and on oxygen and opioids. She developed hospital acquired infections. As it happened, she was staying in the respiratory beds based at the thoracic surgical wards. She was therefore blocking a surgical bed.

With all that, she was communicative with brilliant coherence. She wanted treatment and did not accept that she was entering end of life. Something needed to be offered.

We contacted the UK representatives of the Zephyr Endobronchial Valve (EBV) company. We asked to be offered several valves free of charge as starters. They agreed. I needed the approval of the medical director to do the procedure. They agreed provided that I received training prior to the event and that the procedure was conducted in the surgical theatre, an expert was present, and the patient was aware of all those considerations.

With the help of the Zephyr Endobronchial Valve (EBV) company I flew to Groningen to meet a world-renowned doctor who did the procedure. I showed him the images and lung function tests of this case and other cases. I observed him doing several cases and took tips of how to go forward.

The procedure was done in Bristol Royal Infirmary and was a spectacular success. The patient felt better and less breathless within a few hours, she did not need her oxygen the following day and we were able to discharge her within 48 hours. To the astonishment of everyone, this bed-bound lady was walking in the ward corridors without oxygen and with little breathlessness.

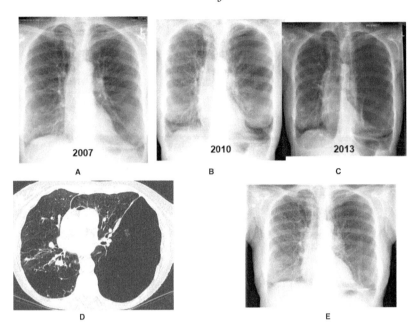

Figure 7
The images of the first patient to receive emphysema treatment by endo-bronchial valve insertion at Bristol Royal Infirmary. Note the increasing expansion of emphysema (left more than right) shown on the chest X-rays from 2007 to 2013 (A to C) with displacement of the heart and mediastinum to the right and diaphragmatic depression. Her CT scan (D) in 2013 showed a large emphysematous bulla on the left and destructive emphysema on the right.
The chest X-ray (E) 24 hours after insertion of valves in the left upper lobe shows the heart to be in a more normal position with loss in volume of the bulla and partial re-expansion of the left lung.

Using this case, we applied to the new procedure committee and for both the surgical and the medical divisions for approval. They approved the procedure given our experience and assurance to form a multidisciplinary team. The team consisted of a respiratory physician, a thoracic surgeon and a thoracic radiologist.

We later adapted in a similar way to introduce endobronchial coils for emphysema patients who were unsuitable for EBV or surgery. Apart from the Brompton Hospital, London, we became the largest clinical unit to provide this service in the UK for the southwest region and beyond.

The Death of Science

Trying and trialling new tools:

Sputum Clearance in Cystic Fibrosis

In addition to endobronchial valves and the remote monitoring for CF exacerbations, we also tried new methods of sputum clearance using hydro-acoustic therapy. Physiotherapy remains one of the most important treatments in sputum clearance in patients with CF. All methods, however, are taxing in terms of time and effort. Adherence to physiotherapy is widely known to be poor. Equipment and devices to assist in sputum clearance have been available for a long time but they have gained differing levels of favour with patients. A new method of physiotherapy was proposed. It is a water bath which generates underwater waves to the chest area. The waves vibrate the chest wall and would mimic chest tapping used by physiotherapists albeit in a gentle way. The method was called "Hydro Acoustic Therapy (HAT)." (Figure 8). The study was a cross-over study in which HAT was compared to flutter and to just sitting in the bath without the hydro-acoustic waves. The study found HAT to be well-tolerated and with no unwanted effects. Patients preferred HAT to flutter. HAT was not inferior to flutter in the degree of sputum production. The aim was to build small baths for commercial purposes. The sponsoring company has not yet done that.

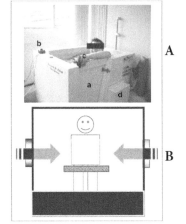

Figure 8.
The hydroacoustic therapy (HAT) bath. The bath [A] creates waves at the chest wall [B] using a wave generator at each side of the chest which works in a similar way to chest percussion.
For safety, there is an easy to open door (a), a button to stop the machine (b) and a pulse oximeter to monitor the blood oxygen level.

The use of Magnetic Resonance Imaging in CF:

Cystic-fibrosis related diabetes (CFRD) has an adverse effect on patients' weight and their ability to reduce pulmonary exacerbations.

We looked at the abdominal organs in patients with and without CFRD using abdominal magnetic resonance imaging (MRI).

The research was helped by the diligent input from Dr Mark Callaway, consultant radiologist. We looked at the pancreas and the spleen. We used, as a comparator, a group of patients with type I diabetes who did not have CF.

We found that the <u>pancreas</u> was almost invisible in most CF patients, in particular in those with CFRD. Whilst pancreatic atrophy was to be expected, the fact that it was almost wiped out even in those *without* diabetes came as a big surprise. This would indicate that insulin production did not need a sizeable pancreas.

The Value of the Research

The work I have described greatly benefitted NHS patients but would have been impossible without my training in research. The research we were involved with enhanced the units I worked in, reduced patients' complaints, and allowed the team to present the research internationally, hence, to visit many parts of the world. It gave me a lot of fun and satisfaction and enhanced my chances of getting merit awards! The research helped me to achieve the honour to be classified as one of the top 100 researchers in the UK in contribution to The National Institute for Health and Care Research (NIHR) .

Figure 9

Dr Jarad receiving the NIHR certificate for being amongst the top 100 UK contributors to NIHR research.

Decline and death of research:

So why is it that most respiratory physicians, and most clinicians generally, do not do any research? These are some of the causes:

1. *Change in training.* Training committees allow specialist respiratory registrars to progress with no need to publish papers, present research or achieve an MD or a PhD. Therefore, when they are appointed as a consultant, they do not have the mind set of researchers.

2. *Lack of incentive* to do research as consultants. This is manifested with many achieving discretionary points or clinical excellence awards without the need to be research leaders (although research leaders tend to achieve these points more easily).
3. *The lack of financial reward.* Previously, proceeds from the research were kept in research pots controlled by the researchers. Now they are owned by organisations that can use the research income and distribute them as they see fit.
4. *The heavy regulatory process* and the need of time-consuming applications for R&D units and time-consuming ethical procedures.
5. *Lack of other researchers in a unit* would create resentment and criticism to those who are research active. Obstacles and lack of co-operation are easily created.

These problems occur in all specialties in the NHS. Unless and until these obstacles are resolved, the death of research in units is almost certain and with it the immense intellectual talents of doctors remain frustrated and unused.

Can we reverse the trend and take advantage of the brain power of doctors?

Research is not for everyone. But most doctors who possess by their nature analytical thinking are attracted to engaging in meaningful research when the grounds and incentives are suitable for it.

What are the remedies?

- The redress should start at **medical school!** Research training needs to be seen as essential.
- During **post-graduate** training, critical analysis of research papers should be part of the training. Those who complete academic degrees should be given priority on jobs in academic centres.
- **Training programme committees** should have academics as university representatives on their composition.
- **All consultant appointments committees** should have a university representative on them, irrespective of what type of Trust is advertising.
- In central hospitals, a senior lecturer or a professor should be **part of the Trust Board** to ensure that academic efforts are introduced

within consultant job plans, recognised and rewarded.
- **Money obtained by research should be controlled by those who generated it**. Control of funding and of medical staff by senior research nurses should stop.
- **Ethics Committee applications** should be short, and decisions should be slick and focused on issues that might harm the patients. Focusing on wording and typos on applications is a welcome part but reviewing, re-submission should be given a quick turnaround. The added application of research proposals to Trusts R&D should be abolished and incorporated in the ethics committee application.

These are my views and the list is not exhaustive. This chapter represents my own experience and the views I put are my own thoughts. I do hope that this chapter will engender enthusiasm for academic work in working clinicians and that they will receive the reward that their research output deserves.

References: At the end of the book

Editorial Comment on the
The value of research in Medical Training

When the editors were at medical school it was possible to become a general practitioner (GP) without further examination after qualifying as a doctor whereas a position as a hospital consultant required many years of further study, higher qualifications from the Royal Colleges, and a track record in medical research including papers published in reputable medical journals. In order to obtain a post in a teaching hospital it was often necessary to have a higher degree such as an MD or PhD. These were definitely required if the medical doctor wished to become an academic and rise to the level of a professorship.

Naturally those who did not aspire to higher academic prowess opted to be GPs and were often very good at their job. However the newly created Royal College of General Practitioners decided that GPs should pass an examination to obtain membership of their college and without it the doctor should not become a GP.

Meanwhile the Royal College of Nursing had come to the conclusion that all nurses should have a degree in nursing. Universities would insist on the applicants for a nursing BSc having appropriate A level qualifications. The Salmon report banged a further nail into the former arrangement. Nurses would not become staff nurses, a potential end career post. Nor would they stop at Sister or Charge Nurse level. There would be a seemingly endless number of nursing officers above the Sister up to the level of Matron and above (since there would be several matrons in a hospital and somebody above them). Nurses stopped being helpful committed carers and became discontented semi-scientists aspiring to being administrators and managers rather than committed to the patients and the ward.

The various governments from Wilson's in the 1970s to Cameron's in the 2010s reiterated their commitment to the NHS and poured in increasing levels of finance. However they also oversaw the growth of private hospitals, which took private patients and their much-needed finance away from the NHS. The movement to increased management massively increased under Thatcher and all following governments.

Not surprisingly the focus on good scientific education in medicine gradually diminished and it became possible for a trainee in a hospital to obtain a consultant post without doing any research, and with no published work. Even professors were being appointed without a higher degree, and now they want to shorten medical training![1]

Daily Telegraph 21.3.2023   **Training for doctors 'could be shortened' to tackle NHS staff shortages**

Having undertaken science degrees were the new breed of nurses publishing successfully? A small proportion, perhaps, but mostly they were simply nurses who, on qualification, were short on practical experience.

Meanwhile there was another move afoot…the insistence on evidence-based medicine. Far too often this has meant and continues to mean that any medical advance or experience not substantiated by a big pharmaceutical trial is totally discarded as not evidence-based.

And who is on the committees that judge the efficacy of drugs and certifies them as safe? The very people who run the companies making the drugs or benefitting from patents for the drugs. This has been particularly obvious in the United States, the country that does by far the most medical research.

Who was foremost in aiding and abetting the takeover by those making a profit? None other than Dr. Anthony Fauci, director of the U.S. National Institute of Allergy and Infectious Diseases. Perhaps the person who explains this best is Robert F Kennedy Junior[2] as stated in his recent book entitled *The Real Anthony Fauci*. Here is a direct quote: *'Dr. Fauci played a historic role as the leading architect of "agency capture"— the corporate seizure of America's public health agencies by the pharmaceutical industry.'*

Just as the medical fraternity are turning their backs on research it has become progressively more important for the medical doctors to have a good working knowledge of medical science, of statistics and the pitfalls of such research. In order that they can check that the research is correct they need to understand how to *do* research.

While this has been happening the medical profession, and health care as a whole, have become progressively risk averse. Whilst avoiding error is extremely important it is necessary to understand that there are errors of omission as well as commission. To avoid error doctors are following mind-numbing protocols that leave little to the doctors' imagination or acumen. This started with guidelines, moved on to protocols and now they are surfacing as directives. Some guidelines were very poorly thought out and published before the scientific papers. We cite as evidence the notorious contraceptive pill scare of 1995.[3,4]

In the last chapter we read about Dr. Nabil Jarad's experience in undertaking research whilst working in the NHS, how he and the patients benefitted and why he believes the lack of research is so detrimental to medicine. In earlier chapters we looked at some of the results from the loss of science particularly with regards to Covid-19, how regulators started telling doctors that they were no longer allowed to do what they always had done (repurpose safe drugs for a new use), nor could they warn patients of the dangers of the new gene-therapy "vaccines" without risk of being struck off.

The role of the medical practitioner in the UK and in the USA has been fatally undermined. The control by management, the shift from guidelines to directives, and the lack of research training has sapped the ability of the doctors to think for themselves. The inevitable has happened: medical care has suffered, medical science has withered on the vine and doctors are discontented. The book now moves into the realm of physicists, astronomers and cosmologists.

References: At the end of the book

Chapter 18

Physics, Astronomy and Cosmology

Professor P Goddard

Introduction

Nearly thirty years ago (1994), whilst researching Magnetic Resonance Imaging, I tried to pick a path through the many problems of physics.[1] I had discussions with physicists and cosmologists. Whilst they all agreed that the main difficulty was reconciling Einstein's theory of relativity with quantum mechanics there was some considerable disagreement as to whether there were many other problems. At a meeting in 1997 held in Jesus College, Cambridge, the physicists purported to be very satisfied with the standard theory of particle physics and with relativity, though the theories seemed incompatible. They were behaving much like Lord Kelvin at the end of the 19th century (see the beginning of chapter 2). The astronomer royal, Martin Rees, actually referred to Fred Hoyle, another famous astronomer, and implied he was a crank because of his criticism of the big bang theory. I pointed out that there were surely major flaws in all their theories. For example Quantum Mechanics appeared to depend on either consciousness, hidden variables or multiple constantly dividing universes…..and none of these problems could fit in with general common sense. Moreover Werner Heisenberg's uncertainty principle states that we cannot know both the position and speed of a particle, such as a photon or electron, with perfect accuracy.

General Relativity, on the other hand, predicted a much greater mass in galaxies than could be observed and at the heart of a black hole there was predicted to be a singularity in which all equations broke down to infinities. Moreover both general and special relativity appeared to do away with time as we perceived it.

I was told that the theories had been proved right. For example time, as measured by atomic clocks, did alter, depending on velocity and gravity, and had been shown to do so. This I did not deny but why did Einstein think that time was a very persistent illusion? Quantum theory, meanwhile, implied that there was no arrow of time.....the equations could go in either direction.

The Arrow of Time

So why does an arrow of time not appear to be fundamental in our theories?
The descriptions of systems using equations by their very nature remove the arrow of time. Of course equations can go backwards as well as forwards for that is how they are written. But reality does not do that, so equations are a poor description of reality.
Fractal theory and chaos mathematics next took up my spare thinking time. From chaos mathematics I understood that complexity was an interesting condition at the edge of order and chaos. It was in this complexity that life and consciousness emerge.
So where are we now? Have the problems been resolved? The answer is a very definite no. In fact things seem to be worse than they were.
Now the physicists are explaining the anomalies in their theories and results by evoking Dark Matter, Dark Energy, the pre-eminence of information and even universal consciousness.
Reductive science is breaking things down into their constituent parts in order to understand them. This will not succeed when the property being observed is an emergent property.

Newton

Newton's laws are a very useful way of calculating forces at the human scale. They break down at the very small level (the quantum level) and at the cosmic scale (the realm of Einstein's deliberations).
But did they ever really make sense and were they really his laws?
I think that understanding Newton's laws is where a lot of children's education in physics becomes unstuck. The laws are taught as if they are actually true whilst the physics teacher should know full well that they are only a useful approximation.
In the first law, an object will not change its motion unless a force acts on it. In the second law, the force on an object is equal to its mass times

its acceleration. In the third law, when two objects interact, they apply forces to each other of equal magnitude and opposite direction.[2]
The first two laws were actually described by Galileo and the last law is completely untrue as a simple demonstration will show. Hold your hands up and push the left against the right with equal force. This is the Newtonian third law of motion which can be paraphrased as *"for every action there is an equal and opposite reaction"*. This works for systems in equilibrium. Now relax the force you are applying with the left hand and the right will push the left hand over to the left. There is no longer an equal and opposite reaction!
When tasked with this at school the physics teacher may say that when you add up all the forces including air resistance, sounds, heating and movement on the left arm you will find that work has been done and no energy was lost. This is another law….the conservation of energy. It does not prove that Newton's third law is correct.
PS. Robert Hooke described the inverse square law for gravity before Newton, though dear Isaac took the glory with the apocryphal story of the falling apple.

Antimatter

Paul Dirac famously predicted the existence of antimatter, in particular the positron. Very small amounts have been detected or produced but only an extremely tiny fraction of the predicted total. Basically half the universe was missing and the theories of symmetry have required fudging.

Dark Matter and why the cosmologists and physicists believe that it must be present.

When the Hubble telescope and other excellent machinery permitted the galaxies beyond the Milky Way to be observed the rotation of the galaxies could be assessed and the number of stars counted. It soon became apparent that, using Newtonian and Einsteinian physics, the mass of visible stars is not sufficient to provide the necessary gravity to keep the galaxies intact. They spin too fast and should therefore fly apart…. the speed is beyond their escape velocity. Even postulating and apparently finding black holes at the centre of the galaxies did not provide sufficient mass. So dark matter was postulated and, by many scientists, accepted as a fact.

Many experiments have followed to try to observe such dark matter but it has not been found. So only 10% of the mass of the universe can be detected.

Observational data on 353 dwarf galaxies in the Fornax Cluster shows that many of them are distorted by the pull of other galaxies indicating that they have little or no dark matter holding them together.[3] Modified Newtonian dynamics (MOND) theories put forward by Mordehai Milgrom in 1983 suggest that the inverse square law for gravity is breached at the galactic level. Such theories can explain the findings without invoking dark matter but are not generally accepted.

The Milky Way, our galaxy but once thought to be the entire universe, apparently has a supermassive black hole in its Galactic Centre, corresponding with the radio source Sagittarius A*. Most large galaxies do appear to have a black hole centrally whilst many dwarf galaxies do not.

However this is not always the case. Some fairly large galaxies do *not* have a large black hole. Despite being one of the largest galaxies so far detected the supergiant elliptical galaxy A2261-BCG has not been found to contain an active supermassive black hole.[4]

It would seem with the lack of dark matter and lack of black holes in the galaxies that are being torn apart that the inverse square law does not appear to work properly in such areas of the universe ! Some form of MOND is likely to be right.

Dark Energy

The observable universe is expanding. That this is the case was a surprise to many and was discovered by the astronomer Edwin Hubble in the 1920s when he showed that the galaxies are nearly all receding away from us.

What was even more unexpected is that there is evidence that this recession is speeding up. The universe is expanding at an accelerating pace. To explain this the concept of **dark energy** has been put forward. However, Dark Energy has not been detected.

Recently it has been shown that the suggested fifth force to explain dark energy probably does not exist.[5] Again a large part of the universe is missing, perhaps as much as 68%.

Universality

The concept of universality is particularly dear to physicists and cosmologists. Universality is the quality or state of being universal. So a law that applies on Earth should also apply elsewhere.

One such law is the inverse square law. This is any scientific law stating that a specified physical quantity is inversely proportional to the square of the distance and it applies in particular to electromagnetic radiation and gravity.

Perhaps the idea of gravity working over less than three full dimensions can explain the conundrum presented by the lack of dark matter? Perhaps it will be possible to test this by comparing predictions of the gravitation effect in the galaxies with the electromagnetic radiation? If dimensions are missing the electromagnetic radiation should also diminish at a lessened extent than the inverse square. This may mean that some galaxies appear to be nearer to us than they actually are.

Extra dimensions or fewer ?

After some deliberation I came to the conclusion in the 1990s that the German mathematician Theodor Kaluza and the Swedish physicist Oskar Klein were right in believing that our descriptions of the universe required at least one more physical dimension in order to describe all the forces.[6] Moreover I surmised that there was no dark matter and no dark energy. The answer lay in the incompleteness of spatial and time dimensions. We assume that everywhere has three complete dimensions of space and one of time but the fractal nature of everything implies partial dimensions and maybe multiple dimensions of time. Where there is an accumulation of matter the three dimensions may seem complete and any other spatial dimensions would have to be very small and only able to be entered at the quantum level. In extremely dense matter, such as a neutron star, there may be multiple spatial and time dimensions.

Between galaxies there is very little matter or energy and there may not even be three complete dimensions.

Luckily some people are still interested in Kaluza-Klein theories and maybe they will come round to testing them. Moreover Mordehai

Milgrom is still working as an almost lone voice on his theories of Modified Newtonian dynamics (MOND).[7]

Measuring G accurately

Newton's equations specified that the force of gravity between two bodies is directly proportional to the product of their masses and inversely proportional to the distance between their gravitational mass centres.

$$F = G \frac{m_1 m_2}{r^2}$$

Where F is the force, m_1 and m_2 are the masses, r is the distance between the two masses and G is the universal constant.

This is, of course, an inverse square law and despite very careful measurement the value of the constant G is still contested with significant discrepancy between readings. Xue et Al[8] state *"Unfortunately, there is still a large discrepancy of about 550 ppm among the thirteen values of G reviewed in this paper, even though the relative standard uncertainties of many results have been less than 50 ppm."*

The Big Bang?

Sir Fred Hoyle (1915-2001) was a very successful British astronomer and cosmologist who was instrumental in working out the mathematics of stellar nucleosynthesis. In other words he and his colleagues were the first people to understand how the fusion in the sun and other stars formed the heavier elements from hydrogen, helium and lithium. [9,10] The initial theory was proposed by Hoyle in 1946 (Hoyle) and later refined in 1954 and 1957 in papers with Willy Fowler. It has been a very successful predictive theory explaining the observed proportions of elements in the universe.

Hoyle also invented the term "the Big Bang" but was not happy with the prevailing theory that the universe appeared in that way. He suggested that there could be creative fields within the cosmos which could give the appearance of a big bang in our locale. Astrophysicists and cosmologists did not agree and he was pilloried as a crank for constantly promoting his ideas as opposed to the widely accepted notion that the universe appeared from nowhere as a point source that expanded rapidly. The other theory that Hoyle proposed with Chandra Wickramasinghe was that of panspermia which will be discussed in the next chapter.

Hoyle was sometimes intolerant of other scientists and supportive of ideas that others had dismissed. In 1974 Anthony Hewish was awarded a Nobel physics prize for his work in discovering a pulsar. Hoyle was of the opinion that Hewish's student, Jocelyn Bell Burnell, should have received the prize. Hoyle's criticism of Hewish and the Nobel committee probably led to his name being crossed off the Nobel list.[11]

In 1983 Fowler, who was 72 years old at the time, was told he would share the Nobel prize with Indian astrophysicist Subrahmanyan Chandrasekhar. The shock to Fowler was the fact that Hoyle, the chief instigator of the stellar nucleosynthesis theory, was not going to receive the prize.[11] This was clearly an example of the Nobel prize committee being petty and manifestly unfair! (Similar unfairness by the Nobel Committee occurred to the initial promoter and inventor of MRI, Raymond Damadian.)

The Big Bang does not have to have happened. The fact that all the galaxies appear to be moving away from a point source does not mean that such a singularity arising from nothingness ever existed. An exploding giant black hole could give the same appearances. Perhaps Hoyle is right and our universe is just one of many eternally existing in a much greater, unseen multiverse. Certainly these theories are beginning to be talked about now and would seem more likely than an almost infinitely massive point of creative origin. Roger Penrose considers that the refusal to consider such ideas, known as cyclic conformal cosmology (CCC), is disturbing. *"This reluctance to consider a new idea in the face of strong evidence is one reason why I think people should worry about science."* Roger Penrose (2022).[12]

The hubristic belief in the 'prevailing wisdom' was where Lord Kelvin went wrong and Penrose is right to be worried about science.

What can explain the accelerating expansion of the Universe?

If there is no dark energy (and it has not yet been detected) what other explanation could there be for the accelerating expansion of the Universe?

As mentioned above perhaps there was no big bang but instead a rebound from a contracted state. This may have occurred in a huge black hole within an even bigger multiverse. If so our universe could be approaching other universes in the cosmos and their gravity could cause the acceleration of expansion.

If the acceleration was not equal in every direction this could be an indication that the other parts of the cosmos, beyond our known universe, are clumped but if it is uniform the outer cosmos may be smooth. Thus we might be able to predict something about the parts of the multiverse that we are unable to detect directly.

Other possibilities include the idea that there might be multiple universes in adjacent dimensions overlapping our universe in the multiverse. They might only be interacting via gravity.

These possibilities deserve consideration.

The Higgs Boson

Eleven years ago in 2012 awed scientists heard researchers at the Large Hadron Collider announce that they had discovered the Higgs Boson. This is purported to be an elementary particle that gives mass to the particles that have mass.

The mathematics had been sorted out in 1964 and the discovery using the LHC paved the way for Higgs to receive the Nobel prize.

What was not sufficiently pointed out was the fact that the discovered particle has a mass many magnitudes less than that predicted by theory. In other words the mathematics is wrong!

According to the standard model each Higgs boson should weigh a few micrograms but it does not– it is apparently one thousand trillion times smaller.[13]

Should it even be called the Higgs boson?

Consciousness

Physicists seem to believe the there is a problem in understanding consciousness. In reductive science this is the case since consciousness is an emergent property of life. Breaking things down into their constituents does not explain emergent properties just as breaking the Mona Lisa down into pieces of painted canvas would never explain its appeal.

Living things have properties that are different from non-living objects. Each of these properties may be present in some regard in the non-living but not all of them. The characteristics of life include order, sensitivity or response to the environment, reproduction, growth and development, regulation, homeostasis, and energy processing. All of these can be considered as emergent properties.

Consciousness is similar.

So what is it? In my definition consciousness is awareness of surroundings and events and understanding of their significance and knowledge of the organism's place in those events and surroundings. It has occurred in living creatures as a result of evolution because it, presumably, provides some advantage. That advantage appears to be the ability to respond to events in novel ways rather than solely by set responses, such as reflexes.

So that is what it is but how does it work?

I reject the recently suggested idea that everything in the universe has a "bit of consciousness". That is too close to Animism and spirits in inanimate objects. It explains precisely nothing. Such ideas are not testable and as such do not yet represent science.

So what do I think consciousness is if it is not some kind of "spirit thing"?

I believe it is the ability of a brain or brain equivalent to learn the nature of surroundings, initially by trial and error with feedback from the senses and motor function. In higher organisms as well as iteration there is learning from teachers and in human beings there is learning from abstract sources such as books. All of these create a virtual model (or models) in the brain of the happenings around the living organism. This allows the creature to understand what is going on in its ecological setting. Sometimes the model is completely wrong or the surroundings are so chaotic that no model can help. Always the model will be incomplete. This is consciousness, and the emergent properties of biology allow it to occur, perhaps utilising effects at the quantum level as suggested in 1989 by Penrose [12]. Required are a brain (or equivalent), a nervous system that holds the model in various levels of memory, sensory organs and probably motor organs. I am hesitant about the latter since it would be possible to devise an organic system that had no intrinsic motor function. Such a system to explore its surroundings sufficiently to create consciousness would require input via its sensory system and the exploration could be done by an external source in a similar way to a computer programmer teaching a neural net by inputting information and checking the outcome for accuracy. This is, however, simply outsourcing the sensory and motor functions.....they still exist but are being provided by another individual.

Thus there is no need to invoke a "bit of consciousness" in every object, animate or inanimate and consciousness can be understood solely as an emergent property of life made up from perfectly normal matter and energy flow.

Gödel's incompleteness theorems

Gödel's incompleteness theorems had profound implications for mathematics and the philosophy of mathematics. But what do the two theorems say and can they be applied to other fields such as Physics or Economics?

Godel's theorems show a limitation to formal mathematical systems. They cannot be completed. For example there is no set of numbers that includes all the numbers. *'Gödel proved fundamental results about axiomatic systems showing in any axiomatic mathematical system there are propositions that cannot be proved or disproved within the axioms of the system.'* [14] Some philosophers might argue that if mathematics cannot be completed then nor can any science since science relies on numbers. That much is true but it does not mean that there is no objective truth...simply that we cannot ever expect to have complete knowledge which seems perfectly reasonable given our limited place in the enormous universe!

Fusion as a source of power

Scientists have been working for three-quarters of a century on fusion, hoping that it will provide an endless source of power. The running joke in physics is that it will be with us as a reality in thirty years time. Unfortunately the time scale remains the same despite years of work, and billions of dollars, euros and pounds having been spent on it.[15]

Meanwhile an endless source of fusion power bathes the world with energy and much of it is wasted. It is, of course, called the sun!

Fraud in Physics

In physics, as in all fields, there are always some people who cheat and lie. Here is just one example.

The Schön scandal: Jan Hendrik Schön, a German physicist, was a prolific writer of research papers on superconductivity. He claimed to be able to attain superconductivity in organic (i.e. Carbon based) materials. This was fraudulent and the experiments could not be repeated successfully. In June 2004 the University of Konstanz issued a press release stating that Schön's doctoral degree had been revoked due to "dishonourable conduct." [16]

Conclusion

It is clear that unless dark matter and dark energy are found it is entirely reasonable to conclude that the theories on which they are based are, at the best, very incomplete and possibly downright wrong. Heralding the discovery of a very small particle and calling it the Higgs boson when what was predicted was enormously larger is tantamount to scientific dishonesty. If a massive particle was needed in the theory but only an infinitesimally small one is found the theory is wrong! Physicists may find consciousness difficult because they either believe in duality (mind and body) or a trinity (mind, body and spirit). Understanding consciousness as an emergent property in an entirely physical living system takes away the difficulty.

Moving on from their broken standard model of quantum mechanics will be difficult but there are some brave souls who have been trying to do so for decades. Hopefully physicists , astronomers and cosmologists will find the new information arising from technological advances such as the Large Hadron Collider and the James Webb space telescope, stimulating their imagination. When the unexpected is found by experimentation it is very exciting and rather than heralding the death of science it should invigorate the scientists to move on to greater theories and greater discoveries.

References: At the end of the book

Chapter 19

ORIGINS OF LIFE AND THE COSMOS

Professor Chandra Wickramasinghe
MBE, ScD, Hon DSc, Hon DLitt, FRAS, FRSA

The entire cosmos originated *ex nihilo* 13.8 billion years ago: life on Earth started 4.2 billion years ago in a primordial soup of organics on the planet. This is the unshakeable orthodoxy that appears today to control and most likely to stifle the progress of science. How was this orthodoxy arrived at and how secure are these pronouncements?

1. Introduction

Our human ancestry stretches back at least 3 million years – representing perhaps a little over 100,000 human generations – the blink of an eye in the very much longer history of the cosmos. This was the time when the skull size of our primate ancestors had doubled resulting in the emergence of a new species *Homo sapiens*. All that we have achieved thus far – progress in the arts of civilisation, technology and science - has been accomplished in this brief timespan. The fossil record shows that before this point in our evolutionary history, life on the Earth evolved in complexity, diversity and sophistication for at least 4 billion years. The age-old question of how this all happened, how we humans and indeed all of lifeforms came into existence, has been approached in a multitude of ways, successively embracing superstition, religion, philosophy and eventually science.

The theory of life's origins that held sway for many centuries, and still continues to have a strong influence in contemporary science, is the "theory of spontaneous generation" – the idea that life arose spontaneously from non-living material in the Earth's oceans, perhaps 4.2 billion years ago. This theory can be traced back to the influential Greek philosopher Aristotle of the 3rd century BCE who posited that life must arise from non-living inorganic matter whenever the right conditions arose. Aristotle cited many instances that he incorrectly regarded as supportive evidence, the most graphic and famous being the statement of "fireflies emerging from a mixture of warm earth and morning dew". In one form or other this basic idea has persisted throughout the centuries, extending into the 20th century and through into modern times.

The modern version of this old Aristotelean idea is the concept known as abiogenesis which began to be cast into a scientific framework by Haldane, Oparin and Stanley Miller in the first half of the 20th century [1-4]. The famous experiment of Stanley Miller and Harold Urey in which they had synthesised amino acids and other monomers of biology from mixtures of inorganic gasses was hailed as a triumph for abiogenesis theories from the mid-1950s onwards. But the production of such organic molecules in the laboratory, by whatever means, was a far cry from synthesising life.

2. The odds against life's origins

The functioning of a living system depends on many thousands of chemical reactions between these organic molecules taking place within a membrane-bound cellular structure. Such reactions, grouped into metabolic pathways, have the ability to harness chemical energy from the surrounding medium in a series of very small steps: transporting small molecules into cells, building biopolymers of various sorts, and ultimately making copies of themselves while also possessing a capacity to evolve under suitable conditions. Batteries of enzymes, composed of chains of amino acids in highly conserved arrangements, play a crucial role as catalysts precisely controlling the rates of chemical reactions. Without enzymes, there could be no life. It is the specificity and conserved information (Shannon information, in IT jargon) represented by the ordering of amino acids in enzymes that is absolutely crucial for life.

Since the twentieth century, the most important metabolic pathways in biology have been unravelled, e.g., the carbon dioxide cycle in plants. However, even if we possessed a complete knowledge of all the metabolic pathways in biology, we would not come any closer to understanding the processes by which the simplest living system emerged. Many types of terrestrial venues for the origin of life have been explored over several decades – deep-sea thermal vents, primordial oceans amongst others – but all such sites of choice are, in my view, grossly inadequate to overcome the enormous hurdles of improbability that are involved.

In present-day biology the information contained in enzymes—the arrangements of amino acids into folded chains—is absolutely crucial for life and this information is transmitted by way of the coded ordering of nucleotides in DNA. In a hypothetical RNA world that may have predated the DNA - protein world in some origin of life models, RNA is posited to serve a dual role as both enzyme and genetic transmitter. If a few ribozymes are regarded as essential precursors to all life, one could attempt to make an estimate of the probability of the assembly of a simple ribozyme which is composed of some 300 bases. This probability turns out to be 1 in 4^{300}, which is equivalent to 1 in 10^{180} - which already defines an event that can hardly be supposed to happen even once in the entire 13.8-billion-year history of the universe. A similar calculation for the ordering of amino acids in a minimal set of bacterial enzymes gives an even more ridiculous probability ~1 in 10^{5000} with plausible assumptions.

On this basis it is impossible to avoid the conclusion that the emergence of the first evolvable cellular life form had of necessity to be a unique event in the cosmos. If this did indeed happen on Earth for the first time, against the most incredible of odds it must be regarded as a near-miraculous event and one that could not be repeated elsewhere, let alone in any laboratory simulation on the Earth. Panspermia is the theory that life did not originate on the Earth but was brought here in the form of components that are omnipresent in the cosmos. The argument often advanced by adversaries that panspermia must be rejected a priori because it merely transfers the problem of origin from Earth to another setting is logically flawed and is by no means scientific. The question of whether life started de novo on Earth or was introduced from the wider universe is a precise and perfectly valid scientific question that merits investigation, and one that is open to testing and verification on many different levels. The invocation of Occam's razor to exclude such a discussion is merely an excuse for keeping scientific discussion within the strict bounds of orthodoxy. It is strikingly reminiscent of the restrictions that stifled science in the Middle Ages, some of which unfortunately continue into the modern era.

3. Societal constraints in acknowledging fundamental Truths

It is an illusion to think that the accepted cannon of scientific ideas is objectively arrived at and is beyond refutation. When it comes to the most important matters of "origins" – the origin of the Universe and the origin of life this is far from being true. The setting up of National Academies devoted to science in the 1660s such as the Royal Society in London and the French Academy in Paris served science well in helping to place empirical science on a sound footing and consequently banishing the evils of superstition and witchcraft that was rampant at the time. Over time, however, such institutions and other state sponsored organisations established their own intractable orthodoxies in science which have been impossible to change in response to new facts and new ideas.

In modern times the involvement of the State or of large organisations – both national and multinational - in the conduct of science has become necessary to varying degrees. This is due mainly to the requirement of funds to set up laboratories, which are often expensive and beyond the reach of individual scientists. Moreover, the so-called "big" projects require large teams of scientists using expensive equipment. So, organisation and central control becomes imperative. Examples of ongoing big projects include the space exploration of planets by NASA and other similar space agencies, the Hadron Collider operated by CERN, and major genome sequencing projects in several countries – to name but a few.

In its earliest beginnings, however, science arose as the solitary pursuit of individual philosophers whose ideas were often opposed to the status quo. The pre-Socratic philosopher Anaxoragas in the 5th century BC declared that the Sun was a red-hot stone and the Moon was made of earth, and for which heresy he was banished from Athens. State-control of science is therefore no new thing. Examples are to be found scattered throughout history – extending from the time of classical Greece, through the long saga of the Ptolemaic epicycles in the Middle Ages, to the control of science by the Papacy.

4. The Rise of the Theory of Panspermia

The origins of panspermia in the tradition of Western philosophy dates back to the pre-Socratic Greek philosopher Anaxoragas (c.500 - 428BC). It was Anaxoragas who first proposed that the sun, moon and planets were not gods or goddesses but physical bodies, and for this heresy he was famously banished from Athens. Thus it is to Anaxoragas, already branded a heretic, that we owe the concept of panspermia – the idea that seeds of life (spermata) are distributed ubiquitously throughout the Universe, taking root whenever and wherever the conditions became favourable. However, this cosmic view of life came for a long time to be denounced and abandoned in favour of the Aristotelian doctrine of spontaneous generation, that dominated science well into the 19th century and onward to the present day.

The modern revival of concept of panspermia began with Louis Pasteur in the early 1860s with his famous declaration that he delivered a 'mortal blow' to the doctrine of spontaneous generation. He referred specifically to his experiments on the fermentation of wine and the souring of milk in which he showed that bacterial activity was responsible for all these processes and that pre-existing bacteria were always required [5]. What was already well known for macroscopic life forms – life being always derived from pre-existing life of a similar kind - was now shown to be valid for bacteria as well. It became clear that the only secure empirical fact relating to the origin of life is encapsulated in a dictum eloquently enunciated by Louis Pasteur *Omne vivum e vivo*—all life is derived from antecedent life.

If life is always derived from antecedent life in a causal chain such as is clearly evident in present day life and throughout the fossil record, the question naturally arises as to when and where this connection may have ceased. The continuation of the life-from-life chain to a time before the first life appeared on our planet and before the Earth itself formed implies the operation of "panspermia" and consequently leads to a theory of a cosmic or cosmological biology. This consequence of Pasteur's work was soon championed by many contemporary physicists in the late 19th century.

Lord Kelvin (Thomson, [6]) declared: *"Dead matter cannot become living without coming under the influence of matter previously alive. This seems to me to be as sure a teaching of science as the law of gravitation...."*

And the German physicist Herman von Helmholtz [7] wrote in 1874: *"It appears to me a fully correct scientific procedure, if all our attempts fail to cause the production of organisms from non-living matter, to raise the question whether life has ever arisen, whether seeds have not been carried from one planet to another..."*.

A similar position was also championed by the Nobel prize-winning Chemist Svante Arrhenius[8] in his book *Worlds in the Making*. Notwithstanding these developments the strong tendency, to prefer a theory of Earth-based abiogenesis–origin of life, prevailed well into the middle of the 20th century and beyond.

Nearly half a century ago (in the 1980s) the earliest evidence for microbial life in the geological record was thought to be in the form of cyanobacteria-like fossils dating back to 3.5 Giga annum (Ga) ago (3.5 billion years ago). There thus seemed to be a comfortable time interval for abiogenesis to occur. From the time of formation of a stable crust on the Earth 4.3 Ga ago, following an episode of violent impacts with comets (the Hadean Epoch), there seemed to be available a brief 800-million year timespan during which the canonical Haldane-Oparin primordial soup may conceivably have developed. Later discoveries, however, have shown that this time interval has all but vanished.

Detrital zircons older than 4.1Ga discovered in rocks belonging to a geological outcrop in the Jack Hills region of Western Australia, have been found to contain micron-sized graphite spheres with an isotopic signature of biogenic carbon [9]. The moment of the first appearance of microbial life on the Earth has now been pushed further back in geological history, to as far as 4.2 billion years ago. This is possibly the first epoch in which microbial life could possibly have survived, and it comes as no surprise that life's first emergence on Earth coincides with a period of intense cometary bombardment, thus forcing the position that life came along with the material of the comets which strongly points to panspermia as its mode of origin.

5. Data from Astronomy

The astronomical origin of the "stuff" of life at the level of atoms has been beyond dispute for some time [10,11]. The chemical elements C,N,O,P... and the metals that are present in all living systems were unquestionably synthesised from the most common element hydrogen in nuclear reactions that took place in the deep interiors of stars. Understanding the origin of the element carbon (12C) in stellar interiors was a milestone in science and this discovery was made by my mentor and collaborator the late Sir Fred Hoyle.

The supernova explosions that take place at the end of the life of a massive star scatter the constituent atoms of biology into interstellar space as vast clouds of gas and dust from which new stars and planets form. The presence of organic molecules in interstellar clouds in large quantity is now beyond doubt. However, the manner by which some of these molecules might form from individual atoms and furthermore relate to life and biology remains a matter of controversy [12]. The question hinges upon whether the wide range of organic molecules that have been discovered in interstellar clouds over the past 3 decades represent steps towards life – prebiotic evolution which are the first steps of "abiogenesis" – or whether they are the products of biological degradation – the detritus of microbial life itself. The latter is the position that has been adopted and vigorously defended by Fred Hoyle and the present author over five decades.

The weight of evidence favours the survival of bacteria under interstellar conditions at any rate to the extent that makes viable interstellar transfers of microbial life between star systems inevitable. We do not require more than one in 10^{24} itinerant microorganisms to survive, until it becomes incorporated (in about a billion years) in a planet/comet forming event by which a new cycle of exponential amplification occurs; a few viable microbes thus turning into trillions [11,12,13]. The strong feedback loop of cosmic biology depicted in Fig.1 can account for all the astronomical data that relates to organic molecules in space.

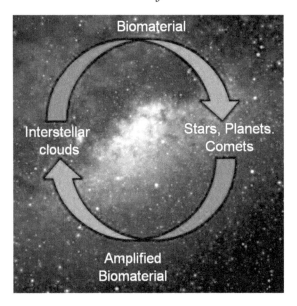

Fig.1 Bacteria and viruses expelled from a planetary system are amplified in the warm radioactively heated interiors of comets and thrown back into interstellar space, where a fraction breaks up into molecular fragments that are observed, but a non-negligible minute fraction remains viable.

This exceedingly modest requirement of microbial survival would be impossible to violate particularly for freeze-dried microorganisms that are embedded within clumps of interstellar dust. This expectation has been borne out in a long series of investigations that have been conducted both in the laboratory and in space from the 1970s to the present day. Most recently the survival of colonies of *Deinococcus radiodurans* on the exterior of the international space station (ISS) for over three years has led to shock and surprise, and an admission by the investigators that life is easily transferable between distant habitats in space.

The vast majority of bacteria in interstellar space do not and need not persist in a viable state, however. Viruses (which carry coded information in the form of DNA or RNA), compared to bacteria, have smaller target areas for cosmic-ray damage and will therefore be expected to have a relatively longer persistence in interstellar space. And both bacteria and viruses within hard frozen interiors of comets would have an almost indefinite persistence, and for this reason comets in our theory serve as long-term cosmic reservoirs of life. Interstellar clouds which would be filled overwhelmingly with the detritus of life escaping from planetary systems as well as comets will naturally include a wide range of organic molecules as has indeed been observed. However, attempts to discover the roots of abiogenesis here, as is currently fashionable, are manifestly futile in my view.[12]

By the late 1970s theoretical studies by myself and the late Sir Fred Hoyle were already converging on the inevitability of life being a cosmic phenomenon with "seeds of life" bacteria and viruses being present everywhere in interstellar space. This idea seemed to us immediately open to astronomical verification. With advances in the new field of infrared astronomy progressing rapidly and with the Anglo-Australian telescope offering the best opportunity available for this verification we made an incredibly bold assertion. If interstellar dust was largely made up of bacteria and viruses, then by observing distant stars that shine through these clouds a spectroscopic signature characteristic of bacteria and viruses should be observed. Having an accomplice at the Anglo-Australian telescope helped enormously. My brother Dayal Wickramasinghe, also an astronomer, was a Professor at the Australian National University in Canberra and had access to the Anglo-Australian telescope. To cut a long story short, he observed the infrared spectrum of a distant star near the centre of the galaxy and verified a prediction we had made earlier – the infrared fingerprint of generic bacteria and viruses. This came as a shock to everyone. Attempts to say that interstellar dust may "look" like bacteria yet not be bacteria began, and they still continue. But the case for non-biologic dust that fortuitously resemble bacteria and viruses seem now to wear thin.

By the mid-1980s together with my many collaborators (including brother Dayal Wickramasinghe) I had accumulated enough spectroscopic evidence to claim that the chemical make-up of cosmic dust as well as cometary dust was uncannily identifiable with generic bacteria and viruses. This is shown in the comparisons astronomical data and theoretical models, based on laboratory measurements, displayed in Fig.2 [11,14,15].

The Death of Science

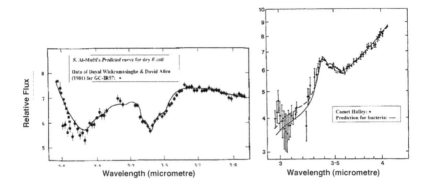

Fig. 2 Left panel: Comparison of the normalised infrared flux from GC-IRS7 (ref.14)(D.T.Wickramasinghe and D.A. Allen, 1981) with the laboratory spectrum of E coli (S. Al-Mufti). Right panel: Emission by dust coma of Comet Halley observed by D.T.Wickramasinghe and D.A. Allen on March 31, 1986 (points) compared with normalised fluxes for desiccated E-coli at an emission temperature of 320K. The solid curve is for un-irradiated bacteria; the dashed curve is for X-ray irradiated bacteria [16].

Although freeze-dried E-coli were used as our model for freeze-dried biomaterial in space, this was merely a representation of a mixture of desiccated microbiology in space. The opportunity to verify our idea that comets were sites of replication for bacteria first arose when Comet Halley approached its last perihelion in 1986. The first infrared spectrum of a comet, Comet Halley, obtained by Dayal Wickramasinghe at the Anglo-Australian telescope clearly showed consistency with bacterial dust emanating from an eruption of the comet in March 1986. This correspondence is shown in the right-hand panel of Fig.2 [16]. More recently the European Space Agency's Rosetta Mission to comet 67P/C-G has provided the most detailed observations that satisfy all the consistency checks for biology and the theory of cometary panspermia [17], as for instance in the infrared reflectivity spectrum of the comet's surface as shown in Fig.3

243

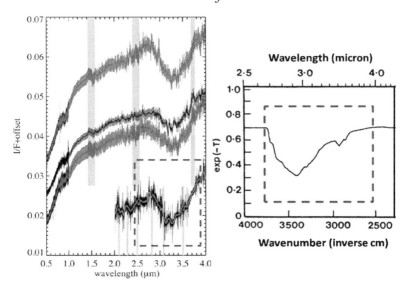

Fig. 3. *The surface reflectivity spectra of comet 67P/C-G (left panel) compared with the transmittance curve measured for E-coli (right panel).*

Many species of fermenting bacteria can produce ethanol from sugars, so the recent discovery that Comet Lovejoy emits ethyl alcohol amounting to 500 bottles of wine per second may well be a further indication that such a microbial process is operating here [18].

Fig.4. *Comet Lovejoy expelling tonnes of ethyl alcohol and sugars per minute (Courtesy NASA)*

The outbursts of comet 67P/C-G (the comet of the ROSETTA mission), as well as many other comets which are now well documented, particularly those erupting at very great distances from the sun could not result from a simple volatilisation of the comet's surface, but rather from gas pressure built up in subsurface (presumed liquid) domains. This was dramatically seen in the case of the giant comet C/2014 UN271 (Bernardinelli-Bernstein) that erupted beyond the orbit of Neptune [19]. In all such cases we are witnessing the contents of pressurised $10^6–10^7$ tonne sub-surface cometary lakes flooding out with some 10% escaping as gases and entrained particles (bacteria and viruses) into the coma. It is the arrival of this type of "biological" dust at the Earth entrained in meteorites and micrometeorites that led to the origin, evolution of life over geological timescales.

6. Capture of comet dust in the stratosphere

An obvious place to find evidence of dust and microorganisms from comets is the Earth's stratosphere, above 30 kilometres from the ground. Cometary meteoroids (fragments of comets) and interplanetary dust particles are known to enter the atmosphere in vast quantity, at a more or less steady rate, averaging about 100 tonne/day. Although much of this incoming debris burns up as meteors a significant fraction of it will in fact survive entry. Cometary dust particles of micrometre sizes, arriving as clumps and dispersing in the high stratosphere, would be slowed down gently and would not all be destructively heated. The Earth's atmosphere could thus serve as an ideal collector of cometary dust, which in my view would inevitably include bacteria and viruses. Such a microbial input would continually interact with and augment the terrestrial biosphere.

In 2001 the Indian Space Research Organisation (ISRO) collaborated with a team led by me in Cardiff UK to launch a balloon into the stratosphere carrying devices to collect stratospheric air under aseptic conditions [20]. The procedure involved the use of cryogenically cooled stainless-steel cylinders that were evacuated and fitted with valves that could be opened when they reached a predetermined altitude. Large quantities of stratospheric air containing dispersed particulate matter (including biomaterial) were thus collected from heights up to 41km and brought back to our laboratories for analysis. The stratospheric samples revealed evidence of 10 micron-sized bacterial clumps that could not be cultured, but were nevertheless confirmed to be biological in character by the use of a fluorescent dye (carbocyanine). The uptake of the dye revealed the presence of viable but not culturable living cells in the clumps (Fig.5).

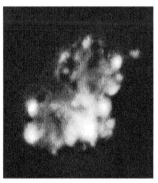

Fig 5. Clump of viable bacteria brought down from 41 km which could not be cultured but fluorescing in a carbocyanine dye.

A later balloon flight in 2008 led to the recovery of more stratospheric material and analysis by Dr. S. Shivaji and his colleagues in India.[21] This yielded cultures of three hitherto unknown microbial species which were all highly resistant to ultraviolet light and presumed to be of extraterrestrial origin. One of the newly discovered species was named Janibacter hoylei, in honour of Sir Fred Hoyle. All the new bacteria that were discovered had a large fraction (80%) of their DNA identical to terrestrially common phenotypes, but they were sufficiently different to be listed as "new" types. Although this similarity of genome has been used by sceptics to assert that they must somehow and against all the odds have been lofted from the Earth, in my view this does not follow. Moreover, if all bacteria on the Earth has originated from space and in a cosmic context in the first place, strong similarities of sequences to "indigenous" terrestrial bacteria are indeed to be expected and will always be found.

Perhaps the most dramatic instance of recovering cometary microorganisms from space was the 2018 report by a team of Russian cosmonauts who claimed the recovery of a variety of rare so-called extremophilic microorganisms from the outside of the International Space Station that orbits the Earth at a height of 400km [22]. No claim of terrestrial contamination appears to be tenable, and this is perhaps the clearest direct proof thus far of cometary organisms entering the Earth's vicinity and splashing on the windows of the ISS.

The best estimate of the total input to the Earth of bacteria and viruses based on stratospheric sampling carried out thus far amounts to an average of three tonnes per day, about 3% of the total input of meteorites that I already mentioned. This converts to a staggering 10^8 bacteria per square metre and some 10^{10} viruses per square metre arriving from space at the Earth's surface every day. The reason that this has gone unnoticed thus far is that such an ongoing ingress of new microbiota is swamped overwhelmingly by many orders of magnitude by the population of the pre-existing terrestrial microbial flora. The "microbiomes" of individual humans and indeed of all members of all living species are replete with trillions of individual bacteria and viruses, a large fraction of which is continually replenished from space.

7. The role of viruses in evolution

After the human genome was fully sequenced at the dawn of the millennium our cosmic ancestry was essentially laid bare. The discovery that only 25,000 genes exist to code for all our proteins left the vast majority of our seemingly redundant DNA to be comprised of viral derivatives. There is now little doubt that much of our genetic inheritance may be comprised of DNA actually delivered by viruses. They show up as LINEs (Long Interspersed Nuclear Elements) (21%), and SINEs (Short Interspersed Nuclear Elements) (13%) which are retroviral derived and controlled, and HERVs (Human Endogenous Retroviruses) and LTRs (Long Terminal Repeats) (9%). These are all relics of viruses that have infected our ancestral lineage over millions of years and left their footprints in our DNA.

Over the past 4.2 billion years of terrestrial evolution of life, viruses appear to have played a key role in the advancement and development of life. When a virus invades a cell it multiplies at the expense of the invaded cell, which it does by stopping the old cell program and inserting its own program. The many viral particles thus produced in this process emerge from their host seeking more cells to invade, and so, on apparently ad infinitum. This behaviour is usually seen as an oddity of biology without any deeper meaning. But mere survival leaves the virus as a disconnected entity without a logical relationship to anything else. Once we see, however, that logical relationship is at least as valid as survival, indeed that survival is impossible without such a logical relationship, the situation becomes different. The virus becomes a program insertion device with the essential capability of forcing cells to take notice of its "will". Many such program insertions by means of viruses are needed to cope with many stages of evolution over millennia for the vast ensemble of lifeforms (species) both on Earth and elsewhere in the cosmos. Hence a cosmically vast – near infinite - population of viruses is needed. If the entry of a particular virus into cells is restricted to situations in which the host cell program and the viral program match together, it will not happen that a virus on entering a cell has precisely the right program insertion to suit the life-form in question exactly at its current stage of evolution. There will have to be very many trials before precisely the right program insertion is accomplished and evolution could then leap forward. What then is the virus to do in the vast majority of instances where the situation is not quite right? Give up the ghost and expire?

Viruses seek cells, not vice versa. In anthropomorphic terms they have the job of driving evolution. They cannot give up the ghost and expire so that nothing more follows. Therefore they augment themselves by increasing their number and then they press on, forever seeking to find cells where they are needed. As soon as one looks for logical design the situation in regard to viruses makes immediate sense. Situations of mismatch between cosmic virus and host species cause pandemic diseases such as influenza. Besides causing disease on occasion viruses are crucially relevant for carrying the information for critical steps in the evolution of life – on our planet and elsewhere throughout the universe.

Our own ancestral line, that led through primates and anthropoids to *Homo sapiens* over hundreds of millions of years, shows clearly the relics of repeated viral or retroviral attacks, some presumably similar to the AIDS virus. The viral inserts at the branching points of the "evolutionary tree" showing the last stages of our cosmic ancestry that led to ourselves is shown schematically in Fig. 6.

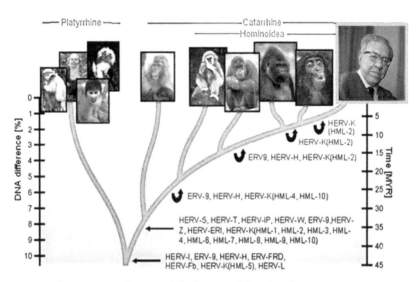

*Fig.6. Schematic evolution of the hominid line leading up to **Homo sapiens**. Note - **Homo sapiens** is represented by a photograph of my mentor the late Sir Fred Hoyle.*

Viral sequences thus added through the mechanism of pandemic disease could provide evolutionary potential that leads to new genotypes and new species at one end of the scale, and to new traits and the capacity to express our genes in novel ways at the other. It is becoming clear that our entire existence on this planet is contingent on the continuing ingress of cosmic viruses, which we had hitherto thought were merely the vehicles for disastrous pandemics of disease. Their positive role in evolution that the late Sir Fred Hoyle and I had predicted in 1982 [2] is only just beginning to be revealed.

According to the theory of cosmic biology viral genes of external origin are continually added to genomes of evolving life-forms. This has become a fact that is now difficult to deny, leaving the role of neo-Darwinian evolution to play a less important role as a fine-tuning, rather than as the main driving force. Major evolutionary traits in the development of complex life are all externally derived, and evolution essentially driven from the universe outside. If this is so the overall impression will be of a pre-programming in the higher levels of development that is manifest in biology.

The mechanism is that the relevant viral genes that were transported to Earth had evolved over cosmological timescales in innumerable locations and suddenly came to be expressed locally in the form of new species. This accounts for the stochastic nature of the geological record of evolution showing long periods of stasis interrupted by temporally bunched episodes of rapid speciation. "Punctuated equilibrium" a term now in common parlance in evolutionary biology is therefore more a description of geological facts than a theory in its own right. The relevant theory for understanding this entire corpus of data is that of cometary panspermia as reviewed in the present article.

8. Viruses and Diseases from Space

With our estimate of some 10^8 bacteria and 10^{10} viruses per square metre arriving from space at the Earth's surface every day, as we discussed earlier, it would come as no surprise to find amongst this vast input a fraction that is potentially pathogenic to plants and animals. Indeed, as we discussed earlier, the whole of evolution occurred against this backdrop of viral and bacterial input giving rise to a continuing alternation of evolutionary progress and disease.

The recorded history of medicine shows clearly that devastating plagues swept across vast tracts of land from time to time seemingly descending from nowhere. They invariably descended suddenly and after running a predetermined course, disappeared equally suddenly. In 430 BC, a devastating plague struck the city of Athens, which was then under siege by Sparta during the Peloponnesian War (431-404 BC). In the next three years, most of the population was infected and perhaps as many a quarter of the city's population died. The historian Thucydides left an eye-witness account of this plague giving a detailed description of its symptoms. Modern physicians examining these facts have not succeeded in identifying the disease with any known plague. A hitherto unknown disease caused by a pathogen – virus or bacterium of space origin seems to have been involved in 430BC.

Careful examination of a vast body of data led Fred Hoyle and one of us to conclude in 1979 that pathogenic bacteria and viruses delivered to Earth from comets provided the best explanation for many pandemics in history (23). Of particular interest to us was the study of influenza, and especially the Spanish Flu pandemic of 1918/1919 that caused some 30 million deaths worldwide. Reviewing all the available data on this pandemic Dr. Louis Wienstein wrote thus in the New England Journal of Medicine of 6 May 1976:

"The influenza pandemic of 1918 occurred in three waves. The first appeared in the winter and spring of 1917-1918..... The lethal second wave, which started at Ford Devens in Ayer, Massachusetts, on September 12, 1918, involved almost the entire world over a very short time.....Its epidemiological behaviour was most unusual. Although person-to-person spread occurred in local areas, the disease appeared on the same day in widely separated parts of the world on the one hand, but, on the other, took days to weeks to spread relatively short distances. It was detected in Boston and Bombay on the same day, but took three weeks before it reached New York City, despite the fact that there was considerable travel between the two cities. It was present for the first time at Joliet in the State of Illinois four weeks after it was detected in Chicago, the distance between those areas being only 38 miles......"

With no air travel in 1918 simultaneous first strikes in Boston and Bombay is strong evidence of a component of the virus falling in from space. Other evidence from archival sources relating to the patchiness of incidence at a more over a wide range of distance scales made us increasingly sceptical about widely-stated assertions about the horizontal spread of influenza in all later pandemics. One such assertion was that the horizontal transmission of influenza (as the main mode of transfer) is proved by the very high attack rates which occur in institutions such as boarding schools and army barracks. Other disease pathogens of space origin, and further implications of panspermia have been discussed elsewhere [24].

9. Cosmic life and emerging trends in Cosmology

In Section 2 the grotesque improbability of the transition from the chemical building blocks of life to the most primitive bacterium was already discussed. The origin of life from non-living matter was argued to require a measure of Shannon information (improbability) that can scarcely be accommodated in any model of a finite universe no matter how big, thus implying that the information needed for life is in essence a cosmological fiat. In this context it is worth reiterating that the currently favoured Big-Bang theory of the Universe – a finite

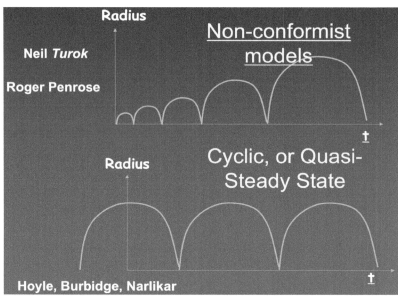

Fig.7. Schematic depiction of non-conformist models of the Universe

Fig. 8. CEERS-93316 presumed to be one of the most distant galaxies discovered thus far, at a redshift of z=16.7 implying it is now at a distance of 35 billion light-years from Earth (courtesy NASA) [30].

universe with an age of 13.8 billion years - is by no means absolutely proved. The recent discovery of a galaxy designated GN-z11 located at a distance of 13.4 billion light years (implying its formation just 420 million years after the posited Big Bang origin of the Universe) already posed a serious problem for the current consensus view of cosmology [25]. Similar problems for the Big Bang cosmological model have been discussed over a period of some three decades by small group of dissenters [26, 27]. More serious problems are to emerge as we shall see after the launch of the new James Webb Telescope scarcely months ago.

Recently Nobel Laureate Roger Penrose has come in amongst a select band of dissenters from the standard view of a unique Big Bang origin of the Universe 13.8 billion years ago [28,29]. In a theory called the "conformal cyclic cosmology" Penrose postulates that the universe undergoes an infinite number of cycles in which the Big Bang event 13.8 billion years ago is the most recent cycle of which we are a part. The difference between the Penrose models and those of Hoyle and Narlikar involving quasi-steady-state cosmologies do not appear to be vast. [26] Both theories posit cyclic models that are in general coincidentally consonant with ancient Vedic-Hindu ideas.

The James Webb Space Telescope was designed to look farther back in space and time than any other telescope, so it is not surprising that it may have detected the most distant galaxy in the cosmos [30]. The object known by the designation CEERS-93316, a galaxy – if indeed it is confirmed as a galaxy – will be some 35 billion light-years away!

One might wonder how such a distance is plausible. The Big-Bang model of the universe is only 13.8 billion years old, so how can anything be farther away than that? The answer is that the universe has expanded greatly since the light first left the galaxy about 13.6 billion years ago, so that the "proper distance" to CEERS-93316 now is in fact 35 billion light-years. This new data poses major problems for standard Big-Bang models of the Universe. And there would surely be more surprises in store – even older galaxies where none is expected, and hopefully spectroscopic data clearly pointing to life at the very dawn of time. Fred Hoyle coined the term "Big Bang" to describe a model of the Universe that he considered untenable. Now after some seven decades this position may seem to have been vindicated.

10. Concluding remarks

Of all the billions of species of life inhabiting the Earth, we humans, Homo sapiens sapiens, are arguably unique in our capacity and our desire to understand the workings and logic of the universe in which we find ourselves. Over tens of thousands of years, and more particularly in the past century, our capacity to conduct such a project has accelerated exponentially. Enormous strides of technical progress has undoubtedly been made, in biology, physics and technology. However, in certain crucial aspects that relate explicitly to our ultimate origins – the origin of life and the origin of the universe itself - the pursuit of objective truth has come under an authoritarian control, and this must spell the end of science.

References: At the end of the book

Chapter 20

Climate Change?

The Editors

Recently a number of eminent scientists have announced that there is no climate emergency.[1] This, of course, flies in the face of the prevailing opinion that global warming due to climate change is the biggest crisis facing the human race.

The Global Climate Intelligence Group (Clintel) state that '*Climate science should be less political, while climate policies should be more scientific.*' [1] We concur with the statement in italics. More science and more careful analysis is what is needed, not politicians and rich plutocrats flying around the world in private jets to climate summits.

What is wrong with climate science?

Climatology has become totally politicised. Since this has happened it is impossible to have a sensible conversation or debate. If you disagree with any part of the prevailing wisdom regarding global warming and in particular the role of carbon dioxide you risk being labelled as a "climate change denier" and being "deplatformed" even if you agree with the majority of the theory and facts.

In 2006 Al Gore turned climate change and global warming into household topics with a video of his presentations. Entitled *An Inconvenient Truth* Gore's video showed a correlation between global temperatures and CO_2 levels. [2]

So where is the problem? Surely CO_2 is important? Well now, stop frame the original video when the graphs are showing and it is clear that CO_2 levels rose **after** the world's temperature had risen, not before. It is therefore wrong to blame the initial warming on the CO_2 rise. It is rather more likely that the rise in temperature is causing the CO_2 levels to go up, released from the sea or land. In other words the interpretation of the graphs was at fault. Although the raised carbon dioxide percentage may have a feedback effect something else was pushing the original climate change. That CO_2 is a "greenhouse gas" is undeniable but it is also a "greening gas". The more CO_2 the more luxurious is the growth of vegetation and this creates an equilibrium. But we, the human race, are not allowing this to happen.

There are presently some worrying climate changes but variations in the global climate occur periodically without being due to human activity. There is, however, sufficient change due to human activity to cause major alteration in local climates. These human activities which are undoubtedly harming the planet include:

- Deforestation
- Pollution and poisoning of land and sea
- Damming rivers
- Taking excessive amounts of water from aquifers
- Overpopulation
- Agriculture and excessive over fishing of rivers and seas
- Building on flood plains, covering land with concrete etc.

Exposé of Climate Change Science Exaggeration and Incorrect Predictions

There have been many examples of climatologists overstating their case. One bad example was the widely publicised and filmed account of a polar bear supposedly dying from climate change. [3] This turned out to be fanciful thinking…yes, the bear was dying but there was no evidence that it was moribund due to climate change. It appears that the bears are not dying due to global warming and receding ice. National Geographic's apology on this was typical in its woke approach: *"Perhaps we made a mistake in not telling the whole story..but we hope that our images of this dying bear moved the conversation about climate change to the forefront…"*[3]

In the 1960s we were told by climatologists that we were heading for a new ice age that was long overdue but definitely should frighten us.

By 1999 the same people, their former prediction shown to be wrong, were telling us that the recent surge in temperatures were the last chance for us to act. Not much was done and here we are in the 2020s and the climate is very little different.

Ice at the Poles

We are frequently being told that when the ice at the poles melts there will be catastrophic effects on sea levels and dire changes for the local

wildlife such as polar bears at the North Pole and penguins at the South Pole. Whilst it may be true that Antarctica has lost ice it has certainly gained snow.[4] Snowfall there has increased by 10% over the last two hundred years and there is some confusion as to whether the loss of ice is as bad now as it has been in the past. Over the past ten years the ice shelves surrounding Antartica have increased by 0.4%![5]
But what about the terrible loss of ice in the Arctic? There was indeed considerable loss of sea ice which, incidentally, is floating and does not affect sea levels. The September minimum occurred in 2012 following the frequent occurrence of central Pacific El Nino events. However since 2012 the ice has recovered.[6] (see also *Part of the graph is missing,* chapter 2). This year's minimum was 4.67 million square kilometres, nearly 40% higher than the nadir of 2012.
Loss of ice from Greenland is worrying but has occurred before. The albedo of the glaciers is important and pollution, from industry and diesel vehicles may have darkened the surface of the glaciers.

The Great Barrier Reef

It was predicted that the Great Barrier Reef had reached the point of no return due to global warming. In fact it has burst back into life with the highest amount of coral cover since monitoring began thirty-six years ago. The reason for the recovery is unknown.[7]

Great Barrier Reef bursting back to life

Daily Telegraph 2022/08/04

Local climate change versus global change

No scientist would deny that there have been local changes in climate. The followers of the Global Warming theory state that this shows the overall effect of climate change.
How do we know that the local warming (or cooling), and the local decrease in rainfall (or increase) are part of a worldwide effect?
It is entirely possible that we do not know this.
Recently (2022) the United Kingdom experienced a very hot summer. This, the public were repeatedly told, was the result of global warming.

Supposedly for the first time ever temperatures over 100^0 F (37.8 C) were recorded. London frequently was the place with the maximum temperature. However, as Liz Osborn states online[8] *"London's temperatures get a boost from the dense concentration of large buildings that create the city's own climate, making London an urban heat-island."* Add to that the fact that the highest temperatures are regularly recorded at Heathrow… a large desert of tarmac where aeroplanes take off and land ….. And you start to question whether there has been any change in the UK at all.

Any English person over the age of fifty-five will remember the hot summer of 1976. Very similar indeed to the hot summer of 2022.

Older people may remember the series of heat waves in the 1950s.

This is weather rather than climate, and heatwaves are bad predictors of global climate change.

Perhaps it is better to look at the vegetation rather than thermometers? Certainly some places have become deserts where previously they were productive. We shall now pursue the local causes of climate change.

Deforestation

Anecdote from Paul Goddard

In 1974 whilst working in Nigeria I was taken north towards Niger and the edge of the Sahara. The agricultural missionary who took myself and a colleague told us about the Sahara. Once the breadbasket of the Roman Empire the area of desert had massively increased over the preceding two millennia. We asked the agriculturalist why this was the case.

'Goats,' was his reply. 'And the semi-nomadic people who keep them. The goats will eat anything within their reach. Any larger trees are cut down by the nomads so that when they return new green shoots will have appeared. The goats eat these and in a few years there is nothing growing and the goat herders move on to another area to despoil.'

This has been apparent for nearly fifty years and there is now fresh information to add to it. The missionary was right and areas do become deserts due to the lack of trees. Rainfall is the all important factor that allows plants to grow. It is also essential to realise that in intra-continental areas this rainfall is dependent on trees, transpiration and particulate matter such as fungal spores.[9]

This simple fact has been ignored (and disbelieved) by climatologists until very recently. There is now growing evidence that shows the importance of trees and vegetation. Tropical land surface air that has passed over extensive vegetation produces twice as much rainfall as areas over little vegetation.[9] Perversely, areas that have been denuded of vegetation are also more prone to catastrophic flooding as the rain that does fall runs straight off the hills into the valleys, the rivers swell and the land is flooded. This is particularly troublesome in built-up areas with a large population as they are also covered with concrete and tarmac.

Australia, an area often cited for its recent climate change, is a perfect place to note the effect of deforestation. An enormous rabbit-proof fence has been erected. On one side is extensive vegetation and on the other farmland. The area of farmland to the west used to be the wettest and now, with deforestation of the farmland, the area to the east with its extensive vegetation gets the most rain. [10,11]

Deforestation must stop and this is vital in rain forests. Cutting down the Amazon forest will result in a desert!

This is not due to CO_2 levels.

Pollution of Rivers and Poisoning the Seas

Run off from agriculture and industry, sewage spillage etcetera have a dire effect on rivers, aquifers and the sea. Damming rivers for hydroelectricity, and for irrigation or reservoirs, massively reduces the distal flow of rivers. Concreting and building over flood plains increases flooding downstream. Taking water out of aquifers for human activity increases flow into the seas. This has probably contributed more to sea level rise than has the melting of ice.[12] We must also stop killing whales. They are vital in the ecosystem.

These effects are not due to global climate change and are not due to the level of CO_2 in the air.

Overpopulation

The reason there is deforestation and many of the changes mentioned above is that there is a demand for it due to the massively increasing population. Overpopulation is the result of increasing longevity due to public health measures and effective medicine. The people need to be fed and they want all the modern conveniences including cars, televisions, air-conditioning and Bitcoin! (Incidentally Forbes reckon that Bitcoin consumes electricity at a rate of 127 terawatt-hours (TWh) per year, exceeding the entire annual electricity consumption of Norway! [13]

In 1950, when the editors were born, the average number of children per female was five. The global average fertility rate is now around 2.3 children per woman. It has more than halved but the population will continue to grow due to the lag. A reduced input does not have much initial effect. Eventually, at the present rate, the population is predicted to stabilise at about 10 billion but it will take another sixty years.

Rewilding

Many people are putting their faith in rewilding projects. In theory they are a very good idea but are they likely to work? As long as the population keeps growing and there is an increasing demand for food there is little incentive for such projects to succeed and if they do they are likely to harm the people living in the immediate vicinity of the rewilding.

One example is flood management. In the South West of England a decision was made, on environmental grounds, to reduce dredging of drainage canals and rivers. Result: dangerous flooding and much loss of income for the farming community. Recently a farmer took it into his own hands to do the dredging himself. He is now in jail for breaking the environmental laws.

Or consider reintroduction of species that have become locally extinct. An obvious one is the wolf. The grey wolf was extirpated from much of the Western world because it preys on livestock. It has been reintroduced in some parts of the USA but has been so successful that *"Idaho has earmarked just over $1 million for wolf killing".*[14] Why do this when the wolf has just been brought back from the edge of extinction? Because wolves and human beings cannot live peacefully together unless the wolf is tamed….and becomes a dog.

In the UK the top predator is the red fox and they have almost become extinct in the countryside following ill-thought out legislation to prevent hunting of foxes with dogs.

Hunting ban leads to 'catastrophic' decline of foxes

Daily Telegraph 9/5/23

The same people who would like to bring back wolves are also in favour of preventing trained dogs (wolves) from being used for hunting. Now farmers are shooting foxes and the fox has retreated to the urban setting. It is interesting to note that the red fox had almost been eradicated in the UK by the middle of the 19th century and, to satisfy the hunting fraternity, one  thousand European red foxes were imported annually for a time so the foxes that do remain in the UK are not truly native any longer.

Reintroduction of beavers is being trialled in the UK. It is hoped that they will alleviate the river flooding problems. It might work but beavers destroy trees in order to make their dams and the UK's rivers have been minutely managed by human beings for some centuries. Exactly which trees will be destroyed by the beavers cannot be predicted and the animals are bound to escape from any enclave they are released into.

Other animals that have been reintroduced in the UK include wild boor, wild bison, wild cats, and the sea eagle and the red kite. There are now so many of the kites that Paul Sargeantson, writing in the *Spectator,* states that they should never have been reintroduced.[15] The sea eagle in Skye famously killed the local golden eagle.

Wolves have made a big comeback in Europe but this has led to calls for a fightback by farmers citing danger to livestock and even humans.

 The Guardian
https://www.theguardian.com › environment › apr › w... ⋮

'The wolf does not belong here': German summit convened ...

28 Apr 2023 — The farmers' union is calling for a relaxation of rules over when **wolves**, strictly protected under **EU** law, can be shot, after a series of highly ...

Which comes to the crux of the problem. Bears, lions, wolves and other predators were hunted to extinction in the British Isles and elsewhere because they were a danger to, and competed with human beings. This has not changed hence their reintroduction would be hazardous. Even the boor and the bison constitute a danger.

As lovers of honey we might think that increasing the number of honey bees in the UK is a good environmentally friendly thing to do. However the honey bees are European bees imported to the UK, bringing diseases with them and competing for food with local bees.[16] But animal lovers believe that animals can do no wrong. An absurd example was recently brought to our attention: pet alpacas were permitted on a paediatric ward at a Staffordshire hospital. The staff, however, were not even allowed to wear a new fleece when it was cold, or wear a tie, and arms must be kept bare from the elbow down. The children loved seeing the cuddly alpacas and what a good job that the alpaca is so good at infection control and does have bare elbows!

The outcome of poor science in climatology

Much climate change is due to large cycles that have always affected the world but certainly some of the changes are due to human activity. Unfortunately there is too little talk about the important human causes of local climate change such as agriculture deforestation, pollution, wars and overpopulation. Concentrating on CO_2 levels has led to many stupid decisions such as pushing the purchase of diesel cars because they produce less CO_2 than petrol vehicles whilst ignoring for many years the obvious effects of increased nitric oxide (NO) and nitrogen dioxide (NO_2) and carbon smuts. Carbon trading was instigated to mitigate against excessive use of oil but the biggest winners in the UK were British Petroleum (BP) and the biggest loser was the National Health Service (NHS). The concept of "carbon footprint" was the brainchild of an advertising firm working for BP.

Big oil coined 'carbon footprints' to blame us for their greed. Keep them on the hook *23 August 2021*

We are being encouraged to buy electric cars with the prospect that all petrol and diesel will eventually be phased out. The polluting effect of making electric cars is being ignored as is the energy tied up in the construction of the petrol, diesel and hybrid cars that will be scrapped. Moreover there simply are not enough easily mineable rare mineral resources as required to make the batteries for the necessary number of electric cars and renewable energy cannot be produced or delivered in sufficient quantities to service and power such vehicles. Until this is overcome the transition is simply impossible. Most people's mobility will simply be curtailed.[17]

The introduction of 20 mph areas in most UK cities is another story. Because people will be travelling round in lower gear for longer it is inevitable that air quality will suffer yet it has been trumpeted as a way to decrease CO_2 levels and improve air quality! Log burning stoves were being encouraged until very recently on the spurious grounds that they are carbon neutral. Not only is burning trees clearly not carbon neutral but it also badly pollutes the air with polycyclic aromatic hydrocarbons to a greater extent than diesel fuel or petrol vehicles. [18] **Wood burners cause nearly half of urban air pollution cancer risk - study** **The Guardian** 17.12.2021

The obsession with CO_2 will lead to other dire effects. Already we are facing fuel shortages which, in the case of electricity generation, could be alleviated by using natural gas and scrubbers. Concentrating on the one cause of anthropogenic climate change that can correct itself risks causing major unrest and economic decline. It also alienates people against science and scientists.

Meanwhile children, and adults who should know better, think that damaging artworks and causing distress by blocking roads is a good way to get their views about climate change taken seriously. Views that simply parrot those put out by other climate extremists, unopposed because alternative ideas are "deplatformed".

We quote from Konstantin Kisin:[19]

"We should, of course, acknowledge that, to some extent, it's not their fault - they have been failed by an education system which indoctrinated them with the belief that the world is about to end, as well as their parents who neglected to explain to them that we live in a democracy where the path to achieving your political goals lies in persuading your fellow citizens to support your views, not in destroying things whose value you do not understand."

Allison Pearson has written very amusingly, and scathingly, about the Cop27 meeting.[20] First she mentions the fact that the conference could have been carried out on Zoom rather than flying 400 private jets to Sharm el-Sheikh. Then she notes that the conference is sponsored by Coca-Cola and ridicules the commitment to "climate reparations". The UK, a massive donor to overseas aid, does not owe Pakistan reparations for climate change. Pakistan's bad flooding occurs due to the deforestation. Quoting from Pearson: *"When the nation was created in 1947, 33 per cent of the total land mass was covered by forest, now that area is only 5 per cent."* In addition the population has massively grown, up from 33.7 million in the 1951 census to 225 million[21].

As noted earlier in this chapter deforestation and overpopulation result in catastrophic local climate change. Sufficient local climate change of that nature can have a global impact.

Having said that it might be prudent to provide more funds to the nations in trouble. This could be couched not as reparations but to pay the developing countries to avoid the harmful developments the Western nations have already undergone. Obviously people in need will do harmful things, such as cut down trees, destroy the rainforest, poach wildlife etcetera. Such activities provide them with a living. Funds we provide should be an alternative to such activities and make rainforests and wildlife a valuable resource.

Weird Technological Suggestions to Combat Climate Change

The dire warnings and scaremongering about climate change have led some scientist to suggest drastic measures to counter it. One possible scheme is to force moon dust from our satellite into space and settle it at the Lagrange points, thus partially shielding the sun and reducing the energy bathing Earth.[22] Such a technique risks causing a continuing winter in marginal parts of the world and moon dust is very toxic. As a correspondent in the letter pages of *New Scientist* remarked: *'Technological advances can improve lives, but the moon dust idea is lunacy.'*[23]

Giant water cannons at the poles have been suggested by one American physicist. Spraying sulphate particles into the atmosphere is another. All of these ideas could have dire consequences.

Lab grown meat has also been put forward as a way of avoiding the methane production and huge use of water, land and feed that conventional animal farming entails. With regard to lab grown meat consider again the points raised in the chapter on nutrition in this book (Chapter 16). And don't put your faith in wind power or solar. They are insufficient for the needs [24] of our enormous population and will harm the environment despite claims to the opposite. In the UK, as in many countries at our latitude, the power demands are huge and "renewables" are unreliable.

Stop Press: (Sept 2023) Dr. Patrick Brown published a paper in *Nature* arguing climate change had increased wildfires in California. One week later he admitted that he had exaggerated the effects of global warming and purposely omitted other factors such as poor forestry management *'so the paper would be published'.* [25]

References: At the end of the book

Chapter 21

Scientific Studies of the Past

Looking up 'archaeology' on Google you might come across this statement. "Because archaeology deals with physical relics, it has a level of legitimacy that no other human science can match".[1]

The proponents of archaeology, history, anthropology and palaeontology all consider themselves to be scientists. They believe that they are using the scientific method when putting the evidence together and creating the best story. But how scientific are they and do they even understand the scientific method?

Let us first define the subjects although it will be seen straight away that considerable overlap occurs.

Palaeontology is the scientific study of life of the geologic past that involves the analysis of plant and animal fossils.[2] History is the study of people, actions, decisions, interactions and behaviours.[3] Archaeology is the scientific study of the material remains of past human life and activities[4] and anthropology is the scientific study of human societies and cultures and their development.

The more ancient the people being investigated the more likely it is that the disciplines overlap.

History tends to depend on written documents or memories from primary source. Naturally such writings and memories may be inaccurate thus some archaeologists may consider their subject to be more scientific because they are dealing with objects and thus less subjective. Palaeontology, when dealing with fossils of ancient man, is straying into the realms of both history, as there may also be written evidence of the era, and archaeology, since as well as the fossils there might be objects such as stone tools found with the fossils.

But how objective or subjective are the actual people studying these subjects? Archaeologists like to consider that using processual archaeology they can develop accurate, objective information about past societies and thus their subject is less subjective than history. Historians may counter that objects cannot tell the story that a written account can give. No number of buttons, bones or bullets from a battlefield will provide the same information as a written account of the event. History, however, tends to be written by the victors. Now much of history is being rewritten to fit with the current ideology, which is mostly politically correct.

Archaeologists and palaeontologists claim to go way back before any written information and once again they consider this makes their pet subject superior. They can study prehistoric societies, carry out surveys and excavations whilst the historians lounge inside looking at old documents.

Added to these subjects, waiting in the wings, are the actual scientists, the usually unsung heroes of the piece. Geologists may be called in to assist with dating the strata that the fossils have been found in. Fossils in stone are often analysed now using palaeoradiological techniques such as computed tomography (CT). By then reconstructing the CT scans in 3D the hidden aspects of the fossils, wrapped mummies etc. can be carefully analysed before removal of the excess material is attempted. This work will often be carried out by highly skilled radiographers, technicians and radiologists who have to explain the appearances to the archaeologists and palaeontologists.

Objects may be dated using radiometric dating methods, based on the natural radioactive decay of certain elements such as potassium and carbon. These techniques provide reliable clocks to date ancient events and are again carried out by experts skilled in the science. Recently it has become possible for molecular biologists to obtain ancient DNA from old bones and even from fossils. Ancient texts may be analysed using multispectral imaging. Again this requires specialised training. Finally there is the use of artificial intelligence to analyse the data and this is the work of the computer programmers.

Despite the assistance of all these scientists, often unpaid, the stories are all written up by the historians, the archaeologists and palaeontologists. They are the ones who get the papers in Nature and they frequently appear to cherry pick the evidence to suit their pre-existing stories and their already written textbooks. Otherwise why have the archaeologists and palaeontologists taken so long to accept that human beings reached the Americas long before the Clovis culture (who were there about 13,000 years ago)? Why do they not want to even consider that the flooding after the last ice age wiped out a vast amount of culture, even perhaps a relatively settled civilisation?

Why do they think that every place they find a body was built as a tomb or that objects found in rivers and wells are all votive offerings? Surely they can understand that old buildings may become resting places for a corpse even though that was not their original purpose or that objects get thrown in rivers, wells etcetera when no longer considered useful? If that is not the case then the old prams, bicycles and shopping trolleys in the canals are all votive offerings, perhaps to the god of mammon? Why do they find it so hard to accept that the ancient Egyptians, whose mummified bodies contain traces of nicotine and cocaine, may have traded with the Americas?[5]

Negationist and Revisionist History

The anthropological subjects being discussed in this chapter are as subject to political whim as all the other sciences, or maybe more so. Recently there has been a huge push to rewrite history, archaeology and anthropology often ignoring the significance of primary source material and concentrating on making the subject politically correct.

Thus people have revelled in pulling down the statue of Colston in Bristol because he was a slaver, ignoring the fact that he was also a major philanthropist. Such is history, people are complex and their histories show conflicting sides of the same person but by removing these historical goads we run the risk of forgetting how unfair the world has always been.

Given that Colston was in many ways a fair target a more worrying example is that of David Livingstone. The PC brigade want him cancelled because, although having always been an ardent abolitionist and totally anti-slavery, he is said to have benefitted from slavery. In what way? From a poor Scottish background he went to work in a factory at the age of ten in order to earn enough money to train as a doctor. The factory is said to have benefitted from slavery and in some people's eyes that is enough to condemn him.

Recently reading a couple of books on the Irish rebellion of 1641 it was clear that the most "up to date" authors favoured much lower figures of protestant plantation owners and settlers killed by the rebelling Irish. A first hand witness had put the number at one hundred thousand and another, just a very few years later, at two hundred thousand but estimates from histories written from the 1800s onwards reduced this figure right down to two thousand. The range accepted nowadays is between two and twelve thousand. However it is clear that the first figure of 100,000 was the primary source. Was the earliest report really fifty times the actual number? The massacres were part of the excuse for Oliver Cromwell taking his army over to Ireland and crushing the Irish. It is, of course, politically incorrect to consider that Cromwell had any justification for his atrocities against the Irish so the contemporary reports must be ignored in favour of the lowest figure.

It is considered important to distinguish between the legitimate revision of history, perhaps based on a re-interpretation of data or discovery of new information, and the falsification or distortion by negationists.[6] However even the serious and legitimate revisers of history succumb to the pressure of political correctness, thus veering in one direction, usually with a left wing bias. The negativists tend to veer dangerously towards the opposite political standpoint. Both sides of the arguments enjoy writing popular books on the subject.

Similar criticism can be made of films and TV series of historical events. A recent example is that of the deeply unpleasant and murderous man, Kenneth Noye. In the BBC One drama *Gold* he is portrayed as a lovable rogue which is very far from the truth. Noye killed an undercover policeman in 1985 and stabbed to death a 21-year old man in a road rage incident in 1996[7]. Noye was known to have been in other road rage assaults and was well-known to be a vicious criminal. Unfortunately fictional versions of events tend to become accepted rather than the historical facts.

Daily Mail
https://www.dailymail.co.uk › femail › article-11744447
'They've made him into a class warrior!'

Conclusion

Presenting evidence about the past is interesting and if all the possibilities are fairly examined can be a true scientific endeavour. But clinging to one cherished interpretation that evidence refutes is clearly not the way that any science progresses. So a little more humility amongst the people writing about the past might be welcome. Perhaps they could give several options relating to their studies not just neatly packaged stories and maybe they should give a lot more credit to the real scientists who actually provide their very interesting subjects with some scientific credibility. As David Wengrow says we must overhaul our ideas about the history of human culture and give up our myths of superiority![8,9]   *References: At the end of the book*

Chapter 22

What is the legal position?

The Editors

Some of the people who have been influencing science in a malign way have definitely been criminal in their actions. Others may have behaved badly but not undertaken illegal activities. They may, of course, be sued at some later date for personal injuries they have inflicted on others. There are, not surprisingly, multiple legal actions being brought at present as a result of the response to the Covid-19 pandemic.

The Research in China

According to the International Committee of the Red Cross[1] *"The international community banned the use of chemical and biological weapons after World War 1 and reinforced the ban in 1972 and 1993 by prohibiting their development, stockpiling and transfer."*

It is very sad that the Chinese military have been so flagrantly in breach of these agreements.

The development of SARS-CoV-2 in the Wuhan Institute of Virology (WIV) was clearly in breach of the agreement. The collaboration with the WIV on gain of function (GOF) experiments, which EcoHealth Alliance were involved in, also broke the moratorium that had been set by the Obama administration.

The experimentation on prisoners without their consent was unjustified and cruel. According to the Nuremberg Code:[2]

• *Informed consent is essential.*
• *Research should be based on prior animal work.*
• *The risks should be justified by the anticipated benefits.*
• *Research must be conducted by qualified scientists.*
• *Physical and mental suffering must be avoided.*
• *Research in which death or disabling injury is expected should not be conducted.*

The WIV research only meets the second of these criteria. They certainly had performed animal work putting the spike proteins onto corona viruses, and working with bats and humanised mice.

They did not obtain informed consent and the risks were not justified. The lack of good bio-safety level 4 techniques indicates that the institute did not even meet the requirement for adequately trained scientists. Suffering of the prisoners was not avoided and the possibility of death from the novel virus or the vaccine could have been predicted. To what extent did EcoHealth Alliance know that these ethical standards were being breached?

United Kingdom

The use of fear to "nudge" the British population during the Covid-19 pandemic was certainly unethical even if courts later decide that it was not specifically illegal. Studying the ethical code of the British Psychological Society it is clear that the behavioural scientists advising the UK Government to use fear to "nudge" people's behaviour were acting unethically. Generating fear without the public's consent breaks the over-riding principles of respect and responsibility. The fact that lockdowns achieved no useful result and that the subsequent damage caused by the social interventions, backed by fear, far outweighs any advantage shows that the behavioural scientists involved were incompetent and lacked integrity. [3]

Looking solely at the issue of integrity the output from the UK Government and NHS regarding Covid-19 lacked honesty, openness and candour; the projections of possible outcomes were inaccurate and biased and there were many examples of conflicts of interest. It would not be unreasonable to suggest that they were criminally negligent and this will be up to the courts to decide….

This negligence extends to people such as Chris Whitty (Chief Medical Officer for England) and Matt Hancock (MP and former Secretary of State for Health and Social Care from 2018 to 2021), both of whom showed enormous incompetence and self interest.

Court cases are going ahead in many countries and will determine whether or not the lockdowns were legal and the mandates for Covid-19 vaccines lawful.

There was considerable confusion in the UK with regard to the difference between guidance and laws. A failure to comply with guidance was not a criminal act whilst not keeping to the law was. The police often overstepped their powers. In April 2021 a cross-party committee of UK Members of Parliament and Peers stated that *"fixed penalty notices (FPNs) - which can be as much as £10,000 - are muddled, discriminatory and unfair."⁴* On that basis they said that all FPNs should be challenged.

Certainly many fines have already been shown to have been issued incorrectly and this is not confined to the UK. Similarly people are challenging their fines in Australia ⁵,⁶ and other countries.

In the UK the climate of fear, the lockdowns and compelling people to self-isolate, the closing of legitimate businesses ….. these measures constituted the biggest infringement of personal liberty in several hundred years. The UK government rewrote the rulebook for the management of a pandemic, ignoring all the previous plans and instituting unscientific programs. To make matters worse the official opposition kept calling for harsher and harder lockdowns and more severe penalties. Effectively there was no opposition. The public did what they were told, particularly with the first lockdown. Subsequent lockdowns have been less well observed as people realised how damaging and ineffective the measure had proven. The excess deaths and the ongoing harm, the mortality and morbidity resulting from these social interventions need thorough investigation.

The vaccines are another story. The Oxford/AstraZeneca vaccine makers were the first to admit that it had rare but serious side effects. Venous thrombosis was demonstrated and could be fatal. Thus the vaccine was sidelined in favour of the mRNA techniques from Pfizer and Moderna. But the latter two companies were hiding their own sorry story. Rather too commonly the mRNA "vaccines" were causing death by myocarditis or pericarditis. Other side effects were showing up and reported to the health authorities. In the UK the NHS 111 emergency advice line was overwhelmed with people complaining about vaccine problems but the people manning the service were told, very strictly, not to let the public know about these complications. One of the co-editors (PRG) was told this confidentially by a paramedic working for 111. The editors of this book have met many people who have complained about such problems and know personally of deaths that occurred within hours of administration of the vaccines.

Refusing to allow the public to know the incidence and severity of the problems, restricting the access to the information leaflets, and mandating the use of vaccines took away the informed consent that any medical intervention is supposed to require. This alone breaches human rights laws.

Doctors and other medical staff have been bullied and penalised if they dared to speak out against the prevailing advice. In some countries laws have been proposed to force doctors to follow government and pharmaceutical industry advice. The Queensland government has passed a particularly dreadful law to this effect which will now be rolled out throughout Australia. [7]

Compelling medical staff to keep in line has been *de rigour* in the UK ever since the Ian Kennedy report on the Bristol cardiac scandal was used as an excuse to curtail medical freedom.[8] Thus the British medical staff were compelled to follow the guidance forbidding the use of repurposed drugs in Covid-19 cases. It is undoubtedly true that many thousands of patients would have been saved if the drugs had been used and this erroneous guidance alone is surely sufficient for Chris Whitty and Matt Hancock to be investigated for negligence.

Dave McGrogan, Senior Lecturer in the Faculty of Law and Business at Northumbria University, asks in a podcast [9] where were all the human rights advocates when: *"…the government was by decree making it a criminal offence to leave one's home without reasonable excuse, that human rights basically don't matter when the chips are down? Didn't they hear that freedom of conscience, the right to liberty and the right to non-discrimination are irrelevant when it comes to the unvaccinated? Weren't they informed that freedom of expression is contingent on speech not being 'harmful'? Didn't they discover during 2020-21 that basic freedoms go out of the window when the government wants to 'keep us all safe'?"*

Very reasonably he points out …

"If you want others to take your principles seriously, you have to defend them when they actually matter. Otherwise, society (usually correctly) concludes that they aren't genuine principles at all, and you're just referring to them when they suit you."

Governments such as that of the UK, and perhaps also the United States, may have colluded together to keep information about the harm caused by the Covid vaccinations out of the public domain. If this is the case prosecutions will have to be brought against ministers and civl servants. This will be difficult but failure to act may permit democracies to slip towards totalitarian control.

The WHO must be resisted in its attempt to gain control over sovereign governments at times of WHO-declared emergency. That would spell the end of democracy as well as the end of science.

Sciences other than medicine

So medical and psychological sciences have been harmed by the Covid-19 pandemic, though the antecedents for that harm stretch way back before the pandemic.

Why are there problems with the other sciences and are the anti-scientific approaches also illegal?

We have seen that the monetisation of universities has had a dire effect on their ability to produce good science in the UK. This is very unfortunate but probably not illegal.

The recruitment of university staff based on ethnicity or gender rather than ability is a different matter. Various laws in the UK state that any discrimination based on sex, religion, disability or ethnicity is illegal. This includes positive discrimination as well as negative since it is impossible to positively discriminate in favour of one group without discriminating negatively against another group.[10] The Equality Act 2010 is also supposed to protect people from harassment, although it does not include doctors as a special group who need such protection![11]

References: At the end of the book

Chapter 23

Can anything be done to halt the death of science?

This book has not been concentrating on the many obviously non-scientific ideas that float around in our society, such as the suggestion that the Earth is flat or that fairies exist. These fantasies are easily disproven and there is no point arguing with people who believe in them.

Instead we have looked at the way that we are being manipulated using bad science and the censorship of scientific debate. These practices are preventing the advancement of science and are endangering democracy. If pursued they will inevitably encourage the backlash against expert opinion and may shake our very civilisation.

Laura Dodsworth in her book *A State of Fear* [1] in addressing the problem of fighting back against "the nudge" brings out some excellent points that might help here.

"Forewarned is forearmed": if we realise that people are trying to manipulate us we can resist. This book is an attempt to show people that things are not quite right in the sciences. We do not want to put people off science, rather the reverse. But science must not be used to fool us…. The misuse of behavioural sciences to control us is very invidious. Look out for virtue signalling in particular. People telling you how good they are and how good you must be are simply tiresome and their take on what is right and proper may not, in fact, be correct. Resist the feeling that you must conform.

If you hang around in a barbershop long enough , sooner or later you are going to get a haircut….this comment by Denzel Washington, (quoted by Dodsworth) reminds me of scientific meetings I have attended recently. People at the meetings reaffirmed their belief in ideas by talking to people who believed the same things. Dodsworth is right, persuasion does occur through affirmation, repetition and contagion rather than by logical, rational discussion and argument. Hang around with the barbers and they'll eventually cut your hair. Socialise with communists or fascists and sooner or later you'll think like one.

Read only one newspaper or watch only one news channel and your outlook also becomes channelled. Even more so is the channelling effect of the social media on computers and smart phones. We should take time off from the smart phone and read books and a variety of newspapers. In this book headlines from the *Daily Telegraph* have been quoted but so have reports from the diametrically opposed *Guardian* and a variety of other news media.

We should encourage good, nuanced argument. Most things in life are not either black or white, it is mostly a pattern of varying grey. Life is complexity on the edge of order and chaos. At times we must embrace the order but at other times, the chaos.

Write letters! We need to fight fire with fire!

It is true that many publishers have sold out to China and to political correctness but there are still newspapers that show some independence and will publish letters. When an article is misleading or a downright lie you should send in your letter to the editor for publication. Here is an example of a letter sent by one of the editors of this book to the *Daily Telegraph* and subsequently published by the paper.

Covid from China

SIR – I agree with Sarah Knapton's analysis (May 20) that the doom-laden warnings concerning the Indian variant are over-egged and that it is no more dangerous than previous incarnations of Covid-19.

However, the original Covid-19 should not be referred to as the "Chinese wild-type" as there is no conclusive proof that the virus evolved naturally in the wild.

Research has shown that the furin cleavage and the charge on the spike protein are unique to Covid-19, and that it is virtually impossible to infect bats with it. Since Chinese virologists have published proof that they have added an identical spike protein to other coronaviruses, it seems the only possibility left is that Covid-19 did escape from a laboratory.

Three laboratories in Wuhan were experimenting with more than 100 different coronaviruses.
Professor Paul R Goddard
Bristol

Daily Telegraph
29/5/2021

You can find the details of how to send a letter online.[2,3,4] Even if the letter is not published it helps to hone your argument.

It is now very difficult to get a dissenting voice onto the main news channels but you can appear online on people's podcasts or write to newer TV channels such as GBNews and they may invite you onto their broadcasts. Failing that why not get somebody to interview you and record it on your smart phone? You can then upload it to Youtube.

Education and Healthcare: We must expect to pay more for education and health care. It is wrong that the essential workers are also the lowest paid. If we want good education for our children we should realise that it is expensive. If we want to be looked after by good, caring people they also need to be paid properly.

Universities need to be funded properly and undergraduates should be given grants, not expected to take out loans to fund their education. Fewer students need to go to university. Vocational courses in practical subjects should be encouraged and grants made available for the students.

Some huge companies are not paying their way. These include Amazon, Starbucks, Facebook, Google, Apple and eBay.[5] In addition many of these companies are pandering and contributing to the censorship crisis. They are in a position of considerable power: they can deplatform people, remove their twitter accounts, their videos and their blogs. Paypal, previously a subsidiary of eBay, has even shut down the financial accounts of people they were unhappy with, though it was forced to reopen them by political pressure.

Apple recently restricted an iPhone tool that was being used to defy China's censors.[6] One Weibo commentator, upset by Apple's compromise with the Chinese Communist Party leaders even asked, semi-seriously, *"So is Tim Cook a Party member or not?"*

Apple restricts iPhone tool used to defy China's censors

By **Our Foreign Staff**

updates". Some Chinese social media

Daily Telegraph Friday 11th November 2022 p15

The big companies must be forced to pay their way and to stop their censorship of science and of people with different political opinions. The way in which Paypal was made to change tack shows that it can be done if the political will is there.

It is important to realise that bad science leads to bad outcome. We saw this with the promotion of diesel cars (because they produced less CO_2 than petrol cars) and wood burning stoves (supposedly carbon neutral) with both interventions leading to a worsening of air quality.

Bad science in a different way, and more directly frightening, is the determination of virologists to make new pathogenic viruses whilst professing to find out which bugs might be a future danger. Such work is highly dangerous and, once published, could become a blueprint for would-be bioterrorists. The creator of the first artificial gene drive, Kevin Esvelt of the Massachusetts Institute of Technology, is certain that legislation and protection is needed against such attacks.[7] He points out that the "advances" in virology are creating a future in which terrorists could easily release multiple pandemics simultaneously. Professor Esvelt has released a road map of how to prevent this using *"Delay, Detect, and Defend"* .[8] This has been published online by the Geneva Centre for Security Policy whose governing body consists of representatives of 52 member states and the Canton of Geneva. At least somebody is taking this seriously!

Remarking in an editorial about cases of fraudulent research in anaesthesiology P Kranke suggested:[9] *"Perhaps a fundamental problem has been the shift towards a view of science as a business, producing 'goods' or 'outputs' to be exchanged in a global market, with the strategic planning and goals that accompany it. This shift has been enshrined in the ways that many (if not all) universities now conduct themselves, and in the methods by which funding bodies provide infrastructure support for science. In turn, this will inevitably influence the way that individual scientists behave. Artificially inflating projects and publication lists may (unfortunately) inflate a researcher's salary and reputation in the short term but it does not lead to better research or more valuable outcomes in the long term . Funding structures and methods of measuring scientific productivity need to be better at identifying quality if they are to become one of the means of discouraging fraudulent practices."*

Kranke published an interesting table of the factors contributing to scientific fraud:[9]

The Death of Science

Examples of potential disincentives and systemic sources constituting hazards with respect to scientific fraud. (Table by Kranke [9])

• Imperative to publish ('publish or perish') to preserve scientific credentials.
• Widespread assumption that research can be organised as efficiently as industry and in a perfect market, with a strong emphasis on 'pay per outcome' (i.e. publications).
• Using the impact factor or other indices such as the h-index as a performance measure determining academics' pay.
• Focus on quantity rather than quality in terms of research output.
• Requirement for large numbers of peer-reviewed scientific publications in order to attain certain academic positions.
• Dependency on (public) funding, with its imperative to have published in the relevant area.
• Focus on publishing in high-ranked (i.e. with high impact factor) journals.
• Lack of emphasis (sometimes considered 'inferior' and with less 'originality') on replication of previous findings.
• Lack of emphasis (sometimes considered 'inferior' and with less 'importance') on publication of 'negative' results (i.e. not showing that one treatment is better than another).

More articles like the one from Kranke are required and fewer people accusing dissenting scientists of being cranks! J L Mackie in his book Ethics[10] states that moralities of universal concern are impracticable: '...Primarily because a large element of selfishness...is a quite eradicable element of human nature.' We have to agree with Mackie so appealing to the better nature of scientists, politicians, civil servants and managers, is simply not going to work. We will have to persuade them that it is in their best interests to be ethical and to follow the rule from the Hippocratic Oath *primum non nocere*, translated as 'first do no harm'.

Perhaps awarding another Nobel prize or equivalent in which ethics are foremost and the *beneficial* nature of the research dominates would help. In addition all scientists, politicians, civil servants and managers should belong to a register, much as doctors do, so that they can be struck off if they offend. Maybe we can stop the rot before it is too late! In 2002 the European Environment Agency published an important report on the precautionary principle as applied to science stating that *misplaced 'certainty' about the absence of harm played a key role in delaying preventive actions.* [11] Scientists and politicians would be well advised to read the work

Artificial Intelligence

And finally we considered it might be interesting to let ChatGPT[12] have almost the last word so here is the result:

If human beings cannot understand AI results is it still science?

Answer from ChatGPT, AI program *"Yes, if human beings cannot understand AI results, it can still be considered as science. The scientific method involves using empirical evidence to test hypotheses and make predictions about the natural world. AI, as a tool, can help generate and analyze data, and provide predictions and insights that may be difficult or impossible for humans to uncover on their own.*

While it is important for scientists to understand the underlying principles and mechanisms of AI algorithms, it is not always necessary for them to fully comprehend the specific output or results generated by the AI. As long as the AI is producing valid and reliable results that are consistent with the scientific method, it can be considered a scientific tool.

However, it is important for scientists to be able to interpret and communicate the results of AI-generated data to other humans, including fellow scientists and the general public. This is important for ensuring the transparency and reproducibility of scientific research, as well as for ethical considerations surrounding the use of AI in research."

Make of that whatever you like but our belief is that it is dangerous to accept what the AI tells you especially if it is incomprehensible. So we asked another question.

Does ChatGPT make mistakes?

Answer from ChatGPT, AI program: *"As an AI language model, ChatGPT is not perfect and can make mistakes from time to time. However, the quality of its responses depends on the accuracy of the information provided to it and the complexity of the task it is asked to perform. Additionally, ChatGPT is constantly learning and improving based on its interactions with users and the feedback it receives. While it may make errors on occasion, it aims to provide helpful and informative responses to the best of its abilities."*

However, in a short article in New Scientist, Chris Stokel-Walker states that a recent investigation showed that search engines using AI generated very plausible but inaccurate results. The AI cannot presently be trusted. [13]

References: At the end of the book

Finale

Sir Richard Dearlove KCMG OBE

The Death of Science.

Science of course is not dead, nor is it even close to death. Why then should a book with this provocative title be published now? I think the question is easily answered. We are living through a period of the most rapid technological advance which potentially allows any individual the ability to communicate and access knowledge without apparent restraint.This empowerment of the individual has happened at such speed that many of the conventions and common sense attitudes that we have hitherto taken for granted are at risk of breakdown. Social and legal structures are stressed, in some instances highly so, and the impact on civic life, especially our politics is profound. However one should draw a distinction between liberal democracies on the one hand and oppressive and controlling autocracies on the other. The same technology which has diffused power away from governments and given so many choices, options and opportunities to the governed, has also become a fearsome instrument of surveillance and control, particularly where the governed are denied their democratic choices. Also those bodies, commercial and governmental, which dominate the collection and interpretation of data, are becoming disproportionately empowered. Thus we are living in a world where the rapidity and extent of technological change has created a series of social and intellectual distortions in areas where we used to enjoy, at least to a degree, comfortable familiarity. These distortions are hard to avoid and now impact us on a daily basis.

The state of scientific inquiry must therefore be judged against the background of a knowledge and communications revolution which, though it adds richness to many aspects of our daily lives, has a profound political and social cost; nor has it been accompanied by any apparent improvement in our common wisdom or judgement. It is the fate of science to be used to compensate for this lack of wisdom and be called upon by governments and interest groups alike to provide the means and the certainty to mitigate those costs. Science has thus become, in a time of great public anxiety, highly politicised. The sound bite 'follow the science' implies that science can and should provide the answers to the multifarious problems driving our anxieties. Good science of course can do just that, contributing well founded policy solutions to the many problems we face as a society, but 'good science' is not about assertion and vested interest; it has always been underwritten by transparent and thorough debate and analysis, and a willingness to admit mistakes and change ones mind in the face of rigorous evidence. However alleged scientific certainty is today being scandalously exploited to serve a perception of truth which is often more about belief in the correctness of a particular argument, and a conviction that this belief must be imposed on others - the motivations for this are variable though 'for their own good' describes the sort of arrogance which drives the refusal to listen to any counter arguments, and leads on to the terrifying concept of 'cancelling' those who disagree with an alleged certainty of view. What ever happened to the spirit of the Age of Enlightenment? It seems that we are being sucked backwards by a proliferation of minority beliefs into a darker world where prejudice and conviction are allowed equal status with our long-nurtured and hard fought for traditions of rational argument.

Many examples come to mind that are subject to this pervasive intellectual infection, because it is a type of cultural illness: the rise and significance of artificial intelligence, issues of gender and identity, the rewilding of nature, regulation of social media and the internet and so on. Two that are discussed extensively in this important book are climate change and the route towards zero carbon, and the Covid 19 pandemic. The current debate that surrounds both issues typifies the way in which the authority of science has been harnessed to the political needs of important and dominant interest groups which brook no disagreement with the programmes they espouse, asserting that their view of the science is definitive and proven, and simply cannot and should not be challenged.

The debate, or rather the lack of debate, around the origins of the pandemic is a shocking and a current example of the manipulation of scientific evidence. The pandemic was the most disruptive social, economic and political event since World War Two; it also probably killed more people globally. There are therefore very strong reasons for explaining how it started and why the SARS CoV2 virus was, in certain instances, so lethal. As the pandemic broke upon a unprepared world, leading scientists in the USA and the UK, though they themselves were immediately suspicious that the virus was an escapee from gain of function experimentation in a Wuhan research laboratory, set about persuading the scientific world that the virus was zoonotic and had jumped species thereby endorsing with all the scientific authority they could muster, and they could muster a great deal, the official narrative put out by the leadership of the Chinese Communist party. The international virological community also largely closed ranks, with a few notable and courageous exceptions, to suppress and actively prevent publication or dissemination of dissenting views. A clearer example of a fatal threat to the health of science it would be hard to find.

The origins case cannot now be proven either way, zoonotic or gain of function creation, but it is now generally accepted that the weight of scientific evidence points strongly towards the latter. However we still lack any explanation why a transparent debate about origins was actively suppressed, and this was in the West not in China where such action might have been expected, and why the scientific evidence was used selectively to push the zoonotic narrative. One hesitates to use the word conspiracy, but a secret agreement amongst a group of important scientists to mislead public and governmental opinion certainly was made, and today we are still waiting for them to acknowledge and explain their extraordinary behaviour. Are there any circumstances where it might be justified? It is hard to think of any, against the background of the catastrophic series of events and governmental decisions that was the pandemic.

The fact that the lexicon now contains the term 'climate science denier' points towards another area where scientific orthodoxy (the mild religious allusion in use of the term 'orthodoxy' is ironical but appropriate) cannot easily be challenged. Manmade climate change, and the prevailing scientific view that we absolutely must reduce the human impact on the climate, is on the cusp of turning the the world we know upside down.....in our homes, places of work and means of travel. Society is about to be forcibly reengineered, using legal instruments, to achieve a lower carbon state by deadlines which many think are simply unreachable. The political stirrings of opposition have recently become evident but a mature scientific debate about adjusting the deadlines, or indeed about the very science of climate change, and the relevance of the UK's very modest contribution to global carbon emissions is still not possible in the majority of the mainstream media or in the majority of scientific journals. The case has been made on our behalf definitively and shall not be seriously challenged. Disagreement is heretical and can have difficult consequences for those brave enough to speak up in the name of 'good science'. We no longer burn heretics at the stake but the way in which they can be marginalised, vilified and excluded from mainline academic debate amounts to a clear attempt to incinerate their contrarian views.

The views expressed in this book are timely and important because they are constructively contrarian and because they challenge a very worrying trend where scientific argument is being used not to promote transparency of investigation, debate, and decision making, but to silence it. They will also be regarded as provocative by significant segments of the scientific community and their associates, especially in the media, but they should be welcomed by the silent majority who should and hopefully will relish this frontal assault on politically correct scientific thinking. Those areas of science which claim ownership of an 'established scientific truth' need to be submitted to the Karl Popper test of the scientific method—that is continuous attempts to disprove any theory. Such an approach is especially relevant to all of us and the way we conduct our daily lives when assertive scientific truth is being used to convince us that we must accept certain decisions and policies, and that we have no longer have any choice in the matter because the consequences if we do not, would be so dreadful - whether it was lockdown and vaccinations, whether it is the accelerated switch to electric vehicles, the way we heat our homes, the introduction of ultra low emissions zones......the list is long and growing fast.

Professors Dalgleish and Goddard and their associates, have in putting together this book which belongs firmly in the polemic tradition, restated something very simple that rational argument was and is the essential building block of human enlightenment. You do not need to share their views and opinions to appreciate the importance of their underlying thesis that belief disguised as and imposed on science cannot be left unchallenged. It is a measure of the difficult and confusing times in which we live that this needs to be said. May this book help to move the dial back towards the rational.

Appendices
Appendix to Chapter 2
1. A Dissection of the Daszak Letter to *The Lancet*.

For the purpose of scientific study we have taken the liberty of reproducing parts of the infamous letter to *The Lancet* penned by Peter Daszak and his pals and available on the internet as open access. You will have to look the whole article up online The bold highlights have been added.

THE *LANCET*, CORRESPONDENCE| VOLUME 395, ISSUE 10226, E42-E43, MARCH 07, 2020
Statement in support of the scientists, public health professionals, and medical professionals of China combatting COVID-19

Four names then ,**Peter Daszak,** 2 names then **Jeremy Farrar,** then 19 more names Published: February 19, 2020

"We are public health scientists who have closely followed the emergence of 2019 novel coronavirus disease (COVID-19) ……..the scientists, public health professionals, and medical professionals of China, in particular, have worked diligently and effectively ……..
We sign this statement in solidarity with all scientists and health professionals in China who continue to save lives and protect global health during the challenge of the COVID-19 outbreak.
The rapid, open, and transparent sharing of data on this outbreak is now being threatened by rumours and misinformation around its origins. We stand together to strongly condemn conspiracy theories suggesting that COVID-19 does not have a natural origin. Scientist…. overwhelmingly conclude that this coronavirus originated in wildlife,2, 3, 4, 5, 6, 7, 8, 9, 10 as have so many other emerging pathogens.11, 12…….. Conspiracy theories do nothing but create fear, rumours, and prejudice that
jeopardise our global collaboration in the fight against this virus. We support the call from the Director-General of WHO to promote scientific evidence and unity over misinformation and conjecture.14 We want you, the science and health professionals of China, to know that we stand with you in your fight against this virus.
…………….. **We declare no competing interests.**"

References: *Look on line*
Published: February 19, 2020IdentificationDOI: https://doi.org/10.1016/S0140-6736(20)30418-9

Was *The Lancet* letter science?

The letter was masterminded by Peter Daszak who wanted to shut down the legitimate scientific debate over the Wuhan lab's involvement. It was widely known that Daszak had been working closely with the Wuhan Institute of Virology. He originally wanted to take his own name off *The Lancet* letter so that it would appear to be a spontaneous epistle from concerned scientists but some of the other people on the list thought it would look strange if his name was not there. Despite having masterminded the letter his name is neither first nor last.

The letter purposely labelled as"Conspiracy Theorists" scientists who were researching the possibility that the virus came from the WIV laboratory. This term usually refers to people who follow weird ideas on the internet, such as suggesting that our leaders are shape changing reptiles. In the context of *The Lancet* letter it is simply a term of abuse and an example of the *The straw man argument set up as a red herring.*

Daszak and pals are conducting an argument by purposely misrepresenting the views of the other side. Very few scientists considered that a conspiracy was behind the escape of the virus from the laboratory. Those who thought it did come from the Wuhan lab thought that it had done so by accident, not as the result of a conspiracy.

The aim of the letter was unscientific in its very nature. Daszak did not want scientists to uncover the truth…. he wanted to shut down debate and he very nearly succeeded.

The letter was not science and should not have been included in *The Lancet*.

Were the statements in the letter true?

Were they really all public health scientists? That is debatable. Public health is a science that specifically involves promoting healthy lifestyles, researching disease and injury prevention, as well as detecting, preventing, and responding to infectious disease. [1] The term often implies that the scientists work for government, local or national, controlling public health interventions. The authors only very loosely met that definition.

Had they watched the Chinese working diligently? Possibly, since they were working with them! But the Chinese scientists already knew the nature of the escaped virus and had patented vaccines by the time the letter was published in February 2020. Daszak, working with them, had stated on video in the autumn of 2019 that adding the spike proteins to coronaviruses was easy but the vaccines had not been successful. Subsequently the Chinese vaccines have indeed shown to be poor, working at 50% efficacy at best. (As shown by illegal tests carried out on political prisoners and the dire results in Chile.)

Daszak decided not to provide that information in the letter.

The Chinese national government (Chinese Communist Party, CCP) prevented the Chinese doctors from letting the world know about the nature of the virus and denied that it was spreading person to person even when it was absolutely obvious. The Chinese scientists were working for the CCP military. They were not protecting global health.

The statements were therefore misleading at best and, at worst, purposely false **Daszak and company chose references** that *"conclude that this coronavirus originated in wildlife"* whilst ignoring references to the opposite. This is an example of *"Ignoring unfavourable evidence".*

Opinion: *"The rapid, open, and transparent sharing of data on this outbreak is now being threatened by rumours and misinformation around its origins."* Where is the evidence for this assertion? None is given and it is purely opinion.

Virtue Signalling *"We want you, the science and health professionals of China, to know that we stand with you in your fight against this virus."*

This is an example of virtue signalling. How can we possibly disagree with these public minded scientists who are so virtuous?

No Conflicts of Interest?

"Revealed: How scientists who dismissed Wuhan lab theory are linked to Chinese researchers......Cover-up alleged over Lancet letter that effectively shut down scientific debate into whether coronavirus was manipulated or leaked from lab. The Telegraph can disclose that 26 of the 27 scientists listed in The Lancet letter had connections to the Chinese lab." Sarah Knapton, *Daily Telegraph* [2]

Knapton has got it right. The writers of the letter had a myriad of conflicts of interest which they did not admit to. Many actually worked for Daszak and EcoHealth Alliance. Daszak had received money from Fauci in order to work with the WIV. **This is an example of appalling nondisclosure**. It could very well be considered as criminal behaviour.

Virologists generally do not want their work shut down because of public concerns over safety (or for any other reason) and that may be the reason for not admitting their involvement with the research in China. The *Lancet* have not come clean over their own conflicts of interest. How much money does Elsevier receive from China? Why does the *Lancet* refuse to publish articles that criticise the Chinese government and that disagree with the Daszak letter?

Conclusion

The *Lancet* letter is still having major repercussions with just exactly the effect that Daszak wanted. It is still difficult talking about the origin of the Covid-19 virus without being called a conspiracy theorist and it is politically incorrect to even suggest that the virus came from the laboratory in Wuhan. In the UK people travelling from China, where the virus originated, have not been quarantined whilst travellers from other countries have been. The lockdowns were a result of governments copying the Chinese reported experience. If the national governments around the world had understood the true origin of the virus and the cover-up that ensued it is likely that they would not have followed the Chinese pseudo-science. This is discussed in a later section of the book.

The letter was a body blow to science in general and, with regard to the science of Covid-19, almost a complete knockout.

Appendix to Chapter 2
2. Head injury and Cycling

In the example we have not been told (and the neurosurgeon did not know) what the prevalence of wearing helmets was amongst his sample of cyclists. If exactly 50% wore helmets and there were equal numbers of equally severe injuries then he might have been right. But if the majority wore helmets and there were equal numbers with equal injuries then wearing a helmet might have been preventing injury. In fact it is entirely possible that the opposite is the case and the majority did not wear helmets…. in which case you might conclude that wearing a helmet is dangerous! But were the cyclists all of the same age and fitness? More figures we do not know! Maybe young, fit and skilful cyclists do not wear helmets but inexperienced, more feeble cyclists do…. in which case it could be that the important factor is the experience, age and fitness of the cyclist and the helmet is incidental.

Appendix to Chapter 2
3. Beauty contest

10 contestants A,B,C,D,E,F,G,H,I,J and 4 judges

Judge 1 results A, B, C, D, E, F, G, H, I, J
               4, 5, 5, 4, 6, 5, 6, 5, 5 ,5
Judge 2 results A, B, C, D, E, F, G, H, I, J
               5, 5, 5, 4, 5, 5, 6, 4, 6, 5
Judge 3 results A, B, C, D, E, F, G, H, I, J
               4, 5, 5, 4, 6 ,5, 6, 5, 5, 5
Judge 4 results A, B, C, D, E, F, G, H, I, J
               10,1,1, 1, 1, 1, 1, 1, 1, 1

Parametric A, B, C, D, E, F, G, H, I, J
          total 23,16,16,13,18,16, 19,15,17,16
A has the highest score and wins
Non-parametric (the scores above have been turned into a rank for each contestant)
Judge 1 results A, B, C, D, E, F, G, H, I, J
          Rank 9=, 3=,3=, 9=, 1=, 3=, 1=, 3=, 3= ,3=
Judge 2 results A, B, C, D, E, F, G, H, I, J
          Rank 2=, 2=, 2=, 9=,2=, 2=, 1=, 9=, 1=, 2=
Judge 3 results A, B, C, D, E, F, G, H, I, J
          Rank 9=, 3=,3=, 9=, 1=, 3=, 1=, 3=, 3= ,3=
Judge 4 results A, B, C, D, E, F, G, H, I, J
          Rank 1, 2=,2=, 2=,2=, 2=, 2=,2=, 2=,2=
Nonparametric: A, B, C, D, E, F, G, H, I, J
          21, 10, 10, 29,6, 10, 5 ,17, 9, 10
G has the lowest score (highest rank) and wins. (A is 2nd from last)

Note also that Judge 3 has exactly the same results as Judge 1 suggesting collusion but this has not seriously affected the results.

Appendix to Chapter 5

"Its science is not criticised but no-one will publish it"

The e-mail chain of rejections for some very important work showing that the Andersen article in *Nature Medicine* was flawed..Blocked for three months!
The correspondence trails with *Nature, Journal of Virology, BioRxiv & Science*
2 April - 2 July 2020
B Sørensen, A Susrud, A.G Dalgleish
****

NOTE: The research has evolved in stages:
1. Virological evidence and implications of engineered origins of SARS-CoV-2 & Bat RaTG13" - combining the Vaccine, the Aetiology of the SARS-Cov-2 spike & the evidence of retro-engineered cover-up. When this proved impossible to publish, on advice the work was split into components, and each significantly up-graded in detail.
2. The "pure' vaccine paper - published on 2 June 2020 in Quarterly Review of Biophysics - Discovery
3. The "pure" aetiology paper reconstructing the history of the Spike - serially refused by Nature (again) and Science. This advances the biochemistry on the virus's dual action construction.
4. A third paper still to be completed on "Three Viruses of interest": two bats and a magical pangolin which will explain the retro-engineered hypotheses.

1. Nature 2 - 9 April 2020

………………………………………

From: Magdalena Skipper <m.skipper@nature.com>
Date: Thursday, 2 April 2020 at 11:52
To: Gus Dalgleish <dalgleis@sgul.ac.uk>, Joao Monteiro
<joao.monteiro@us.nature.com>
Cc: Ritu Dhand <R.Dhand@nature.com>, Alison Wright <A.Wright@nature.com>
Subject: *FW: Reply to Andersen et al paper*

Dear Professor Dalgleish,
Thank you for your email and your letter. As the letter pertains to a publication in *Nature Medicine*, I am including in this reply Chief Editor of this journal – Dr Joao Monteiro. In line with our editorial policies, the journal in which the original work was published needs to have the opportunity to consider your correspondence first.
Kind regards,
Magdalena
Magdalena Skipper, PhD, D.Sc. (h.c.)
Editor in Chief, *Nature*
Chief Editorial Advisor, Nature Research
https://www.nature.com/nature
https://www.nature.com/immersive/d42859-019-00121-0/index.html
@nature | @NatureNews | @magda_skipper
ORCID: 0000-0001-8707-8369

……………………………………………

From: Gus Dalgleish <dalgleis@sgul.ac.uk>
Date: Thursday, 2 April 2020 at 20:35
To: Magdalena Skipper <m.skipper@nature.com>, Joao Monteiro
<joao.monteiro@us.nature.com>
Cc: Ritu Dhand <R.Dhand@nature.com>, Alison Wright <A.Wright@nature.com>
Subject: Re: *Reply to Andersen et al paper*
Dear Dr Skipper,
Thank you for your prompt response to our submission. We look forward to hearing from Dr Monteiro as soon as possible
This is because we believe that there is real urgency in clarifying the aetiology of Covid-19, as we have now done, most especially because, as you will appreciate from the paper itself, we approach this issue as very experienced vaccine designers who have identified a difficulty in vaccine design in this case that presents a significant hazard to public health. The need for a vaccine is very pressing, but extreme care is required given the characteristics of Covid-19 that are now revealed.
Therefore we trust that *Nature/Nature Medicine* will publish our observations without delay so that the many international teams now working on candidate vaccines can consider the points made and hopefully avoid the pitfalls that we have indicated.
We also note with some surprise that an Editorial Note was attached on 30 March 2020 to the Menachery et al 2015 paper which, as you will have seen, we have thoroughly analysed from a virological point of view. You now know from our paper that there is indeed serious scientific evidence which says that this note is no longer

correct.
Yours sincerely
Angus Dalgleish
....

From: Gus Dalgleish <dalgleis@sgul.ac.uk>
Date: Monday, 6 April 2020 at 14:56
To: Magdalena Skipper <m.skipper@nature.com>, Joao Monteiro
<joao.monteiro@us.nature.com>
Cc: Ritu Dhand <R.Dhand@nature.com>, Alison Wright <A.Wright@nature.com>
Subject: Re: *Reply to Andersen et al paper*
Dear Dr Skipper and Dr Monteiro,
We have received no communication from Dr Monteiro.
May we know please whether and when you intend to publish our reply to Andersen
et al.
Public interest demands it occurs now.
Yours sincerely
Angus Dalgleish
....

From: Gus Dalgleish <dalgleis@sgul.ac.uk>
Date: Monday, 6 April 2020 at 16:55
To: Magdalena Skipper <m.skipper@nature.com>, Joao Monteiro
<joao.monteiro@us.nature.com>
Cc: Ritu Dhand <R.Dhand@nature.com>, Alison Wright <A.Wright@nature.com>
Subject: Re: **Reply to Andersen et al paper**
Dear Dr Skipper and Dr Monteiro
With reference to my email enquiry of 1456, I and my colleagues do find your
apparent reluctance to engage with us odd.
Unless we hear from you by 5.30pm UK time today we will be obliged to draw the
conclusion that you are, in fact, not willing even to discuss in a timely fashion the
publication of our paper, a reluctance that we find extraordinary given the crisis of
global public interest with which it engages.
We hope, of course, that we are wrong because it both logical and proper for your
pages to carry our work given that you published the papers which we have
anatomised.
But if by close of business we do not have your agreement to publish at once and in
full, we will immediately take appropriate other steps in the public interest which
will, of course, include reference to our first submission being to *Nature*.

Yours sincerely
Angus Dalgleish
....

From: Joao Monteiro <joao.monteiro@us.nature.com>
Date: Monday, 6 April 2020 at 17:29
To: Gus Dalgleish <dalgleis@sgul.ac.uk>, Magdalena Skipper
<m.skipper@nature.com>
Cc: Ritu Dhand <R.Dhand@nature.com>, Alison Wright <A.Wright@nature.com>

Subject: RE: *Reply to Andersen et al paper*

Dear Dr Dalgleish,

Thank you for your follow up. We did receive your inquiry. Please be aware we are receiving a large number of inquiries and submissions at the moment. Therefore, timelines for a response are longer than usual. We appreciate your patience in the meanwhile. However, if you are not able to wait, there is the option to take your correspondence elsewhere.

Best regards,

Joao

Joao Monteiro MD PhD

Chief Editor

Nature Medicine

Springer Nature

One New York Plaza, Suite 4500, NY, NY 10004-1562

Office: +1-212-726-9355

Mobile: +1-347-266-8398

Email: joao.monteiro@us.nature.com

…………………………………………………………..

From: Joao Monteiro <joao.monteiro@us.nature.com>

Date: Tuesday, 7 April 2020 at 15:19

To: Gus Dalgleish <dalgleis@sgul.ac.uk>

Subject: RE: *Reply to Andersen et al paper*

Dear Dr. Dalgleish,

Thank you for your patience. We have now had the chance to discuss your proposed correspondence in response to 'Anderson and colleagues' published in *Nature Medicine* in March 2020. While we appreciate that the points you have raised extend the discussion about the origin of SARS-CoV2 further our opinion is that the content complements other viewpoints that have been considered and published elsewhere, and therefore would be as appropriate for publication in the specialized literature. Please note that this is not a criticism regarding the importance of the matter or the quality of your analyses, but rather an editorial assessment of priority for publication, in a time when there are many pressing issues of public health and clinical interest that take precedence for publication in *Nature Medicine*, and limited space in the journal. We also would encourage you to share your viewpoint by posting your Comment in our of the accepted preprint repositories so that it remain visible and adds to the discussion about the origin of the virus.

I am sorry that I cannot be more encouraging at present.

Kind regards,

Joao

Joao Monteiro MD PhD

Chief Editor

Nature Medicine

……………………………………………………

From: Gus Dalgleish <dalgleis@sgul.ac.uk>

Date: Thursday, 9 April 2020 at 12:07

To: Joao Monteiro <joao.monteiro@us.nature.com>
Cc: Magdalena Skipper <m.skipper@nature.com>, Alison Wright
<A.Wright@nature.com>, Ritu Dhand <R.Dhand@nature.com>
Subject: Re: Reply to Andersen et al paper
Dear Dr Monteiro
Thank you for your extraordinarily unhelpful replies. We can only conclude that the Nature editorial team does not understand that there is no scientific issue in the world at present more important than establishing with scientific precision the aetiology of the Covid-19 virus.

Your initial claim regarding volume of work is puzzling, to say the least. We bring to your attention, as we did in first writing to Dr Skipper, that Nature found it possible to publish Zhou et al within seven days of deposition of Bat RaTG13, of which virus we found evidence of recent retro-engineering.

Why you find yourselves unable to meet the same time scale for publication of the paper which we believe shows gross error in the Chinese paper, as well as in the Andersen et al Letter which stands upon it, is quite baffling. The reputational consequences for Nature of this lack of objectivity and balanced scientific viewpoints is regrettable, but a choice you have made and will have to own.

Yours sincerely
Angus Dalgleish
....

2. Journal of Virology: 7 - 20 April 2020

Professor R Sandri-Goldin,
Editor-in-Chief,
The Journal of Virology,
by personal email: rmsandri@uci.edu
7 April 2020

Dear Professor Sandri-Goldin,
Forgive us for writing to you directly to request the earliest possible publication of our attached article in the Journal of Virology. It comments on a Letter to Nature/Medicine (Andersen et al, 17 March) also attached for convenience.

We are taking this unusual step because, during our four decades' careers in virology - fifteen of them working together on vaccine design - our research on the origins of SARS-CoV-2, presented in our paper, has been unlike any other experience, and likewise the conduct of Nature. As you will see, one clear implication of our paper is that there have been two major failures in peer-review in that journal: Andersen et al 17 March and Zhou et al 2 February, both of which we anatomise.

Naturally we first submitted our paper to Nature; but we have experienced an unsatisfactory exchange of communications with the editors which revealed that journal was not willing to discuss in a timely or sensible fashion the publication of our paper. Our confidence in the collective editorship of Nature has been entirely eroded. That full correspondence is, of course, available should you and your colleagues wish to peruse it.

On virological analysis in our paper we show that, beyond reasonable doubt,

The Death of Science

Covid-19 is an engineered virus; and, almost more shocking, that Bat RaTG13 reported in Zhou et al was similarly retro-engineered aligning it with SARS-CoV-2, we surmise in order to sustain a narrative of natural causation of the current pandemic.

Our principal concern in seeking immediate publication of our paper is that as highly experienced vaccine designers, we are concerned that an incorrect understanding of the aetiology of SARS-CoV-2 may cause vaccine designers now focused on this virus to make dangerous errors. This is, in our opinion, a matter of the highest scientific responsibility in the public interest. Acting upon our aetiological findings, we have, ourselves, designed a vaccine to be effective and safe against SARS-CoV-2 that is now in preparation and will be ready for trials in September/October, which is a different topic upon which we shall write and report in due course.

Naturally we are aware of the political impact that our paper will occasion, but that cannot be our main concern as scientists and clinicians. In our profession we have an over-riding duty of truth.

Accordingly, may we ask you to expedite your review processes so that we may seek the favour of your reply at the very earliest convenience? A great deal is at stake here, Yours sincerely,

Birger Sørensen
Angus Dalgleish

……………………………………………………..

Fra: Rozanne Sandri-Goldin <rmsandri@uci.edu>
Sendt: onsdag 8. april 2020 17:52
Til: Gus Dalgleish <dalgleis@sgul.ac.uk>
Kopi: Birger Sørensen <bs@birgersorensen.no>
Emne: Re: Submission of Reply to Andersen et al and origin of COVID-19
Dear Dr. Dalgleish,

The Journal of Virology cannot consider a Letter to the Editor that discusses a manuscript that was published in another journal. Letters to the Editor for JVI must refer to articles published in JVI.

Sincerely,

Rozanne Sandri-Goldin, PhD
Editor-in-Chief, Journal of Virology

……………………………………………………..

Fra: Birger Sørensen <bs@birgersorensen.no>
Sendt: torsdag 9. april 2020 00:06
Til: 'Rozanne Sandri-Goldin' <rmsandri@uci.edu>
Kopi: 'Gus Dalgleish' <dalgleis@sgul.ac.uk>
Emne: SV: Submission of Reply to Andersen et al and origin of COVID-19
Dear Professor Rozanne Sandri-Goldin,

Thank you for your reply. Of course you are correct. We (and others) were so shocked by the conduct of Nature to whom we had first written in the normal expectation of the profession that we failed to remove traces of that earlier format. Our apologies.

Therefore, since our paper presents significant new analysis, we herewith enclose it as

293

an autonomous paper for your most urgent consideration

Kind regards,

Birger Sørensen

+47 4040 7565

…………………………………………..

Fra: asm@msubmit.net <asm@msubmit.net>

Sendt: lørdag 18. april 2020 01:15

Til: birger.sorensen@immunor.com

Emne: JVI00718-20: Manuscript Receiv

Dear Dr. Sørensen,

On April 17, 2020, we received the manuscript "Virological evidence and implications of engineered origins of SARS-CoV-2 & Bat RaTG13" by Birger Sørensen, Andres Susrud, John-F Moxnes, and Angus Dalgleish. The submission form indicates that this paper should be processed as a(n) Full-Length Text intended for publication in the section Virus-Cell Interactions.

The manuscript has been assigned the control number JVI00718-20. Take note of this number, and refer to it in any correspondence with the Journals Department or with the editor.

………………………………………………………

Fra: asm@msubmit.net <asm@msubmit.net>

Sendt: mandag 20. april 2020 21:53

Til: birger.sorensen@immunor.com

Emne: Final Decision made for JVI00718-20

Dear Dr. Sørensen:

Here is a copy of the decision letter for manuscript "Virological evidence and implications of engineered origins of SARS-CoV-2 & Bat RaTG13" by Birger Sørensen, Andres Susrud, John-F Moxnes, and Angus Dalgleish (JVI00718-20), for which you were a contributing author.

Sincerely,

Rozanne Sandri-Goldin

Editor

Journal of Virology

Subject: JVI00718-20 Decision Letter

Prof. Angus George Dalgleish

St George's, University of London

Institute of Infection and Immunity

Cranmer Terrace

London

United Kingdom

Re: JVI00718-20 (Virological evidence and implications of engineered origins of SARS-CoV-2 & Bat RaTG13)

Dear Prof. Dalgleish:

Thank you for your submission to the Journal of Virology (JVI). It was editorially evaluated by three JVI editors and I regret to inform you that we do not feel this work meets the criteria for JVI. Thus, we will not be able to consider your manuscript

further for publication.
Sincerely,
Rozanne Sandri-Goldin
Editor-in-Chief, *Journal of Virology*
....
3. BioRxiv 23 - 26 April 2020
Fra: biorxiv@cshlbp.org <biorxiv@cshlbp.org>
Sendt: torsdag 23. april 2020 14:24
Til: birger.sorensen@immunor.com; birger.sorensen@immunor.com
Emne: bioRxiv Manuscript Received
MS ID#: BIORXIV/2020/057273
MS TITLE: Virological evidence and implications of engineered origins of SARS-CoV-2 & Bat RaTG13
Dear Birger Sorensen;
This is an automatic message acknowledging your online submission to bioRxiv.
Completion of article screening typically completes within 48 hours, however, it may take longer over a weekend or holiday.
If you would like to make changes to your submission prior to it being approved for posting on bioRxiv, please contact bioRxiv at biorxiv@cshl.edu and we will return your submission. Do not create a new submission to update your manuscript as this will create a duplicate submission and will significantly delay the screening of your manuscript.
In addition, note that bioRxiv now allows you to save time submitting to certain journals or review services by transmitting your manuscript files and metadata directly. To submit your paper to a journal, please click on the link below to access your "Submit bioRxiv Preprint to a Journal or Peer Review" queue:
(https://submit.biorxiv.org/submission/
queue?queueName=send_paper_away_author)
Thank you for your submission.
Best wishes,
The bioRxiv team
....
Fra: biorxiv@cshlbp.org <biorxiv@cshlbp.org>
Sendt: søndag 26. April 2020 02:51
Til: birger.sorensen@immunor.com; birger.sorensen@immunor.com
Emne: Your submission to bioRxiv
MS ID#: BIORXIV/2020/057273MS TITLE: Virological evidence and implications of engineered origins of SARS-CoV-2 & Bat RaTG13
Dear Birger Sorensen;
We regret to inform you that your manuscript is inappropriate for bioRxiv. As part of a two-step screening process, every submitted manuscript is examined by affiliate scientists to determine its suitability for posting. bioRxiv is intended for full research papers and on screening, our affiliate scientists determined that this manuscript fell short of that description.
 Please be assured that this conclusion simply refers to the manuscript's appropriateness for bioRxiv and is not a judgment on the merits of the work

described.
You may wish to consider submitting your manuscript to preprints.org or OSF preprints. We hope you will find this information useful.
Thank you so much for your interest in bioRxiv.
Best regards,
The bioRxiv team
26 April 2020
Dear Editors,
With reference to your rejection letter that we received this morning, we have removed phrases which we can only guess you feel are 'inappropriate'. The suggestion that this is not a full paper of course we reject. It is demonstrably incorrect: this paper is packed full of new science and self-evidently new discoveries as well as critiquing previously published work – just like any other research paper, as the peer review process which preceded submission to you affirmed. We have also taken the opportunity of this slight delay to respond to further peer review in order to specify and clarify more the concept of 'charge' which we have discovered that some virologists do not appear to understand correctly.
Thus revised, we re-submit our paper to BioRxiv for earliest publication,
Thank you,
With kind regards
……………………………………………………
Fra: biorxiv@cshlbp.org <biorxiv@cshlbp.org>
Sendt: tirsdag 28. April 2020 19:05
Til: birger.sorensen@immunor.com; birger.sorensen@immunor.com
Emne: **Your submission to bioRxiv**
MS ID#: BIORXIV/2020/062620MS TITLE: Virological Evidence of Engineered Origins of SARS-CoV-2 & Bat RaTG13 and a Consequent Hypothesis of Covid-19's General Method of Action for Infectivity
Dear Birger Sorensen;
We appreciate you have edited this manuscript from your initial submission. However, bioRxiv is intended for full research papers to encourage the rapid sharing of new data and complete research manuscripts that contain such sections as Methods and Results. Our screening process has been developed to maintain the focus of the bioRxiv mission by limiting content to new research rather than perspectives, commentaries or theories. Therefore, we regret to inform you, that during screening, our affiliate scientists determined that your manuscript was not suitable for bioRxiv.
You may otherwise wish to consider submitting your manuscript to preprints.org or OSF preprints, which are preprint servers with different submission criteria compared to bioRxiv.
Best regards,
The bioRxiv team

3. The 'pure' Aetiology paper

Nature 19- 24 June 2020
From: "birger.sorensen@immunor.com" <birger.sorensen@immunor.com>

Date: Friday, 19 June 2020 at 11:32
To: "M.Skipper@nature.com" <m.skipper@nature.com>
Cc: "dalgleis@sgul.ac.uk" <dalgleis@sgul.ac.uk>, "andres.susrud@immunor.com" <andres.susrud@immunor.com>
Subject: An Historical Aetiology_180620

Dear Dr Skipper,
Greetings from Norway!
I am writing further to our earlier correspondence.
Our Vaccine candidate Biovacc-19 has now been published by Quarterly Reviews of Biophysics - Discovery, as you may have seen and now I and my co-authors wish and need to publish the attached research into the reconstructed historical aetiology of the SARS-CoV-2 Spike.
Since we sought to correct Andersen et al by a simple letter which your colleague declined to publish in *Nature Medicine*, we have advanced much more deeply into the biochemistry of the matter where we have made new discoveries, and have added a more extensive diachronic examination of published papers. We posit that the attached paper reverses the burden of proof in this very significant scientific discussion, which we seek to advance.
We have observed that several parts of this story are now appearing on pre-print servers and in journals worldwide. But there is need for an authoritative combination of the various parts, which we submit that we have done in the attached paper. Also, there is need for a lead from a journal of Nature's standing in order that this well-evidenced debate is normalised and conducted henceforth within mainstream scientific channels so that well established scientists can participate in formal investigation of these competing hypotheses, as we have done here, without accusations of conspiracy theorising.
 In view of the topicality of our findings may I request that you accept this responsibility to lead and now publish our findings in the primary Nature journal via your established accelerated route?
Mvh/Kind regards,
Birger
…………..
Birger Sørensen
Chairman
IMMUNOR
Immunor AS
Karenslyst Alle 6
NO-0278 Oslo, Norway
Mobile: +47 4040 7565
birger.sorensen@immunor.com

Fra: Magdalena Skipper <m.skipper@nature.com>
Sendt: fredag 19. juni 2020 15:02
Til: birger.sorensen@immunor.com
Kopi: dalgleis@sgul.ac.uk; andres.susrud@immunor.com

The Death of Science

Emne: Re: An Historical Aetiology_180620

Dear Dr Sorensen,
Thank you for your email and for asking that this manuscript be considered at *Nature*. We will discuss it within our editorial team and get back to you as soon as we can.
Kind regards,
Magdalena
Magdalena Skipper, PhD, D.Sc. (h.c.)
Editor in Chief, Nature
Chief Editorial Advisor, Nature Research
https://www.nature.com/nature
https://www.nature.com/immersive/d42859-019-00121-0/index.html
@nature | @NatureNews | @magda_skipper

Fra: c.thomas@nature.com <c.thomas@nature.com>
Sendt: onsdag 24. juni 2020 11:19
Til: birger.sorensen@immunor.com
Emne: Decision on Nature submission 2020-06-11495
 24th June 2020
Dear Dr. Sørensen
Thank you for submitting your manuscript entitled "A Reconstructed Historical Aetiology of the SARS-CoV-2 Spike" to be considered for publication in *Nature*. After careful review of the work, we regret to say that we are unable to publish it.
It is our policy to decline a substantial proportion of manuscripts without sending them to referees so that they may be sent elsewhere without further delay. In making this decision, we are not questioning the technical quality or validity of your findings, or their value to others working in this area, only assessing the suitability of the study based on the editorial criteria of the journal. In this case, we do not believe that the work represents a development of sufficient scientific impact such that it might merit publication in Nature. We therefore feel that the study would find a more suitable audience in another journal.
I am sorry that we cannot respond more positively on this occasion but hope that you will receive a more favourable response elsewhere soon.
Yours sincerely
Clare Thomas
Senior Editor
Nature

Correspondence with 'Science' 1- 2 july 2020
Fra: birger.sorensen@immunor.com <birger.sorensen@immunor.com>
Sendt: onsdag 1. juli 2020 23:12
Til: 'hthorp@aaas.org' <hthorp@aaas.org>
Kopi: 'Gus Dalgleish' <dalgleis@sgul.ac.uk>; 'andres.susrud@immunor.com' <andres.susrud@immunor.com>
Emne: An Historical Aetiology_July1,2020

The Death of Science

The Editor,
Science

Dear Professor Holden Thorp:

On 2 June 2020, after benefitting from extensive peer review, we published our candidate vaccine for SARS-CoV-2 in the Quarterly Reviews of Biophysics - Discovery, as you may know. Our candidate is created by a design methodology unlike any of the eight methodologies underlying the ninety or so research projects in Nature's review of projects currently in progress. Axiomatic to our method was a detailed biochemical analysis of the Spike protein of this unusual virus. We had not expected it, but the clear implication of what we found and reported in QRB-D, is that this chimera displays characteristics better explained by an hypothesis of purposive manipulation than one of natural evolution.

We have now extended our analysis into the attached paper which seeks to reconstruct the historical aetiology of the SARS-CoV-2 virus, adding a diachronic review of published papers to our fundamental bio-chemical research.

Now that Dr. Tedros Adhanom Ghebreyesus has indicated that WHO will pursue a long-overdue inquiry into the aetiology of the SARS-CoV-2 virus, which we welcome, we hope that you will support the very necessary debate that is now breaking in a second wave, following the publication of our vaccine. We are aware of significant responsible mainstream media interventions that are imminent. We are glad that this important question will now be addressed where it should be, in mainstream media and science journals, and not left to internet speculations, some of which have been both uninformed and therefore unhelpful, in our view.

It is germane to this submission that we tell you that the Editors of Nature have twice refused to publish our work – accepting neither the vaccine paper nor that on the aetiology – both times citing 'inappropriateness within their editorial policies', but explicitly excluding any criticism of the quality of our work from their refusals. We found this most peculiar. We have been disturbed to find egregious error in several prominent papers that Nature has published, as reported in the present submission. We are aware that journalists who have interviewed us are currently pressing the Editor-in-Chief Dr M. Skipper for precise answers to specific questions although at this moment of writing we do not, of course, know what answers she has given. In any event, we are convinced of our collective responsibility to conduct a fact-based scientific debate on the topic now prescribed by Dr Ghebreyesus and we earnestly hope that you share this conviction. We have a duty to pursue our research without fear or favour and regardless of political implications; and that is what we have done.

We seek publication in your journal as a contribution to advance debate, and it is as such, and solely upon its own merits, that we ask you and your colleagues to review it with all the speed due to this critical matter and with a view to swift publication in the global public interest.

Mvh/Kind regards,

Birger

Birger Sørensen

Chairman

IMMUNOR
Immunor AS
Karenslyst Alle 6
NO-0278 Oslo, Norway
Mobile: +47 4040 7565
birger.sorensen@immunor.com
………………………………………..
Fra: Holden Thorp <hthorp@aaas.org>
Sendt: torsdag 2. juli 2020 15:11
Til: birger.sorensen@immunor.com
Kopi: 'Gus Dalgleish' <dalgleis@sgul.ac.uk>; andres.susrud@immunor.com
Emne: Re: An Historical Aetiology_July1,2020
Dr. Sorenson,
Thank you for your interest. We do not publish papers that are critiques of works in other journals, so we cannot consider something along these lines.
Holden
Holden Thorp
Editor-in-Chief
Science Family of Journals
American Association for the Advancement of Science
1200 New York Ave NW
Washington, DC 20005
Landline: 202-326-6505
Cell: 202-288-6896
hthorp@aaas.org

Sorensen to Holden Thorp 2 July 2020
Dear Dr Holden Thorp
You will have read the paper by now and see that it is not a critique of papers in Nature per se; it is a discussion of the aetiology of coronavirus which happens to contradict and on richly evidenced grounds papers published elsewhere, in Nature as it happens. This is perfectly normal in science, why not in Science?

NO REPLY TO DATE

References and Bibliography

Chapter 1
Introduction and Overview

1. https://www.medscape.com/viewarticle/ 925178?src=wnl_tp10_daily_221021_MSCPEDIT&uac=285238SV&impID=4778683
2. https://en.wikipedia.org/wiki/Scientific_Revolution
3. https://www.philosophybasics.com/movements_rationalism.html).
4. https://www.london.edu/think/who-needs-experts
5. A level data Guardian 10 Aug 2021
6. Ilaria Lievore & Moris Triventi (2022): Do teacher and classroom characteristics affect the way in which girls and boys are graded?, British Journal of Sociology of Education,DOI:10.1080/01425692.2022.2122942
7. https://www.bloomberg.com/opinion/articles/2022-02-23/-follow-the-science-is-a-slogan-not-a-policy
8. https://www.merck.com
9. https://www.astrazeneca.com/our-company/great-place-to-work.html
10. A level data Guardian 10 Aug 2021
11. Ilaria Lievore & Moris Triventi (2022): Do teacher and classroom characteristics affect the way in which girls and boys are graded?, British Journal of Sociology of Education, DOI: 10.1080/01425692.2022.2122942
12. https://www.bbc.co.uk/news/entertainment-arts-57486272
13. https://commonslibrary.parliament.uk/research-briefings/cbp-9018/
14. *The War on the West*, Douglas Murray   Harper Collins
15. Racism is the Public Health Crisis *The Lancet* April 10 2021
16. "Tackling systemic racism requires the system of science to change." *Nature* May 19 2021

Chapter 2
Philosophy of Science

1. https://en.wikipedia.org/wiki/Philosophy_of_science
2. https://en.wikipedia.org/wiki/Occam%27s_razor
3. Smart M-ways show Tories' child-like faith in technology, Daily Telegraph 24/4/2023
4. No more deadly "smart" motorways to be built Daily Mail 6/4/2023
5. William R. Klemm Ph.D. Psychology Today https://www.psychologytoday.com/us/blog/ memory-medic/202104/specious-reasoning-how-spot-it-and-stop-it
6. Cline, Austin. 2019, Begging the question. https://www.thoughtco.com/begging-the-question-petitio-principii-250337
7. http://www.shakespeare-online.com/biography/ shakespeareeducation.html#:~:text=One%20can%20see%20that%20Shakespeare,his%20plays%20and%20their%20sources.
8. https://shakespeareoxfordfellowship.org/shakespeare-oxford-and-the-grammar-school-question/
9. https://allthatsinteresting.com/mother-teresa-saint
10. How to Lie with Statistics, Darrell Huff 1954 Penguin
11. https://en.wikipedia.org/wiki/Rhyme-as-reason_effect
12. Marsh, Robert (2017). "Timex and Beowulf and a copywriting secret you should know"
13. "The Rhyme-as-Reason Effect: Why Rhyming Makes Your Message More Persuasive". 2019.
14. McOwan, Peter William; Curzon, Paul (2017). The Power of Computational Thinking: Games, Magic and Puzzles to Help You Become a Computational Thinker.
15. McGlone, M. S.; J. Tofighbakhsh (2000). "Birds of a feather flock conjointly (?): rhyme as reason in aphorisms". Psychological

The Death of Science

Science11 (5):424–428. doi:10.1111/1467-9280.00282. PMID 1122891.

16. McGlone, M. S.; J. Tofighbakhsh (1999). "The Keats heuristic: Rhyme as reason in aphorism interpretation". Poetics. 26 (4): 235–244. doi:10.1016/s0304-422x(99)00003-0.
17. Kahneman, Daniel (2011). Thinking, Fast and Slow. New York: Farrar, Straus and Giroux.

Chapter 3
Politics and Science
Part 1 Political Lying, Political Correctness and the Managerial Process

1. P Goddard. The history of Medicine, Money and Politics, 2008 Clinical Press, Bristol UK
2. https://en.wikipedia.org/wiki/Political_correctness
3. https://www.independent.co.uk/life-style/catgender-bristol-university-pronoun-guide-b2010087.html
4. Tik Tok culture leaves Gen Z unfit for work says C4 head, Daily Telegraph 21.9.23
5. Paul R Goddard, Fake News, Clinical Press 2018
6. Paul R Goddard, The History of medicine, Money and Politics, pages 208-209, Clinical Press Ltd. 2008
7. Laura Dodsworth, A State of Fear, Pinter and Martin 2021
8. https://www.hepi.ac.uk/2020/03/07/mind-the-gap-gender-differences-in-higher-education/
9. https://www.ethnicity-facts-figures.service.gov.uk/education-skills-and-training/higher-education/first-year-entrants-onto-undergraduate-degrees/
10. https://www.indexmundi.com/united_kingdom/demographics_profile.html
11. https://www.ethnicity-facts-figures.service.gov.uk/work-pay-and-benefits/pay-and-income/household-income/latest)
12. Daily Telegraph: Universities accused of stifling free speech
13. https://www.thetimes.co.uk/article/dont-call-the-obese-chunky-doctors-told-szz9rjh2g)15/7/2022))
14. vCMAJ. 2010 Aug 10; 182(11): 1161–1162.
15. https://www.niddk.nih.gov/health-information/weight-management/adult-overweight-obesity/health-risks):
16. https://www.worldobesity.org/news/one-billion-people-globally-estimated-to-be-living-with-obesity-by-2030)
17. https://www.ncbi.nlm.nih.gov/pmc/articles/PMC9077150/Embryologic and hormonal contributors to prostate cancer in transgender women Simita Gaglani,1 Rajveer S Purohit,1 Ashutosh K Tewari,1,2 Natasha Kyprianou,1,2,3,4 and Dara J Lundon1,2)
18. https://www.sbs.com.au/news/the-feed/article/myth-busting-the-true-picture-of-gendered-violence/hbbqupyt8
19. https://www.ons.gov.uk/peoplepopulationandcommunity/crimeandjustice/articles/homicideinenglandandwales/yearendingmarch2021.
20. https://www.sbs.com.au/news/the-feed/article/myth-busting-the-true-picture-of-gendered-violence/hbbqupyt8.
21. https://www.independent.co.uk/voices/rotherham-grooming-gang-sexual-abuse-muslim-islamist-racism-white-girls-religious-extremism-terrorism-a8261831.html
22. https://www.military.com/daily-news/2021/05/10/nearly-half-of-female-soldiers-still-failing-new-army-fitness-test-while-males-pass-easily.html).
23. https://www.independent.co.uk/news/army-ap-washington-rand-national-guard-b2042243.html.
24. Paul R Goddard re: Bristol Cardiac Scandal in The History of Medicine, Money and Politics pp184-186 Clinical Press 2008
25. *Nearly 10 Million Patients Now Waiting for Some Form of NHS* CareDr Sheena Meredithhttps://www.medscape.co.uk/viewarticle/nearly-10-million-patients-now-waiting-some-form-nhs-care-2022a100211q?uac=285238SV&faf=1&sso=true&impID=4523476&src=mkm_ret_2

302

20812_mscpmrk_trdalrtuk03_int.

26. DIY dentistry swells amid shortfall of appointments: *Daily Telegraph* 21/9/2022
27. How the NHS fostered a serial killer by Allison Pearson, Features, The Daily Telegraph 23/8/2023
28. https://www.cato.org/study/risks-of-cbdcs

Chapter 4
Politics and Science, Part 2: Censorship

1. http://www.bristolmedchi.co.uk/the-west-of-england-medical-journal/wemj-volume-115-no1-march-2016)
2. https://www.dsma.uk/standing-notices/.
3. https://www.theoldie.co.uk/blog/why-does-the-bbc-censor-the-news JUL 07, 2020.).
4. https://www.medscape.com/viewarticle/ 976855?src=mkm_ret_220722_mscpmrk_exclusiveuk_int&uac=285238SV&impID=4448 515&faf=1
5. How secretive units tackling Covid disinformation 'strayed towards censorship' The Telegraph 2/6/2023
6. Covid critic unit broke its own rules Daily Telegraph 12/6/2023
7. https://www.hartgroup.org/cdu/

Chapter 5
Malpractice in Scientific Research? Peer Review Including the Origin of the Covid-19 Pandemic

1. Darwin's theory of evolution or Wallace's https://www.npr.org/transcripts/92059646?t=1660425164138
2. Computed Tomography in Pulmonary Emphysema, Goddard P, Nicholson E, Laszlo G and Watt I Clinical Radiology (1982) Vol 33, 379-387
3. Pathological Evaluation of Computed Tomography Images of Lung. Coddington R, Goddard P and Bradfield J Journal of Clinical Pathology (1982) Vol 35, 356-540
4. "Diagnosis of Pulmonary Emphysema by Computerised Tomography. Hayhurst, Flenley et al Lancet Vol 324, pp320-322, 1984
5. https://en.wikipedia.org/wiki/Yoshitaka_Fujii
6. https://en.wikipedia.org/wiki/Joachim_Boldt
7. Andersen, K.G., Rambaut, A., Lipkin, W.I. et al. The proximal origin of SARS-CoV-2. Nat Med 26, 450–452 (2020). https://doi.org/10.1038/s41591-020-0820-9
8. THE LANCET, CORRESPONDENCE| VOLUME 395, ISSUE 10226, E42-E43, MARCH 07, 2020 Statement in support of the scientists, public health professionals, and medical professionals of China combatting COVID-19. Charles Calisher (plus Daszak and his cronies)
9. Sorensen et al (https://www.cambridge.org/core/journals/qrb-discovery/article/biovacc19-a-candidate-vaccine-for-covid19-sarscov2-developed-from-analysis-of-its-general-method-of-action-for-infectivity/DBBC0FA6E3763B0067CAAD8F3363E527
10. P Goddard. The history of Medicine, Money and Politics, 2008 Clinical Press, Bristol UK)
11. (COVID UPDATE: What is the truth? Russell L. Blaylock Surg Neurol Int. 2022; 13: 167.https://www.ncbi.nlm.nih.gov/pmc/articles/PMC9062939/#__ffn_sectitle
12. "Could Vaccines Make Omicron Infection Worse? Scientists Weigh in on Antibody Dependent Enhancement BY JENNIFER MARGULIS AND JOE WANG." https://www.theepochtimes.com/covid-vaccines-ade_4607583.html?utm_source=healthnoe&utm_campaign=health-2022-07-21&utm_medium=email&est=Q0IaNJjhpPkwHV5B5ZM035bJJRAdkATi%2FTXac9Pe53f0HHXGF%2F17IBwKk8VFJeQ%3D
13. https://www.covidtruths.co.uk/2021/06/dr-samuel white-nhs-gp-speaks-about-the-fraud/
14. https://evidencenotfear.com/tag/dr-sam-white/
15. https://www.bmj.com/content/382/bmj.p1549.full,
16. https://www.gponline.com/doctors-vote-no-confidence-gmc-mpts-demand-new-leadership/article/1828746
17. mRNA Vaccines Contain DNA That May Turn Human Cells Into Long-Term Spike Protein Factories – Study By Will Jones Daily Sceptic 2.3.2023
18. The Real Anthony Fauci by Robert F. Kennedy Jr. Children's Health Defense
19. https://en.wikipedia.org/wiki/Hwang_Woo-suk
20. Fake News, Paul R Goddard, Clinical Press Ltd. Clinical Press 2018
21. https://simple.wikipedia.org/wiki/Thomas_Midgley

22. https://articles.mercola.com/sites/articles/archive/2023/06/14/paraquat-parkinsons.aspx?ui=8da75069bc1d7422588afebfeb52eaecf898d12796c58447a12b2fd081884b85&sd=20220211&cid_source=dnl&cid_medium=email&cid_content=art1ReadMore&cid=20230614_HL2&mid=DM1416671&rid=1828037424
23. https://www.theguardian.com/us-news/2023/jun/02/paraquat-parkinsons-disease-research-syngenta-weedkiller

Chapter 6
Virology: Gain-of-function studies

1. https://www.gmwatch.org/en/news/archive/2021-articles2/19691)
2. https://www.ncbi.nlm.nih.gov/pmc/articles/PMC3712877/)
3. https://gmwatch.org/en/news/archive/2020-articles/19437)
4. Paul R Goddard, PANDEMIC 2nd edition 2021 Clinical Press Ltd.
5. https://www.cell.com/cell/pdf/S0092-8674(20)31012-6.pdf
6. https://www.foxnews.com/opinion/fauci-covid-lab-leak-origin-theory-china-jason-chaffetz)
7. https://nypost.com/2022/01/24/emails-reveal-suspected-covid-leaked-from-a-wuhan-lab-then-censored-themselves/
8. https://www.theepochtimes.com/behind-the-scenes-of-the-natural-origin-narrative_4023181.html)
9. https://www.nature.com/articles/s41591-020-0820-9
10. https://theintercept.com/2021/09/09/covid-origins-gain-of-function-research/)
11. https://www.ncbi.nlm.nih.gov/books/NBK285579/)
12. Virus Hunters by Greer Williams
13. PANDEMIC by Paul R Goddard 1st and 2nd editions
14. https://armyhistory.org/major-walter-reed-and-the-eradication-of-yellow-fever/
15. https://www.historyofvaccines.org/content/jesse-lazear)
16. https://www.ajtmh.org/view/journals/tpmd/s1-11/6/article-p365.xml)
17. https://en.wikipedia.org/wiki/Biosafety_level#:~:text=The%20first%20prototype%20Class%20III,Laboratories%2C%20Camp%20Detrick%2C%20Maryland.
18. 1967 https://www.who.int/news-room/fact-sheets/detail/marburg-virus-disease
19. 11966 and 1978 https://en.wikipedia.org/wiki/1978_smallpox_outbreak_in_the_United_Kingdom
20. 1971 Aral smallpox incident: https://en.wikipedia.org/wiki/1971_Aral_smallpox_incident
21. 1973 https://api.parliament.uk/historic-hansard/written-answers/1973/apr/12/smallpox
22. 1977,1979 The History of Lab Leaks Has Lots of Entries: https://www.bloomberg.com/opinion/articles/2021-05-27/covid-19-and-lab-leak-history-smallpox-h1n1-sars
23. 2003- 2017 Breaches of safety regulations are probable cause of recent SARS outbreak, WHO says BMJ. 2004 May 22; 328(7450): 1222 and The Origin of the Virus (Clinical Press, Bristol) 2021
24. 2007 https://en.wikipedia.org/wiki/2007_United_Kingdom_foot-and-mouth_outbreak
25. 2015 https://doi.org/10.1038/nature.2015.17653 US military accidentally ships live anthrax to labs
26. https://www.ncbi.nlm.nih.gov/books/NBK285579/
27. Herfst, S. et al., 2012. Airborne transmission of influenza A/H5N1 virus between ferrets. Science, 22, pp. 1534-1541
28. https://osp.od.nih.gov/biotechnology/gain-of-function-research/
29. The Origin of the Virus by Paolo Barnard, Steven Quay and Angus Dalgleish
30. https://www.avert.org/professionals/history-hiv-aids/origin
31. Genetics for good or bad New Scientist 27 August 2022 p 35
32. Mercola: https://articles.mercola.com/sites/articles/archive/2022/10/26/lab-made-hybrid-covid-

virus.aspx?ui=8da75069bc1d7422588afebfeb52eaecf898d12796c58447a12b2fd081884b85
&sd=20220211&cid_source=dnl&cid_medium=email&cid_content=art1HL&cid=202210
26_HL2&cid=DM1273454&bid=1629609872

33. MP Told to 'check his behaviour' (Bristol) Weekend Post March 31ˢᵗ 2023
34. https://ici.radio-canada.ca/rci/en/news/1800416/wake-up-call-for-canada-security-experts-say-case-of-2-fired-scientists-could-point-to-espionage
35. https://www.dailymail.co.uk/health/article-11678281/Undercover-footage-reveals-Pfizer-exploring-manipulating-COVID-make-potent.html

Bibliography Chapter 6

• Paul R Goddard *PANDEMIC*, a personalised history of plagues, pestilence and war, Clinical Press Ltd August 2020 and *PANDEMIC* 2nd Edition 2021 (Clinical Press, Bristol.)
• *The Origin of the Virus* (Clinical Press 2021) Barnard, Quay and Dalgleish

Chapter 7
The Response to the Covid-19 Pandemic: Repurposed drugs

1. Chloroquine and Hydroxychloroquine in covid-19 Paul R Goddard, Nabil Jarad, Angus Dalgleish BMJ 2020;369;m1432
2. https://www.recoverytrial.net/results/dexamethasone-results
3. Hydrocortisone https://www.bmj.com/content/370/bmj.m3472
4. Davidson S and Macleod J, The Principles and Practice of Medicine 10th edition, Churchill and Livingstone 1972 page 429. High dose corticosteroids in circulatory collapse due to severe pneumonia
5. Gibbons JB, Norton EC, McCullough JS, Meltzer DO, Lavigne J, Fiedler VC, Gibbons RD. Association between vitamin D supplementation and COVID-19 infection and mortality. Sci Rep. 2022 Nov 12;12(1):19397. doi: 10.1038/s41598-022-24053-4.
6. https://articles.mercola.com/sites/articles/archive/2022/11/10/paxlovid-fraud.aspx?ui=8da75069bc1d7422588afebfeb52eaecf898d12796c58447a12b2fd081884b85
&sd=20220211&cid_source=dnl&cid_medium=email&cid_content=art1ReadMore&cid=
20221110&cid=DM1283865&bid=1641483882
7. The Real Anthony Fauci by Robert F. Kennedy Jr. Children's Health Defense

Chapter 8:
Social Interventions, Part1: Background, Inception, Definitions and Effectiveness

1. A State of Fear: How the UK government weaponised fear during the Covid-19 pandemic
2. The epidemiological relevance of the COVID-19-vaccinated population is increasing, Günter Kampf https://www.thelancet.com/journals/lanepe/article/PIIS26667762(21)00258-1/fulltext
3. Rapid Response Goddard and Dalgleish https://www.bmj.com/content/376/bmj.030/rapid-responses)
4. Cambridge Advanced Learner's Dictionary & Thesaurus Cambridge University Press
5. Oxford English Dictionary
6. International Encyclopedia of Public Health. 2008 : 454–462. Published online 2008 Aug 26. doi: 10.1016/B978-012373960-5.00380-4 PMCID: PMC7150140 Quarantine Through History A.A. Conti
7. PANDEMIC, Paul R Goddard, Clinical Press Ltd. 2020
8. Wikipedia https://en.wikipedia.org/wiki/Quarantine
9. https://www.nhs.uk/conditions/coronavirus-covid-19/self-isolation-and-treatment/when-to-self-isolate-and-what-to-do/#:~:text=Self-isolation%20is%20when,COVID-19).
10. https://en.wikipedia.org/wiki/Social_distancing
11. https://www.nhs.uk/conditions/coronavirus-covid-19/social-distancing/what-you-need-to-do/
12. https://www.nhs.uk/conditions/coronavirus-covid-19/people-at-higher-risk/advice-for-people-at-high-risk/
13. The Daily Telegraph 19/8/22 Also reported in The Week, Independent, and the Daily Mail

14. Scientific Advice at a Time of Emergency. SAGE and Covid-19 Lawrence Freedman First published: 01 August 2020 https://doi.org/10.1111/1467-923X.12885
15. https://gbdeclaration.org
16. The Independent Scientific Advisory Group for Emergencies (SAGE), The Independent SAGE Report. COVID-19: What are the Options for the UK? Recommendations for Government Based on an Open and Transparent Examination of the Scientific Evidence, 12 May 2020; https://www.the-eps.org/wp-content/uploads/The-Independent-SAGE-Report.pdf (accessed 4 July 2020)
17. Vitamin D Deficiency and Covid-19: Its Central Role in a World Pandemic by Dr David C Anderson and Dr David S Grimes Jul 31, 2020

Chapter 9
Social Interventions Part 2: The harmful effects on cancer, cardiac and respiratory conditions

1. 1 PANDEMIC P Goddard Clinical Press 1st edition 2020, 2nd edition 2021
2. 2 https://articles.mercola.com/sites/articles/archive/2022/10/25/mortality-risk-covid.aspx?ui=8da75069bc1d7422588afebfeb52eaecf898d12796c58447a12b2fd081884b85&sd=20220211&cid_source=dnl&cid_medium=email&cid_content=art1HL&cid=202210 25&cid=DM1272722&bid=1628836160
3. 3 A State of Fear: How the UK government weaponised fear during the Covid-19 pandemic, Laura Dodsworth, Pinter and Martin Ltd
4. Lord Sumption: https://www.33bedfordrow.co.uk/print-insight?id=3052:Article&printpage=true
5. Ferguson: https://theferret.scot/fact-check-neil-ferguson-covid-19-predictions/
6. HART: https://www.hartgroup.org
7. https://www.hartgroup.org/covid-19-evidence/
8. Stock Markets bounce back: https://www.bbc.co.uk/news/business-55301996
9. https://assets.publishing.service.gov.uk/government/uploads/system/uploads/attachment_data/file/902466/CCS0320353028-001_NHSPRB_Book_WEB_ACCESSIBLE__4_.pdf
10. Camille Maringe et al, The impact of the COVID-19 pandemic on cancer deaths due to delays in diagnosis in England, UK: a national, population-based, modelling study.. The *Lancet* VOLUME 21, ISSUE 8, P1023-1034, AUGUST 01, 2020
11. Impact of the COVID-19 pandemic on the detection and management of colorectal cancer in England: a population-based study Prof Eva J A Morris et al The *Lancet* Volume 6, Issue 3, March 2021, Pages 199-208
12. Hanna et al, Mortality due to cancer treatment delay: systematic review and meta-analysis. BMJ 2020; 371:m4087.
13. Nef HM et al Impact of the COVID-19 pandemic on cardiovascular mortality and catherization activity during the lockdown in central Germany: an observational study Clin Res Cardiol 2021 Feb;110(2):292-301
14. https://news.sky.com/story/coronavirus-lockdown-may-have-indirectly-caused-16-000-excess-deaths-study-12044923
15. https://statistics.blf.org.uk/
16. James le Fanu, The Surgery, Doctor's Diary, Covid has been a boon for bad GPs, Daily Telegraph April 2021
17. https://www.ons.gov.uk/peoplepopulationandcommunity/birthsdeathsandmarriages/deaths/articles/analysisofdeathregistrationsnotinvolvingcoronaviruscovid19englandandwales28december2019to1may2020/28december2019to10july2020#causes-of-non-covid-19-deaths
18. https://www.blf.org.uk/taskforce/get-in-touch/media/patients-needing-urgent-care-for-lung-conditions
19. https://digital.nhs.uk/dashboards/ers-open-data.
20. https://www.gov.uk/government/publications/respiratory-disease-applying-all-our-health/

respiratory-disease-applying-all-our-health
21. https://www.sleepreviewmag.com/sleep-treatments/therapy-devices/cpap-pap-devices/covid-19-pandemic-insomnia-cpap-use-sleep-apnea-osa/
22. https://www.news-medical.net/news/20210218/Changes-in-drinking-and-smoking-during-Englande28099s-first-COVID-19-lockdown.aspx

Chapter 10

PART 2 Mental health

1. https://www.psychiatrist.com/jcp/depression/separation-anxiety-measures-of-suicide-risk-among-patients-mood-anxiety-disorders/?utm_source=jcp-gl&utm_medium=email&utm_campaign=jcp040121a&utm_content=20m13299&mc_cid=45c5443ce3&mc_eid=84ed32a4c0 Pini S, Abelli M, Costa B, et al. Separation anxiety and measures of suicide risk among patients with mood and anxiety disorders. J Clin Psychiatry. 2021;82(2):20m13299
2. https://www.medscape.com/viewarticle/949020?src=WNL_infoc_210416_MSCPEDIT_Markle&uac=285238SV&impID=3314037&faf=1#vp_2
3. https://www.medscape.com/viewarticle/949324?src=wnl_newsalrt_uk_210415_MSCPEDIT&uac=285238SV&impID=3313417&faf=1#vp_2
4. Tanaka, T., Okamoto, S. Increase in suicide following an initial decline during the COVID-19 pandemic in Japan. Nat Hum Behav 5, 229–238 (2021). https://doi.org/10.1038/s41562-020-01042-z
5. https://www.healthline.com/health/covid-brain-fog
6. https://www.nytimes.com/2020/12/28/us/vaccine-first-patients-covid.html
7. Thomson H, Why going back to offices may affect mental health, New Scientist 17 April 2021 p10
8. https://www.who.int/news/item/08-04-2020-joint-leader-s-statement---violence-against-children-a-hidden-crisis-of-the-covid-19-pandemic#:~:text=The%20situation%20is%20aggravated%20by,marriage%20and%20child%20trafficking.
9. https://www.mirror.co.uk/news/uk-news/20000-kids-missing-school-amid-23966700
10. 10 https://www.theguardian.com/education/2018/jun/21/thousands-of-pupils-missing-from-english-school-rolls-study
11. Daily Telegraph 29 6 2021
12. https://www.healthline.com/health/respiratory-acidosis#symptoms
13. https://jamanetwork.com/journals/jamapediatrics/fullarticle/2781743 Experimental Assessment of Carbon Dioxide Content in Inhaled Air With or Without Face Masks in Healthy Children A Randomized Clinical Trial Harald Walach, PhD1; Ronald Weikl, MD2; Juliane Prentice, BA3; et al
14. We need a plan to fix the NHS backlog. Editorial . Daily Telegraph Friday 16 April 2021
15. 14 https://www.rcplondon.ac.uk/news/rcp-calls-urgent-measures-protect-and-safeguard-medical-workforce
16. 15 Daily Telegraph, Editorial, 20 April 2021
17. 16 Jonathan Sumpton : Starmer betrayed a chilling truth about lockdown. Daily Telegraph, 21 April 2021
18. 17https://www.thetimes.co.uk/article/civil-servants-must-disclose-outside-work-as-greensill-scandal-widens-qcvrbqjnc
19. 18https://homecareassistance.com/blog/health-benefits-of-socialization
20. 19Robert S Wilson 1, Kristin R Krueger, Steven E Arnold, Julie A Schneider, Jeremiah F Kelly, Lisa L Barnes, Yuxiao Tang, David A Bennett Loneliness and risk of Alzheimer disease Arch Gen Psychiatry 2007 Feb;64(2):234-40.doi:10.1001/archpsyc.64.2.234.
21. 20 https://www.medscape.com/viewarticle

944943?src=WNL_ukmdpls_210508mscpedit_gen&uac=285238SV&impID=3358561&faf=1

22. https://www.cdc.gov/obesity/adult/causes.html
23. Obesity, eating behavior and physical activity during COVID-19 lockdown: A study of UK adults EricRobinsonEmmaBoylandAnnaChisholmJoanneHarroldNiamh G.MaloneyLucileMartyBethan R.MeadRobNoonanCharlotte A.Hardman https://www.sciencedirect.com/science/article/abs/pii/S0195666320310060?via%3Dihub)
24. Fears grow of nutritional crisis in lockdown UK BMJ 2020; 370 doi: https://doi.org/10.1136/bmj.m3193
25. https://www.cancer.gov/about-cancer/causes-prevention/risk/obesity/obesity-fact-sheet#what-is-known-about-the-relationship-between-obesity-and-cancer-
26. https://www.thetimes.co.uk/article/two-million-hidden-unemployed-are-masking-true-cost-of-the-pandemic-wrfznsrcm
27. Quarter of diabetes cases missed over lockdown as obesity soars: Daily Telegraph 26.4.2021
28. Only a third could access the NHS Daily Telegraph 26.4.2021
29. Indirect effects of covid-19 pandemic on type 2 diabetes diagnosis and monitoring across the UK Matthew Carr. Virtual Diabetes UK Professional Conference 2021
30. https://www.mayoclinic.org/diseases-conditions/type-2-diabetes/symptoms-causes/syc-20351193
31. https://www.theguardian.com/business/2020/jun/14/the-past-three-months-have-proved-it-the-costs-of-lockdown-are-too-high
32. https://www.dailymail.co.uk/news/article-9386889/The-shattering-price-lockdown-health-economy-revealed-year-Covid-restrictions.html
33. https://iea.org.uk/media/lockdowns-were-a-costly-failure-finds-new-iea-book/

Chapter 11
Vaccines and Gene Therapy

1. Scarlett Yan personal communication to A Dalgleish 2021
2. Tortured in Uyghur Prison Camp, Good News September 2022 www.goodnews-paper.ork.uk
3. https://www.bmj.com/content/380/bmj.p2
4. Sørensen B, Susrud A, Dalgleish AG (2020). Biovacc-19: A Candidate Vaccine for Covid-19 (SARS-CoV-2) Developed from Analysis of its General Method of Action for Infectivity. QRB Discovery, 1: e6, 1–11 https://doi.org/10.1017/qrd.2020.8
5. The epidemiological relevance of the COVID-19-vaccinated population is increasing. Günter Kampf. The *Lancet* LETTER| VOLUME 11, 100272, DECEMBER 01, 2021Open AccessPublished:November 19, 2021https://doi.org/10.1016/j.lanepe.2021.100272
6. Rapid Response: Re: Covid-19: Fourth vaccine doses—who needs them and why? Goddard and Dalgleish https://www.bmj.com/content/376/bmj.o30/rr-1
7. https://www.gov.uk/government/publications/myocarditis-and-pericarditis-after-covid-19-vaccination/myocarditis-and-pericarditis-after-covid-19-vaccination-guidance-for-healthcare-professionals
8. https://www.ema.europa.eu/en/medicines/human/EPAR/vaxzevria-previously-covid-19-vaccine-astrazeneca
9. https://dailysceptic.org/2022/08/04/covid-vaccines-are-killing-one-in-every-800-over-60s-and-should-be-withdrawn-immediately-says-leading-vaccine-scientist/
10. https://www.floridahealth.gov/newsroom/2022/10/20220512-guidance-mrna-covid19-vaccine.pr.html
11. https://www.greekradiofl.com/en/ute-kruger-οι-επιθετικοί-και-ασυνήθιστοι-καρκ/
12. UK Health Security Agency COVID-19 vaccine surveillance report Week 40 6 October 2022
13. Covid-19: Irish GP who refused to vaccinate patients is suspendedBMJ 2021;373:n987

14. Pandemic, Paul R Goddard Clinical Press 2020
15. https://www.independent.co.uk/life-style/health-and-families/health-news/time-line-how-the-andrew-wakefield-mmr-vaccine-scare-story-spread-8570591.html
16. https://www.mctlaw.com/vaccine-injury/encephalitis-vaccine-reaction/
17. https://www.cdc.gov/vaccines/vpd/should-not-vacc.html
18. Schneider et al. Postmortem investigation of fatalities. Int J Legal Med. 2021; 135(6): 2335–2345
19. Innate immune suppression by SARS-CoV-2 mRNA vaccinations: The role of G-quadruplexes, exosomes, and MicroRNAs. Seneff et al https://doi.org/10.1016/j.fct.2022.113008
20. 20. Risk of Coronavirus Disease 2019 (COVID-19) among Those Up-to-Date and Not Up-to-Date on COVID-19 VaccinationNabin K. Shrestha, Patrick C. Burke, Amy S. Nowacki, Steven M. Gordondoi: https://doi.org/10.1101/2023.06.09.23290893
21. Carissa Wong, Subvariant 'soup' may drive wave. New Scientist 5th November 2022 p11
22. Olivier Restif1, and Bryan T GrenfellJ R Soc Interface. 2007 Feb 22; 4(12): 143–153. Published online 2006 Oct 3. doi: 10.1098/rsif.2006.0167 PMCID: PMC2358969 PMID: 17210532 Vaccination and the dynamics of immune evasion
23. Philip L. F. Johnson et al, J Virol. 2011 Jun; 85(11): 5565–5570. doi: 10.1128/JVI.00166-11 PMCID: PMC3094965 PMID: 21411537 Vaccination Alters the Balance between Protective Immunity, Exhaustion, Escape, and Death in Chronic Infections.
24. COVID-19 bivalent vaccine effectivenessNabin K. Shrestha et al https://www.medrxiv.org/content/10.1101/2022.12.17.22283625v1.full.pdf
25. https://dailysceptic.org/2023/07/06/lancet-study-on-covid-vaccine-autopsies-finds-74-were-caused-by-vaccine-journal-removes-study-within-24-hours/

Chapter 12
A Closer look at Covid-19 vaccines

1. Covid vaccine will not be available in UK before spring, says Sir Patrick Vallance (20th October 2020) https://www.youtube.com/watch?v=eDcjQHRmdqw
2. WHO doctor says lockdowns should not be main coronavirus defence. https://www.abc.net.au/news/ 2020-10-12/world-health-organization-coronavirus-lockdown-advice/12753688
3. Exercise Cygnus Report: Tier One Command Post Exercise Pandemic Influenza, 18 to 20 October 2016. https://assets.publishing.service.gov.uk/government/uploads/system/uploads/attachment_data/file/927770/ exercise-cygnus-report.pdf
4. UK needs to get COVID-19 for 'herd immunity'. Sir Patrick Vallance, Sky News (13th March 2020). https:// www.youtube.com/watch?v=2XRc389TvG8
5. Common Cold Unit. https://wellcomecollection.org/works/bhtpkxjx
6. Tseng CT, Sbrana E, Iwata-Yoshikawa N et al. Immunization with SARS coronavirus vaccines leads to pulmonary immunopathology on challenge with the SARS virus. PLoS One. 2012;7(4):e35421. https:// doi:10.1371/journal.pone.0035421
7. Su S, Du L & Jiang S. (2021) Learning from the past: development of safe and effective COVID-19 vaccines. Nat Rev Microbiol 19, 211–219. https://doi.org/10.1038/s41579-020-00462-y
8. Kanduc D, Shoenfeld Y. Molecular mimicry between SARS-CoV-2 spike glycoprotein and mammalian proteomes: implications for the vaccine. Immunol Res. 2020 Oct 68(5):310-313. https://doi:10.1007/ s12026-020-09152-6 .
9. https://www.ukmedfreedom.org/open-letters/ukmfa-open-letter-to-mhra-jcvi-and-matt-hancock-re-safety- and-ethical-concerns-of-proposed-covid-19-vaccine-authorisation-and-rollout
10. https://www.telegraph.co.uk/news/2023/03/07/covid-not-deadly-enough-fast-track-vaccines-chris-whitty- advised/
11. Minute of the JCVI Extraordinary Meeting on COVID-19 Immunisation, Thursday 29

July 2021 08:15-11:45 https://app.box.com/s/iddfb4ppwkmtjusir2tc/file/941427448413
12. https://www.sec.gov/Archives/edgar/data/1682852/000168285220000017/ mrna-20200630.htm#i8ebe2c9c2ccd487c851f72dd23b1630b_121 see page 69
13. WHO (2020). Evaluation of the quality, safety and efficacy of RNA-based 6 prophylactic vaccines for infectious diseases: regulatory considerations. https://cdn.who.int/media/ docs/default-source/biologicals/ ecbs/reg-considerations-on-rna-vaccines_1st-draft_pc_tz_22122020.pdf?sfvrsn=c13e1e20_3
14. Public Health and Medical Professionals for Transparency. https://phmpt.org/
15. Australian Government Therapeutic Goods Administration (January 2021). Nonclinical Evaluation Report BNT162b2 [mRNA] COVID-19 vaccine (COMIRNATYTM) https:// www.tga.gov.au/sites/default/files/ foi-2389-06.pdf (see p45, Table 4-2)
16. https://assets.publishing.service.gov.uk/government/uploads/system/uploads/ attachment_data/file/1112667/ COVID-19_mRNA_Vaccine_BNT162b2__UKPAR___PFIZER_BIONTECH_ext_of_indi cation_11.6.2021.pdf
17. https://www.icmra.info/drupal/en/covid-19/ statement_on_continuation_of_vaccine_trials
18. Walter EB, Talaat KR, Sabharwal C et al (2022). Evaluation of the BNT162b2 Covid-19 Vaccine in Children 5 to 11 Years of Age. https://www.nejm.org/doi/full/10.1056/ NEJMoa2116298
19. Thomas SJ, Moreira ED Jr, Kitchin N et al (2021). Safety and Efficacy of the BNT162b2 mRNA Covid-19Vaccine through 6 Months. https://www.ncbi.nlm.nih.gov/pmc/articles/ PMC8461570/
20. https://www.gov.uk/government/publications/coronavirus-covid-19-vaccine-adverse-reactions/coronavirus-vaccine-summary-of-yellow-card-reporting--2
21. Oster M. mRNA COVID-19 Vaccine-Associated Myocarditis. https://www.fda.gov/media/ 153514/download
22. Pfizer-BioNTech COVID-19 Vaccine Emergency Use Authorization Review Memorandum (November 2020). https://www.fda.gov/media/144416/download
23. Shrotri M, Krutikov M, Palmer T et al (2021). Vaccine effectiveness of the first dose of ChAdOx1 nCoV-19 and BNT162b2 against SARS-CoV-2 infection in residents of Long-Term Care Facilities (VIVALDI study). https://www.ncbi.nlm.nih.gov/pmc/articles/ PMC8221738/
24. Bar-On YM, Goldberg Y, Mandel M et al (2022). Protection by a Fourth Dose of BNT162b2 against Omicron in Israel. https://www.nejm.org/doi/full/10.1056/ NEJMoa2201570
25. Code of Practice for the Pharmaceutical Industry 2021. https://www.abpi.org.uk/ publications/code-of-practice-for-the-pharmaceutical-industry-2021/
26. https://www.theguardian.com/world/2021/jan/19/covid-related-deaths-in-care-homes-in-england-jump
27. Siglaugsson T (2022). Eleven Children Report Serious Injury From the Vaccines Versus Zero Serious Cases of Covid, Official Data From Iceland Show. https://dailysceptic.org/ 2022/07/24/eleven-children-report- serious-injury-from-the-vaccines-versus-zero-serious-cases-of-covid-official-data-from-iceland-show/
28. MHRA. The Blue Guide - Advertising and Promotion of Medicines in the UK. 3rd Edition (November 2020) https://assets.publishing.service.gov.uk/government/uploads/system/ uploads/attachment_data/file/956846/ BG_2020_Brexit_Final_version.pdf
29. https://www.gov.uk/drug-safety-update/yellow-card-please-help-to-reverse-the-decline-in-reporting-of- suspected-adverse-drug-reactions
30. Guetzkow J (2022). The Israeli Ministry of Health Actually Did a Survey of Adverse Events after The Booster Dose. https://jackanapes.substack.com/p/the-israeli-ministry-of-health-

actually-db7
31. 400,000 Cases of COVID Vaccine Injuries Found in Data Analyzed by German Health Insurer. https:// childrenshealthdefense.org/defender/covid-vaccine-injuries-german-health-insurer/? utm_source=salsa&eType=EmailBlastContent&eId=8c8ff710-927d-47ca-a1b6-6b7742002a1f
32. Hause AM, Baggs J, Marquez P et al. COVID-19 Vaccine Safety in Children Aged 5–11 Years — United States, November 3–December 19, 2021. https://www.cdc.gov/mmwr/volumes/70/wr/mm705152a1.htm
33. Mansanguan S, Charunwatthana P, Piyaphanee W et al (2022). Cardiovascular Effects of the BNT162b2 mRNA COVID-19 Vaccine in Adolescents. https://www.mdpi.com/2414-6366/7/8/196
34. Jain SS, Steele JM, Fonseca B et al (2021). COVID-19 Vaccination-Associated Myocarditis in Adolescents. https://pubmed.ncbi.nlm.nih.gov/34389692/
35. Yang F, Wang J, Li W et al (2020). The prognostic value of late gadolinium enhancement in myocarditis and clinically suspected myocarditis: systematic review and meta-analysis. Eur Radiol 30, 2616–2626 (2020). https://doi.org/10.1007/s00330-019-06643-5
36. Minute of the JCVI Extraordinary Meeting with cardiologists on COVID-19Immunisation, 1st September 2021, published 15th December 2021. https://app.box.com/s/iddfb4ppwkmtjusir2tc/file/941427461613
37. Gazit S, Shlezinger R, Perez P et al (2021). Comparing SARS-CoV-2 natural immunity to vaccine-induced immunity: reinfections versus breakthrough infections. https://www.medrxiv1101/2021.08.24.21262415v1.full
38. León TM, Dorabawila V, Nelson L et al. COVID-19 cases and hospitalisations by COVID-19 vaccination status and previous COVID-19 diagnosis. https://www.cdc.gov/mmwr/volumes/71/wr/mm7104e1.htm#
39. Raw RK, Kelly CA, Rees J et al (2021). Previous COVID-19 infection, but not Long-COVID, is associated with increased adverse events following BNT162b2/Pfizer vaccination. https://www.ncbi.nlm.nih.gov/pmc/ articles/PMC8164507/
40. Menni C, Klaser K, May A et al (2021).Vaccine side-effects and SARS-CoV-2 infection after vaccination in users of the COVID Symptom Study app in the UK: a prospective observational study. https:// www.ncbi.nlm.nih.gov/pmc/articles/PMC8078878/
41. Universal Declaration on Bioethics and Human Rights (2005). https://www.unesco.org/en/legal-affairs/ universal-declaration-bioethics-and-human-rights
42. Public Health England (2021). SARS-CoV-2 variants of concern and variants under investigation in England.https://assets.publishing.service.gov.uk/government/uploads/system/uploads/attachment_data/file/ 1009243/Technical_Briefing_20.pdf
43. Woodbridge Y, Amit S, Huppert A et al. Viral load dynamics of SARS-CoV-2 Delta and Omicron variants following multiple vaccine doses and previous infection. Nat Commun 13, 6706 (2022). https://doi.org/ 10.1038/s41467-022-33096-0
44. Collier AY, Miller J, Hachmann MP et al (2022). Immunogenicity of the BA.5 Bivalent mRNA Vaccine Boosters.https://www.biorxiv.org/content/ 10.1101/2022.10.24.513619v1.full.pdf? utm_source=substack&utm_medium=email
45. Javid: Valneva vaccine would not have got UK approval. https://www.bbc.co.uk/news/business-58510519
46. https://assets.publishing.service.gov.uk/government/uploads/system/uploads/attachment_data/file/ 1066759/Vaccine-surveillance-report-week-13.pdf See page 45, Table 14.
47. Shrestha NK, Burke PC, Nowacki AS et al. Effectiveness of the Coronavirus Disease 2019 (COVID-19) Bivalent Vaccine (2022). https://www.medrxiv.org/content/ 10.1101/2022.12.17.22283625v5.full-text
48. Class switch toward noninflammatory, spike-specific IgG4 antibodies after repeated

SARS-CoV-2 mRNA vaccination. https://doi/10.1126/sciimmunol.ade2798

49. Buhre JS, Pongracz T, Künsting I et al (2023). mRNA vaccines against SARS-CoV-2 induce comparably low long-term IgG Fc galactosylation and sialylation levels but increasing long-term IgG4 responses compared to an adenovirus-based vaccine.https://doi.org/10.3389/fimmu.2022.1020844

50. https://www.conservativewoman.co.uk/other-cancer-specialists-agree-with-me-about-vaccine-harm-but- the-authorities-still-wont-listen/

51. Open Letter to the MHRA Regarding Child Death Data – HART (hartgroup.org)

52. Machl F (November 2021). Excess mortality shock in Austria:up to 33 percent increase from the age of 15. https://report24.news/uebersterblichkeits-schock-in-oesterreich-bis-zu-33-prozent-zunahme-ab-15-jahren/? feed_id=7298

53. In the matter of The Queen (on the application of AB and CD, by their mother and Litigation Friend EF) v The Secretary of State for Health and Social Care and The Joint Committee Vaccination and Immunisation, CO-3001-2021, a non-party application was made for provision by the ONS of disclosure of information as set out in this letter.

54. Matt Hancock Grilled By Tory MP's Over Vaccine Effects Data Collection Failures - YouTube

55. Cumulative excess deaths 2020-2022 — an international comparison – HART (hartgroup.org)

56. Comparison of European deaths – HART (hartgroup.org)

57. Aarstad J, Kvitastein OA. Is There a Link between the 2021 COVID-19 Vaccination Uptake in Europe and 2022Excess All-Cause Mortality? Asian Pac. J. Health Sci., 2023;10(1):25-31. https://www.researchgate.net/publication/369204376_Is_There_a_Link_between_the_2021_COVID-19_Vaccination_Uptake_in_Europe_and_2022_Excess_All-Cause_Mortality#fullTextFileContent

58. Spieker F (2022). Excess deaths and boosters by state in Germany. https://vigilance.pervaers.com/p/ excess-deaths-and-boosters-by-state?utm_campaign=post_embed

59. Inquiry into increased neonatal deaths in Scotland gets underway – HART (hartgroup.org)

60. Carpenter D, Zucker EJ, Avorn J (2008). Drug-Review Deadlines and Safety Problems. https://doi.org/10.1056/NEJMsa0706341

61. Doshi P (2018). Pandemrix vaccine: why was the public not told of early warning signs? https:// archive.hshsl.umaryland.edu/bitstream/handle/10713/8270/Doshi_Pandemrix2018.pdf? sequence=1&isAllowed=y

62. Doucleff M (2019). Rush To Produce, Sell Vaccine Put Kids In Philippines At Risk. https://www.npr.org/ sections/goatsandsoda/2019/05/03/719037789/botched-vaccine-launch-has-deadly-repercussions

63. Dr June Raine (5th March 2022). From Watchdog to Enabler – Regulation in Covid and after. https:// www.youtube.com/watch?v=xUQfzTqPUm4

Chapter 13
The Erosion of Trust: Science in the Age of Covid

1. The origins of a critical covid myth. HART. 2023.https://www.hartgroup.org/the-origins-of-a-critical-covid-myth/ (accessed 28 Mar 2023).

2. Jimenez J-L. Shockingly, @Twitter has done what @WHO has REFUSED to do for 2.5 years. Tell us that the 'FACT: COVID-19 is NOT AIRBORNE' message from !WHO 'was not proven at the time, and is NOW CONFIRMED FALSE'Will @WHO please confirm they agree and apologize?@mvankerkhove? @DrTedros? pic.twitter.com/wcRvMW8wsV. Twitter. 2022.https://twitter.com/jljcolorado/status/1578063884400971777 (accessed 28 Mar 2023).

3. Lewis D. Why the WHO took two years to say COVID is airborne. Nature 2022;604:26–31.

4. Sagan C. The Demon-Haunted World: Science as a Candle in the Dark. Random House 1995.
5. Horton R. Offline: What is medicine's 5 sigma? *Lancet* 2015;385:1380.
6. Watson C. Many researchers say they'll share data - but don't. Nature. 2022;606:853.
7. Steinbrook R, Kassirer JP, Angell M. Justifying conflicts of interest in medical journals: a very bad idea. BMJ 2015;350:h2942.
8. Khalsa KP. Frequently asked questions (FAQ). J Herb Pharmacother 2006;6:77–87.
9. Rose J, McCullough PA. WITHDRAWN: A Report on Myocarditis Adverse Events in the U.S. Vaccine Adverse Events Reporting System (VAERS) in Association with COVID-19 Injectable Biological Products. Curr Probl Cardiol 2021;:101011.
10. Rose J. Predators in the legacy media... a personal story. Unacceptable Jessica. 2022.https://jessicar.substack.com/p/predators-in-the-legacy-media-a-personal?utm_source=%2Fsearch%2Fmccullough&utm_medium=reader2 (accessed 28 Mar 2023).
11. Oster ME, Shay DK, Su JR, et al. Myocarditis Cases Reported After mRNA-Based COVID-19 Vaccination in the US From December 2020 to August 2021. JAMA 2022;327:331–40.
12. White EM, Yang X, Blackman C, et al. Incident SARS-CoV-2 Infection among mRNA-Vaccinated and Unvaccinated Nursing Home Residents. N Engl J Med 2021;385:474–6.
13. Bermingham C, Morgan J, Nafilyan V. Deaths involving COVID-19 by vaccination status, England - Office for National Statistics. 2021.https://www.ons.gov.uk/peoplepopulationandcommunity/birthsdeathsandmarriages/deaths/bulletins/deathsinvolvingcovid19byvaccinationstatusengland/deathsoccurringbetween2januaryand24september2021 (accessed 28 Mar 2023).
14. Jones W. ONS slapped down by UK statistics watchdog for misleading claim that unvaccinated have '32 times' risk of Covid death –. The Daily Sceptic. 2021.https://dailysceptic.org/2021/11/26/ons-slapped-down-by-uk-statistics-watchdog-for-misleading-claim-that-unvaccinated-have-32-times-risk-of-covid-death/ (accessed 28 Mar 2023).
15. Thomas SJ, Moreira ED Jr, Kitchin N, et al. Safety and Efficacy of the BNT162b2 mRNA Covid-19 Vaccine through 6 Months. N Engl J Med 2021;385:1761–73.
16. Pfizer, Inc. , on behalf of Pfizer and BioNTech. Emergency Use Authorization (EUA) for an Unapproved Product Review Memorandum. Published Online First: November 2020.https://www.fda.gov/media/144416/download
17. It gets worse before it gets better. HART. 2021.https://www.hartgroup.org/it-gets-worse-before-it-gets-better/ (accessed 28 Mar 2023).
18. Why hide what happens in the first two weeks after vaccination? HART. 2021.https://www.hartgroup.org/why-do-they-hide-what-happens-in-the-first-two-weeks-after-vaccination/ (accessed 28 Mar 2023).
19. Public Health Scotland. Public Health Scotland COVID-19 Statistical Report. Published Online First: 17 November 2021.https://publichealthscotland.scot/media/10181/21-11-17-covid19-publication_report.pdf
20. New CDC study: Vaccination Offers Higher Protection than Previous COVID-19 infection. CDC. 2021.https://www.cdc.gov/media/releases/2021/s1029-Vaccination-Offers-Higher-Protection.html (accessed 28 Mar 2023).
21. Harris RJ, Hall JA, Zaidi A, et al. Effect of Vaccination on Household Transmission of SARS-CoV-2 in England. N Engl J Med 2021;385:759–60.
22. UK Health Security Agency. SARS-CoV-2 variants of concern and variants under investigation in England Technical briefing 24. Published Online First: 1 October 2021.https://assets.publishing.service.gov.uk/government/uploads/system/uploads/attachment_data/file/1030146/technical-briefing-24.pdf
23. Landray PHAP. Statement from the Chief Investigators of the Randomised Evaluation of

COVid-19 theRapY (RECOVERY) Trial on hydroxychloroquine. 2020;:2.

24. Wise J, Coombes R. Covid-19: The inside story of the RECOVERY trial. BMJ 2020;370:m2670.

Chapter 14
Other medical services suffering from a lack of science

1. https://www.bbc.co.uk/news/uk-england-shropshire-60925959)
2. https://www.gov.uk/government/publications/final-report-of-the-ockenden-review/ockenden-review-summary-of-findings-conclusions-and-essential-actions
3. https://www.theguardian.com/society/2022/oct/19/this-cannot-go-on-nhs-maternity-care-report-author-calls-for-fresh-approach
4. Safety on maternity wards 'at lowest level'. The Daily Telegraph on 20/10/22
5. Paul R Goddard *The history of medicine, money and politics*. (Clinical Press Ltd 2008)
6. Daily Telegraph letter Dr Hilary Aitken 22/4/22
7. https://www.medscape.co.uk/viewarticle/about-1-4-say-they-did-not-get-help-needed-crisis-care-2022a1002535?uac=285238SV&faf=1&sso=true&impID=4809019&src=wnl_ret_221030_mscpmrk-GB_wir_active
8. Not such a class act. Lucy Foulkes, New Scientist, 20 August 2022 p25)

Bibliography
• Goddard P 2008 The History of Medicine, Money and Politics

Chapter 15 Drugs and drug policy

1. Nutt, King, Saulsbury and Blakemore: development of a rational scale to assess the harms of drugs. *Lancet* 2007 https://doi.org/10.1016/S0140-6736(07)60464-4
2. https://assets.publishing.service.gov.uk/government/uploads/system/uploads/attachment_data/file/119154/ACMD-multi-criteria-report.pdf
3. Nutt DJ King LA Phillips LD (2010) Drug harms in the UK: a multicriteria decision analysis *Lancet* 376: 1558-66 DOI: 10.1016/S0140-6736(10)61462-6
4. Kyzar et al Psychedelic Drugs in Biomedicine. Trends in Pharmacol. Sci. https://pubmed.ncbi.nlm.nih.gov/28947075/
5. Goodwin et al (2022) N Engl J Med 2022;387:1637-48. DOI: 10.1056/NEJMoa2206443

Chapter 16 Nutrition

1. https://academic.oup.com/jn/article/133/3/638/4688006
2. Magendie, F. (1816) Sur les propriétés nutritives des substances qui ne contiennent pas d'azote. Ann. Chim. (ser. 2)3:66–77 408–410.
3. The discovery of the vitamins: https://pubmed.ncbi.nlm.nih.gov/23798048/
4. Lind, J. (1753) Memoir upon the germination and fermentation of grains and farinaceous substances. A Treatise of the Scurvy :60 Millar Edinburgh, UK (Reprinted 1953 by University of Edinburgh Press).
5. Burr, G. O. Prog. Lipid Res.20, xxv–xxvi (1981).
6. https://www.asbmb.org/asbmb-today/science/100412/the-discovery-of-essential-fatty-acids
7. Low-dose tryptophan depletion in recovered depressed patients induces changes in cognitive processing without depressive symptoms Gail Hayward , Guy M Goodwin, Phil J Cowen, Catherine J Harmer. https://pubmed.ncbi.nlm.nih.gov/15737667
8. Regulation of osteoarthritis by omega-3 (n-3) polyunsaturated fatty acids in a naturally occurring model of disease. L Knott 1 , N C Avery, A P Hollander, J F Tarlton 2011 Sep;19(9):1150-7. doi: 10.1016/j.joca.2011.06.005. Epub 2011 Jul 1
9. https://usrtk.org/sweeteners/aspartame_health_risks/
10. https://www.sciencedaily.com/releases/2022/03/220324143800.htm
11. https://www.medscape.com/viewarticle/988721?ecd=wnl_tp10_daily_230301_MSCPEDIT&uac=285238SV&impID=5208069#vp_2

12. https://www.ncbi.nlm.nih.gov/pmc/articles/PMC6539761/
13. https://en.wikipedia.org/wiki/Body_mass_index
14. A weighty matter, Clare Wilson, New Scientist 10 Sept, 2022 p 28
15. Warning to elderly slimmers: Losing weight later in life may RAISE risk of an early death, study warns, Caitlin Tilley, Health Reporter, Daily Mail 11.4.2023 https://www.dailymail.co.uk/health/article-11960483/Losing-weight-later-life-RAISE-risk-early-death-study-warns.html

Chapter 17
Medical Training and the NHS: The value of research in Medical Training

• Jarad NA. The History and Future Treatment of Emphysema: Emphysema Valves, Emphysema Coils and Volume Reduction Surgery- Proceeding of the Bristol Medico- Historical Society, West of England Medical Journal 2018; Vol 117 No 1 .
• Criner GJ, Sue R, Wright S, Dransfield M, Rivas-Perez H, Wiese T, Sciurba FC, Shah PL, Wahidi MM, de Oliveira HG, Morrissey B, Cardoso PFG, Hays S, Majid A, Pastis N Jr, Kopas L, Vollenweider M, McFadden PM, Machuzak M, Hsia DW, Sung A, Jarad NA, et al.. LIBERATE Study Group. A Multicentre RCT of Zephyr® Endobronchial Valve Treatment in Heterogeneous Emphysema (LIBERATE). Respir Crit Care Med. 2018 May 22. doi: 10.1164/rccm.201803-0590OC.
• Creber P, Bendall O, Jarad NA. Delayed Response to Endobronchial Emphysema Valve Insertion. Clinics in Respiratory Medicine 2018; 1: 1001- 1003.
• Jarad NA. Clinical Review - Endo-bronchial valve treatment of emphysema. Chronic Respiratory Disease 2016; May; 13(2):173-188
• Jarad NA, Patel P, Buswell J. Epidemiology and risk factors of urinary incontinence in patients with chronic obstructive pulmonary disease (COPD). West of England Medical Journal 2015;114(3)- September: Article 3 pp:1-3.
• Williams R, Krishnadas R, Patel B, Jarad NA. Endobronchial valves in the management of bronchial fistulae caused by bronchopulmonary aspergillosis. British Medical Journal Case Report. 2015 Dec 1;2015. pii: bcr2015211955. doi: 10.1136/bcr-2015-211955
• Jarad NA. The Riddle of Breathlessness- Life of breath.2015 https://lifeofbreathblog.wordpress.com/2015/07/01/the-riddle-of-breathlessness/
• Sequeiros IM, Jarad NA. Cystic Fibrosis Pulmonary Exacerbation – Natural History, Causative Factors and Management. In Amer Amal - Respiratory Disease and Infection – InTec Publications 2013 – PP 173 – 204
• Sequeiros IM, Jarad NA. Radiological Features of cystic fibrosis – In Dinesh Sriramulu- Cystic Fibrosis - Renewed Hopes through Research, InTec Publications 2012: PP 31-50.
• Hessey SM, Jarad N A. Prevention of exacerbations of chronic obstructive pulmonary disease. West of England Journal of Medicine 2012; Volume 111, Number 2, Article 1.
• Jarad NA. Chest Sounds Multimedia presentation of normal and abnormal lung sounds. http://rubble.heppell.net/chestnet/t/chestsounds/chestsounds.htm
• Jarad N A, Sequeiros IM, Sund Z, Bristow K. Fatigue in Cystic Fibrosis. A novel prospective study investigating subjective and objective factors associated with fatigue. Chron Respir Disease, 2012, 9 (4): 241-249.
• Sequeiros IM, Jarad N A. Extending the course of intravenous antibiotics in adult patients with cystic fibrosis with acute pulmonary exacerbations. Chron Resp Disease 2012;9 (4):213-20.
• Sequeiros IM, Jarad N A. Factors associated with a shorter time until the next pulmonary exacerbation in adult patients with cystic fibrosis. Chron Respir Dis. 2012; 9(1):9-16
• Jarad N A, Sequeiros IM. A novel respiratory symptom scoring system for CF pulmonary exacerbations. QJM. 2012, 2012; 105(2) 137-143.
• Jarad N A, Sund ZM. Telemonitoring in chronic obstructive airway disease and adult patients with cystic fibrosis. J Telemed Telecare. 2011; 17(3):127-32.
• Jarad N A, Powell T, Smith E. Evaluation of a novel sputum clearance technique-- hydro-acoustic therapy (HAT) in adult patients with cystic fibrosis: a feasibility study. Chron Respir Dis. 2010;7(4):217-27.
• Sequeiros IM, Hester K, Callaway M, Williams A, Garland Z, Powell T, Wong FS, Jarad N A. MRI appearance of the pancreas in patients with cystic fibrosis: a comparison of pancreas volume in diabetic and non-diabetic patients. Br J Radiol. 2010 ;83(995):921-6.
• Sarfaraz S, Sund Z, Jarad N A. Real-time, once-daily monitoring of symptoms and FEV in cystic fibrosis

patients--a feasibility study using a novel device. Clin Respir J. 2010 Apr;4(2):74-82.

• Jarad N A, Sequeiros IM, Hester K, Callaway M, Williams AJ, Sund Z, Powell T, Wong FS. The size of the spleen by magnetic resonance imaging in patients with cystic fibrosis; with and without diabetes--a novel observational study. QJM. 2010;103(4):237-42.

• Sequeiros IM, Jarad N A. Home intravenous antibiotic treatment for acute pulmonary exacerbations in cystic fibrosis - Is it good for the patient? Ann Thorac Med. 2009 Jul;4(3):111-114

• Sund ZM, Powell T, Greenwood R, Jarad N A. Remote daily real-time monitoring in patients with COPD -a feasibility study using a novel device. Respir Med. 2009;103(9):1320-8.

• Jarad N A, Johnson N et al BTS statement on criteria for specialist referral, admission, discharge and follow-up for adults with respiratory disease. Thorax. 2008 Mar; 63 Suppl 1:i1-i16.

• Jarad N A, Giles K. Risk factors for increased need for intravenous antibiotics for pulmonary exacerbations in adult patients with cystic fibrosis. Chron Respir Dis. 2008;5(1):29-33.

• Jarad N A, Higgs S, Jeffcote T, Giles K. Factors associated with reduced FEV1 in adult patients with cystic fibrosis in a relatively affluent area. Chron Respir Dis. 2005;2(3):133-7.

• Jarad N A. Asbestos-Related Disease. Journal of the Royal College of Physicians, London 1999; 33:532-536.

• Jarad N A, Wedzicha JA, Burge PS, Calverley PM. An observational study of inhaled corticosteroid withdrawal in stable chronic obstructive pulmonary disease. ISOLDE Study Group. Respir Med. 1999 Mar;93(3):161-6.

• Jarad N A, Empey DW, Duckworth G. Administration of the BCG vaccination using the multipuncture method in schoolchildren: a comparison with the intradermal method. Thorax. 1999 Sep;54(9):762-4.

• Jarad N A, Demertzis P, Jones DJ, Barnes NC, Rudd RM, Gaya H, Wedzicha JA, Hughes DT, Empey DW. Comparison of characteristics of patients and treatment outcome for pulmonary non-tuberculous mycobacterial infection and pulmonary tuberculosis. Thorax 1996 Feb;51(2):137-9.

• Jarad N A, Parastatides S, Paul EA, Sheldon CD, Gaya H, Rudd RM, Empey DW. Characteristics of patients with drug resistant and drug sensitive tuberculosis in East London. Thorax 1994 49(8):808-810

• Jarad NA, Carroll MP, Laroche C, Poulakis N, Moxham J, Green M, Rudd RM. Respiratory muscle function in patients with asbestos-related pleural disease. Respir Med. 1994 Feb;88(2):115-20.

• Jarad N A, Hui KP, Barnes N. Effects of a thromboxane receptor antagonist on prostaglandin D2 and histamine induced bronchoconstriction in man. Br J Clin Pharmacol. 1994 Jan;37(1):97-100.

• Jarad N A, Davies SW, Logan-Sinclair R, Rudd RM. Lung crackle characteristics in patients with asbestosis, asbestos-related pleural disease and left ventricular failure using a time-expanded waveform analysis--a comparative study. Respir Med. 1994 Jan;88(1):37-46.

• Jarad NA, Underwood SR, Rudd RM. Asbestos-related pericardial thickening detected by magnetic resonance imaging. Respir Med. 1993 May;87(4):309-12.

• Jarad N A, Strickland B, Bothamley G, Lock S, Logan-Sinclair R, Rudd RM. Diagnosis of asbestosis by a time expanded wave form analysis, auscultation and high resolution computed tomography: a comparative study. Thorax 1993 Apr;48(4):347-53.

• Jarad NA, Wilkinson P, Pearson MC, Rudd RM. A new high resolution computed tomography scoring system for pulmonary fibrosis, pleural disease, and emphysema in patients with asbestos related disease. Br J Ind Med. 1992 Feb;49(2):73-84.

• Jarad N A, Poulakis N, Pearson MC, Rubens MB, Rudd RM. Assessment of asbestos-induced pleural disease by computed tomography--correlation with chest radiograph and lung function. Respir Med. 1991 May;85(3):203-208.

Comment

References

1. Training for Doctors…Laura Donnelly; https://www.telegraph.co.uk/news/2023/03/21/training-doctors-could-shortened-tackle-nhs-staff-shortages/
2. Robert Kennedy, *The Real Anthony Fauci,* Children's Health Defence.
3. Szarewski et al, The 'pill scare'. Human Reproduction Update 1999 Vol 5 No 6 pp627-632
4. Drife, This Gynaecological Life, Clinical Press 2023 (in press)

Chapter 18
Physics, Astronomy and Cosmology

1. Paul R Goddard, Time and Space-The Conceptual Answer, Clinical Press 1995
2. https://www.britannica.com/science/Newtons-laws-of-motion
3. Nearby galaxies may lack dark matter to hold them together Leah Crane New Scientist

10/8/22 p15
4. https://astronomynow.com/2021/01/25/the-case-of-the-missing-supermassive-black-hole/
5. Bang goes the theory New Scientist 3 Sept 2022 p 13).
6. https://plus.maths.org/content/kaluza-klein-and-their-story-fifth-dimension
7. https://en.wikipedia.org/wiki/Mordehai_Milgrom
8. Precision measurement of the Newtonian gravitational constant. Chao Xue, Jian-Ping Liu, Qing Li, Jun-Fei Wu, Shan-Qing Yang, Qi Liu, Cheng-Gang Shao, Liang-Cheng Tu, Zhong-Kun Hu, Jun Luo National Science Review, Volume 7, Issue 12, December 2020, Pages 1803–1817, https://doi.org/10.1093/nsr/nwaa165
9. https://en.wikipedia.org/wiki/Stellar_nucleosynthesis
10. Hoyle, F. (1946). "The synthesis of the elements from hydrogen". Monthly Notices of the Royal Astronomical Society. 106 (5): 343–383. Bibcode:1946MNRAS.106..343H. doi:10.1093/mnras/106.5.343.
11. vhttps://www.theguardian.com/science/2010/oct/03/fred-hoyle-nobel-prize).
12. Cosmic Thoughts, interview with Roger Penrose pp46-49 *New Scientist* 19 November 2022
13. The Universe by numbers, Antonia Padilla, pp42-45 *New Scientist*, 13 August 2022
14. https://mathshistory.st-andrews.ac.uk/Biographies/Godel/
15. https://www.lppfusion.com/technology/brief-history-of-fusion-power/
16. https://en.wikipedia.org/wiki/Schön_scandal

Chapter 19
Origins of life and the cosmos

1. Wickramasinghe, C., The Search for Our Cosmic Ancestry, World Scientific, 2015
2. Hoyle, F. and Wickramasinghe, N.C., 1982. Evolution from Space, J.M. Dent, Lond
3. Wickramasinghe, C., Wickramasinghe, K. and Tokoro, G., Our cosmic ancestry in the stars, Bear and Co. Rochester, 2019
4. Wickramasinghe, J.T., Wickramasinghe, N.C.. and Napier, W.M. Comets and the Origin of Life, World Scientific Press, 2009
5. Pasteur, Louis, 1857. Comptes rendus de l'Académie des Sciences, 45, 913.
6. Thompson, W. (Lord Kelvin), 1871. British Association for the Advancement of Science, Presidential address.
7. von Helmholtz, in W. Thomson & P.G. Tait (eds).. 1874 Handbuch de Theoretische Physik, Vo.1. Part 2., Brancsheig.
8. Arrhenius, S., 1908. Worlds in the Making, Harper, Lond.
9. Bell, E.A., Boehnke, P., Harrison, T. et al, 2015. Potentially biogenic carbon preserved in a 4.1 billion-year-old zircon, PNAS, 112 (47) 14518-14521
10. Hoyle, F. and Wickramasinghe, N.C., 2000. Astronomical Origins of Life: Steps towards Panspermia (Kluwer Academic Press)
11. Wickramasinghe, C., Where did we come from? Life of an astrobiologist, 2015, World Scientific Publ. Singapore
12. Wickramasinghe, N.C., 2010 Astrobiological Case for our Cosmic Ancestry. International Journal of Astrobiology, 9(2), 119
13. Steele EJ, Al-Mufti S, Augustyn KK, Chandrajith R, Coghlan JP, Coulson SG, Ghosh S, Gillman M. et al 2018 "Cause of Cambrian Explosion: Terrestrial or Cosmic?" Prog. Biophys. Mol. Biol. 136: 3-23, https://doi.org/10.1016/j.pbiomolbio.2018.03.004
14. Wickramasinghe, C., 2004. A Journey with Fred Hoyle: The search for cosmic life, World Scientific, Singapore
15. Wickramasinghe, C., 2015. The search for our cosmic ancestry, World Scientific, Singapore
16. Wickramasinghe, D.T. and Allen, D.A., 1986. Discovery of organic grains in Comet Halley, Nature, 323, 44-46

17. Capaccione F, Coradini A, Filacchione G., et al 2015, The organic-rich surface of comet 67P/Churyumov-Gerasimenko as seen by VIRTIS/Rosetta, Science 347 (6220).
18. Biver, N. et al, 2015. Ethyl alcohol and sugar in Comet C/2014Q2 (Lovejoy)
19. Wickramasinghe, N.C. 2022. Giant comet C/2014 UN271 (Bernardinelli-Bernstein) provides new evidence for cometary panspermia, International Journal of Astronomy and Astrophysics, 12, 1-6
20. Harris, M.J., Wickramasinghe, N.C., Lloyd, D., Narlikar, J.V., et al, 2001. The detection of living cells in stratospheric samples. Proc SPIE 4495, 192–198; Lloyd, D., Wickramasinghe,N.C., Harris, M.J., Narlikar, J.V.et al, (2002. Possible detection of extraterrestrial life in stratospheric samples. Proceedings of the International Conference entitled "Multicolour Universe" eds R.K. Manchanda and B. Paul (Tata Institute of Fundamental Research, Mumbai, India, pages 367ff
21. Shivaji, S., Chaturvedi, P., Begum, Z. et al, 2009. Janibacter hoylei sp. nov., Bacillus isronensis sp. nov. and Bacillus aryabhattai sp. nov., isolated from cryotubes used for collecting air from the upper atmosphere. Int. J Systematics Evol. Microbiol, 59, 2977–2986
22. Grebennikova, T.V., Syroeshkin, A.V., Shubralova, E.V. et al, 2018. The DNA of Bacteria of the World Ocean and the Earth in Cosmic Dust at the International Space Station, Scientific World Journal 2018: 7360147. Published online 2018 Apr 18. doi: 10.1155/2018/7360147; (https://www.hindawi.com/journals/tswj/aip/7360147/).
23. Hoyle, F. and Wickramasinghe, N.C., 1979. Diseases from Space, J.M. Dent, London
24. Hoyle, F. and Wickramasinghe, N.C., 1979. Life on Mars? The case for a cosmic heritage, Clinical Press, Bristol
25. Brammer, P.A. and van Dokkum, P.G., 2016. A Remarkably Luminous Galaxy at z=11.1 Measured with Hubble Space Telescope Grism Spectroscopy, The Astrophysical Journal, 819(2), article id. 129
26. Hoyle, F., Burbidge, G. and Narlikar, J.V., 2008. A Different Approach to Cosmology: From a Static Universe through the Big Bang towards Reality (Cambridge University Press)
27. Narlikar, J.V., Burbidge, G., and Vishwakarma, R.G., 2007 Cosmology and Cosmogony in a Cyclic Universe, Astrophys. Astron., 28, 67
28. Penrose Roger, 2006. "Before the Big Bang: An Outrageous New Perspective and its Implications for Particle Physics". Proceedings of the EPAC 2006, Edinburgh, Scotland: 2759–2762.
29. Gurzadyan, VG and Penrose, R, 2013. "On CCC-predicted concentric low-variance circles in the CMB sky". Eur. Phys. J. Plus. 128 (2): 22. arXiv:1302.5162
30. Brammer, P.A. and van Dokkum, P.G., 2016. A Remarkably Luminous Galaxy at z=11.1 Measured with Hubble Space Telescope Grism Spectroscopy, The Astrophysical Journal, 819(2), article id. 129

Chapter 20
Climate Change?

1. https://clintel.org/world-climate-declaration/
2. Al Gore - An Inconvenient Truth full documentary https://www.youtube.com/watch?v=I-SV13UQXdk
3. Dying Polar Bear, National Geographic https://www.dailysabah.com/environment/2018/08/05/national-geographic-admits-lying-to-its-readers-about-the-dying-polar-bear
4. https://climate.nasa.gov/news/2836/antarcticas-contribution-to-sea-level-rise-was-mitigated-by-snowfall/
5. https://tc.copernicus.org/articles/17/2059/2023/ Change in Antarctic ice shelf area from 2009 to 2019 Julia R. Andreasen et al
6. https://dailysceptic.org/2022/10/02/climate-bombshell-greenland-ice-sheet-recovers-as-scientists-say-earlier-loss-was-due-to-natural-warming-not-co2-emissions/).

7. The Great Barrier Reef bursting back to life https://www.telegraph.co.uk/world-news/2022/08/04/great-barrier-reef-bursts-back-life-climate-change-still-poses/
8. Hottest Places in the UK, Liz Osborn https://www.currentresults.com/Weather-Extremes/UK/hottest-place-in-uk.php
9. Spracklen, D., Arnold, S. & Taylor, C. 2012, Observations of increased tropical rainfall preceded by air passage over forests. Nature 489, 282–285 doi:10.1038/nature11390 (https://www.nature.com/articles/nature11390)
10. Nair et al-2011-Journal of Geophysical Research-Atmospheres (1984-2012) The role of land-use change on the development and evolution of the west coast trough, convective clouds, and precipitation in southwest Australia (https://agupubs.onlinelibrary.wiley.com/doi/epdf/10.1029/2010JD014950)
11. https://www.learningfromnature.com.au/drought-proof-increasing-rainfall/
12. https://blogs.egu.eu/divisions/gd/2017/09/13/modern-day-sea-level-rise/
13. https://www.forbes.com/advisor/investing/cryptocurrency/bitcoins-energy-usage-explained/
14. https://e360.yale.edu/features/americas-new-war-on-wolves-and-why-it-must-be-stopped
15. Red kites should never have been reintroduced to Britain Paul Sargeantson *Spectator* 1/10/2022
16. https://www.nature.scot/doc/guidance-honey-bees-and-beekeeping-protected-areas#:~:text=Under%20certain%20conditions%2C%20honey%20bees,a%20threat%20to%20other%20pollinators.
17. Energy Transition Delusion: Mark P Mills. https://www.youtube.com/watch?v=sgOEGKDVvsg
18. https://www.theguardian.com/environment/2021/dec/17/wood-burners-urban-air-pollution-cancer-risk-study
19. https://konstantinkisin.substack.com/p/the-suicide-cult-of-the-climate-emergency
20. Allison Pearson Daily Telegraph Features, p6. 9th Nov 2022
21. https://en.wikipedia.org/wiki/Demographic_history_of_Pakistan
22. https://space.nss.org/making-sun-shades-from-moondust/
23. John Fewster, p32 18 March 2023 *New Scientist*
24. Wade Allison: The Inadequacy of Wind Power: https://www.thegwpf.org/content/uploads/2023/03/Allison-Wind-energy.pdf?mc_cid=5c197dfa62&mc_eid=c926002e71
25. Climate change findings inflated 'so paper would be published' Thursday 7 September 2023 *The Daily Telegraph*

Chapter 21
Scientific Studies of the Past

1. https://www.vedantu.com/question-answer/are-the-advantages-and-disadvantages-of-class-6-social-science-cbse-60c18969b8444500abb96209
2. https://www.britannica.com/science/paleontology
3. https://www.historytoday.com/archive/head-head/what-history
4. https://www.britannica.com/science/archaeology
5. http://www.faculty.ucr.edu/~legneref/ethnic/mummy.htm
6. https://en.wikipedia.org/wiki/Historical_negationism
7. Noye: https://www.dailymail.co.uk/femail/article-11744447/Theyve-class-warrior-Viewers-slam-boring-BBC-drama-Gold.html
8. https://magazine.ucl.ac.uk/this-idea-must-die-david-wengrow/
9. The Dawn of Everything: A New History of Humanity, Graeber and Wengrow (Penguin)

Chapter 22
What is the legal position?

1. https://www.icrc.org/en/war-and-law/weapons/chemical-biological-weapons
2. https://en.wikipedia.org/wiki/Nuremberg_Code
3. https://www.bps.org.uk/guideline/code-ethics-and-conduct
4. https://committees.parliament.uk/committee/93/human-rights-joint-committee/news/154842/joint-committee-on-human-rights-every-fixed-penalty-notice-issued-under-coronavirus-regulations-must-be-reviewed/
5. https://www.smh.com.au/national/nsw/recipient-of-covid-fine-tells-of-confusion-as-he-challenges-ticket-in-court-20220720-p5b36k.html

6. https://www.dailymail.co.uk/news/article-11026365/Thousands-Covid-fines-worth-millions-dollars-overturned-landmark-test-case.html
7. Daily Sceptic: The End of Doctors' Freedom to Ignore What the Government and Pharmaceutical Industry Say Should Worry Us All, By Dr Frank Mercy
8. https://www.ncbi.nlm.nih.gov/pmc/articles/PMC1120824/
9. David McGrogan https://newsfromuncibal.substack.com/p/on-human-rights-advocates-and-having
10. https://www.gov.uk/discrimination-your-rights/discrimination-at-work
11. https://www.equalityhumanrights.com/en/advice-and-guidance/your-rights-under-equality-act-2010

Chapter 23
Can anything be done?

1. Laura Dodsworth: *A State of Fear* Pinter and Martin 2021
2. https://www.telegraph.co.uk/contact-us/editorial/
3. https://www.theguardian.com/info/2015/jan/28/contact-the-guardian-letters-desk
4. https://www.thetimes.co.uk/static/contact-us/
5. https://realbusiness.co.uk/six-companies-that-avoid-paying-their-taxes
6. Apple restricts iPhone tool used to defy China's censors. *Daily Telegraph* 11th November 2022 p15
7. Risk of pandemic terrorism, New Scientist, p11, 19th November 2022
8. https://drive.google.com/file/d/1YF0F7DHrxen09IxChsf_px49RPuJQtm2/view
9. Kranke P, Putting the record straight: granisetron's efficacy as an antiemetic 'post-Fujii https://doi.org/10.1111/j.1365-2044.2012.07318.x
10. J.L Mackie, page 132 in Ethics Penguin Books 1990
11. Late lessons from early warnings: the precautionary principle 1896–2000https://www.eea.europa.eu/publications/environmental_issue_report_2001_22
12. https://chat.openai.com
13. Can we trust AI search engines? Chris Stokel-Walker News Scientist 6 May 2023 p 12

Appendix to Chapter 2

1 https://www.goodwin.edu/enews/health-science-vs-public-health/).
2 Sarah Knapton, Daily Telegraph: SCIENCE EDITOR 10 September 2021

Bibliography

- *Sir Francis Bacon, Philosopher, Polymath, Poet and Playwrigh*t, by Peter M. Dunn, Clinical Press Ltd 2018
- *How to Lie with Statistics*, Darrell Huff 1954 Penguin
- *A State of Fear*; Laura Dodsworth Pinter & Martin Ltd
- *The War on the West: How to Prevail in the Age of Unreason*, Douglas Murray HarperCollins Publishers
- *Life on Mars?* Hoyle and Wickramasinghe Clinical Press
- *The history of Medicine, Money and Politics*, P Goddard 2008 Clinical Press, Bristol UK
- *The Origin of the Virus, Barnard, Quay*, Dalgleish, Clinical Press, Bristol UK 2021 and *L'origine del virus* Chiarelettere
- *PANDEMIC* 1st and 2nd editions P Goddard 2020/2021 Clinical Press, Bristol UK
- *Vitamin D Deficiency and Covid-19*: Its Central Role in a World Pandemic by Dr David C Anderson and Dr David S Grimes Jul 31, 2020
- *The Dawn of Everything: A New History of Humanity*, D Graeber and D Wengrow (Penguin)
- Fake News, Paul R Goddard, Clinical Press Ltd. Clinical Press 2018

About the Authors and Conflicts of Interest

Professor Paul R Goddard
MD, FRCR, FBIR

Paul is a retired consultant radiologist and retired Professor of Radiology, (University of the West of England). He is also a director and co-owner of Clinical Press Ltd and author of some thirty books including *Diagnostic Imaging of the Chest* (1987), *PANDEMIC* (1st and 2nd editions) and *The History of Medicine, Money and Politics*. He won the Kodak Scholarship, the Couch Award and the Twining Medal of the Royal College of Radiologists and the Barclay Prize and Honorary Fellowship of the British Institute of Radiology. He developed the generally used CT technique for the assessment of pulmonary emphysema and established the clinical method of reporting MRI scans.

Professor Angus Dalgleish
FRCP FRCPath FMedSci

Gus is Professor of Oncology at St Georges Medical School, London and Visiting Professor at the Institute of Cancer Research in London and also at the Earle Childes Research Institute in Portland, Oregon, USA, and the University of Stellenbosch, South Africa. He was the co-discoverer of the CD4 receptor as the major cellular receptor for HIV and produced the first report of a link between Slim Disease in Africa and HIV infection. He received the Joshua Lederberg prize from Celgene in 2011. He has worked closely with Dr Birger Sørensen of Norway in producing vaccines against AIDS and against Severe Acute Respiratory Syndrome Coronavirus 2 (SARS-Cov-2: the virus that has caused the Covid-19 pandemic). He is a Fellow of many learned societies including the Academy of Medical Sciences, the Royal College of Physicians, the Royal College of Pathologists and the Royal Australasian College of Physicians. He is co-author of the best selling book *The Origin of the Virus*.

The Death of Science

Professor Chandra Wickramasinghe
MBE, ScD, Hon DSc, Hon DLitt, FRAS, FRSA

Sri Lankan-British astronomer, astrobiologist, co-proponent with the late Sir Fred Hoyle of the theory of cometary panspermia. Chandra is a pioneer of the new science of astrobiology, and is a prolific writer both of technical scientific papers as well as popular expositions of his ideas. His total count of technical journal papers exceeds 400, and some 60 of these have appeared in the journal Nature. Chandra was born in Colombo, Sri Lanka in 1939, and received his early education at Royal College, Colombo and the University of Ceylon. In 1961 he went to Cambridge, UK, where he began his life-long collaboration with Sir Fred Hoyle. Recent books include: Cosmic Genetic Evolution (Academic Press), Diseases from Outer Space, A Journey with Fred Hoyle, The Search for Our Cosmic Ancestry, Where did we come from? (World Scientific Publishing Singapore), and Our Cosmic Ancestry in the Stars (Inner Traditions USA).
He was a Fellow of Jesus College, Cambridge from 1963-1973, Professor at University College Cardiff and Cardiff University from 1973-2011. Currently he is an Honorary Professor at the University of Buckingham UK, and also at the University of Ruhuna, Sri Lanka, the Sir John Kotelawala Defence University, Sri Lanka, and an Adjunct Professor at the National Institute of Fundamental Studies, Sri Lanka

Professor David Nutt
Mbbch (Cantab) DM (Oxon) FRCP FRCPsych FMedSci DLaws

David is Professor of Neuropsychopharmacology at Imperial College London, Director of the Centre for Psychedelic Research there and also Chief Research Officer of Awaknlifesciences. He obtained an Open Scholarship in Medicine at Downing College Cambridge then completed his clinical training at Guy's hospital London. After MRCP he trained in psychiatry at Oxford where he did his DM at the MRC Clinical Pharmacology Unit, subsequently becoming a University Lecturer and then a Wellcome Trust Senior Fellow in psychiatry. He then spent two years as head of the research ward at NIAAA in the USA before setting up the Psychopharmacology unit at Bristol University in 1988, where he later became Prof of Psychopharmacology and Dean of Clinical Medicine before moving to Imperial in 2008. He has held presidencies of the EBC, BAP, BNA and ECNP, was chair of the ACMD and founded the charity DrugScience and now chairs PAREA the European association for access to research with psychedelics.

David's contributions to pharmacology include GABA and noradrenaline receptor function in anxiety disorders, serotonin function in depression, endorphin and dopamine function in addiction and the neuroscience and clinical utility of psychedelics. He has over 500 original research papers, a similar number of reviews/book chapters, eight government reports and 36 books. In 2013 he was awarded the John Maddox Prize from Nature/Sense about Science for standing up for science and in 2017 a Doctor of Laws hon causa from the University of Bath.

Dr Nabil Jarad
PhD FRCP

Dr Jarad completed his clinical and research training in London and was awarded a PhD from London University (Imperial College).
He worked in Bristol where he founded and lead the Cystic Fibrosis Centre, the community COPD service and Bronchiectasis Service.
He established the South West Lung Volume Reduction Service using endobronchial valves and coils to treat emphysema.
He was the Training Program Director for General Medicine in the South West. He also chaired the General and Acute Medicine Training Committee in the Severn Deanery. He served as a Severn Royal College of Physicians adviser for over a decade.
He is a national and international examiner for the MRCP (UK)
He published textbooks, book chapters and original research included Cystic Fibrosis, Lung Fibrosis induced by asbestos, COPD and volume reduction therapies in Emphysema. He was recognised as one of the UK Leading UK Principal Investigators by The Chief Medical Officer. He is the current Honorary Secretary and the Science Secretary for the Bristol Medico Chirurgical (Surgical) Society.

Jeremy Goddard
MAPhilosophy (Edin)

Jeremy is the elder son of Paul and Lois Goddard. He studied philosophy at Edinburgh University and has since pursued a successful international career as a pianist, vocalist and songwriter. He currently lives and performs in Barbados.

Mark Goddard
BSc (UCL).

Mark is the younger son of Paul and Lois Goddard. He studied art at Weston College of Art and architecture at the Bartlett (UCL) and the Royal College of Art. He has a current exhibition of photography and artworks at the Karma Sanctum, Soho, London, and is the author of *Losing Eldorado, Searching for the Soul of America.*

Dr Rosamond Jones,
MBBS, MD, FRCPCH

Dr Jones is a retired NHS consultant paediatrician, whose main clinical interests were newborn intensive care and paediatric infectious diseases. Throughout her career, she was active in clinical research including drug trials. She was at one time on the Advisory board of the National Perinatal Epidemiology Unit. She was also a regular peer reviewer for a number of medical journals.
Since 2020, she has been a pioneer of children's rights, speaking out against school closures and other harmful restrictions for children. She set up the Children's Covid Vaccine Advisory Council to lobby against the rollout of Covid-19 vaccines to healthy children.

Dr Clare Craig
BM BCh FRCPath.

Dr Clare Craig has been a tireless voice, on and offline, over the past several years in advocating for evidence based policy around covid policy, and the importance of upholding basic medical ethical principles including informed consent and bodily autonomy. She is Co-Chair of the Health Advisory and Recovery Team, HART, a voluntary body of professionals educating the public on covid issues. Dr Clare Craig is a qualified diagnostic pathologist reaching consultant level in 2009. She specialised in cancer diagnostics including within mass screening programmes and was the day to day pathology lead for the cancer arm of the 100,000 Genomes Project.

Prof Karol Sikora
MA, MBBChir, PhD, FRCR, FRCP, FFPM

Professor Karol Sikora, Founding Dean of Medicine and Honorary Professor of Professional Practice at The University of Buckingham, studied medical science and biochemistry at Cambridge, where he obtained a double first. After clinical training he became a house physician at The Middlesex Hospital and registrar in oncology at St Bartholomew's Hospital. He later became a research student at the MRC Laboratory for Molecular Biology in Cambridge working with Nobel Prize winner, Dr Sydney Brenner. He obtained his PhD and became a clinical fellow at Stanford University, California before returning to direct the Ludwig Institute in Cambridge. He has been Clinical Director for Cancer Services at Hammersmith for 12 years and established a major cancer research laboratory there funded by the Imperial Cancer Research Fund. He chaired Help Hammer Cancer, an appeal that raised £8m towards the construction of the new Cancer Centre at Hammersmith. He became Deputy Director (Clinical Research) of the ICRF. From 1997 to 1999 he was Chief of the WHO Cancer Program and from 1999 to 2002, Vice President, Global Clinical Research (Oncology) at Pharmacia Corporation.

He has published over 300 papers and written or edited twenty books and is on the editorial board of several journals and is the founding editor of Gene Therapy and Cancer Strategy. He was a member of the UK Health Department's Expert Advisory Group on Cancer (the Calman-Hine Committee), the Committee on Safety of Medicines and remains an adviser to the WHO. He currently directs a cancer drug donation program in Africa.

Sir Richard Dearlove KCMG OBE

Sir Richard, who has had a successful and distinguished career in government and education, joined MI6 in 1966 undertaking various overseas postings. He was appointed Director of Personnel and Administration in 1993, going on to become Director of Operations in 1994, before being promoted to Chief of the Secret Intelligence Service in 1999. He retired from the Service in 2004. Sir Richard was the Master of Pembroke College, Cambridge from 2004 – 2015 and also served as a Deputy Vice-Chancellor of the University of Cambridge between 2005 and 2010. He became Chair of the Board of Trustees of London University on1 August 2014.

He is also Chairman of Ascot Underwriting at Lloyd's of London and a Director of Kosmos Energy, a trustee of Kent School Connecticut and is a senior adviser to several international companies including AIG and an Honorary Fellow of Queens' College Cambridge.